Vetch
  Hairy — Vicia sativa
  Common — " villosa
Lupine
  white — Lupinus alba
  yellow — Lupinus lutens
  Blue — " angustifolius
Peanut — arachis hypogaea
Peas — Pisum sativum
Timothy — Phleum pratense
BROOME — Bromus inermis
Meadow Tescue — Festuca elatior
  Tall Tescue — Festuca arundinacea
Orchard grass — Daclylis glomerata
Crested Wheat Grass — Agropyron cristatum
  Slender " " — " panciflorum
  Reed Canary — Phalaris arundinacea
    Red Top — agrostis alba
Creeping Bent — " plustris
Sudan Grass — Sorghum vulgare sudanense
Toptail Millet — Setaria italica
Proso Millet — Panicum miliaceum
  Jap " — Echinochloa frumentacea
Sorghum — sorghum vulgare .

CHAPTER 1

HISTORY AND DEVELOPMENT

The early history of forage-crop growing and utilization is lost in the unwritten pages of time. Prehistoric man had no need for such crops since he supported himself probably by picking berries, digging roots, fishing, and hunting wild game. It was not until he started taming some of the animals that roamed his domain that the need for forage developed.

The animals which inhabited the forest and field were numerous and of diverse types. Many, of course, consumed other animals, but many others were mostly herbivorous. These probably fed primarily on grasses, legumes, tree and bush leaves, and other green and succulent plants. The first animals to be domesticated were those which still inhabit the hills and fields of the farmer. These include dogs, horses, cattle, water buffalo, sheep, swine, poultry, and various others.

As mankind increased in numbers and tamed more and more animals, it became necessary to consider how these could be fed the essentials for maintenance, growth, and reproduction. At first, the animals were doubtless left to shift for themselves. This presented no problem in areas where the climate was mild the year around. It was the northward migration to regions where there was an abundance of crops in summer and a severe shortage in winter that brought on the forage problem. As time went by and as man's responsibility to his animal properties increased, it became necessary for him to produce the feed with which to supply the animals entrusted to his possession. Since these animals were mostly of a herbivorous type, the primary need was for hay and pasture crops.

Early Efforts to Harvest Forage. As the centuries passed and the human population became larger, man's dependence on animals increased. Undoubtedly, he observed the crops consumed by the herbivora and sought to harvest them for winter feeding. Wild hay from meadows and low moist areas may have been used at an early date. Tree leaves, bushes, weeds, and other rank vegetation were probably popular in cave-man days.

The first attempts to harvest hay or other bulky products must have been very crude. It probably was first collected by hand pulling and later in the Stone and Iron Age by means of semisharpened implements. It may have been cured before being moved to stacks or storage places. It is likely that curing was adopted not as a result of knowledge of the nutri-

1

tional value of this process, but because less labor was required to move the cured materials.

Hay Plants for Shelter.   The hay type of plant was put to other uses during this early period of mankind's development.   Many of the early huts and buildings established by the Europeans and Asiatics were covered, at least in part, with the hay type of grasses.   In some cases the grasses also were used to fill the chinks and openings between logs or rough-hewn timbers.

FIG. 1.   There is no substitute for high-quality hay in the dairy-cow ration.

Even within the last century, forage plants were used in this manner by the pioneers who settled the great prairie regions of North America. Grasses are still used for housing in the tropical and semitropical lands surrounding the Pacific basin, as any veteran who saw action in that theater during the Second World War can testify.   Housing is not, of course, the principal use to which the forage crops are put today, nor does this manner of utilization belong in the subject matter of this book, but it is an indication of the long and varied service these crops have rendered to mankind.

SPREAD OF FORAGE CROPS

As populations continued to increase and to become concentrated, pressure on the food supply made itself felt, and warfare developed as one means of relieving this pressure.

McGRAW-HILL PUBLICATIONS IN THE
AGRICULTURAL SCIENCES

R. A. BRINK, *Consulting Editor*

FORAGE CROPS

Selected Titles From

McGRAW-HILL PUBLICATIONS IN THE AGRICULTURAL SCIENCES

R. A. Brink, *Consulting Editor*

The late Leon J. Cole was Consulting Editor of this series from 1937 to 1948.

There are also the related series of McGraw-Hill Publications in the Botanical Sciences, of which Edmund W. Sinnott is Consulting Editor, and in the Zoological Sciences, of which A. Franklin Shull is Consulting Editor. Titles in the Agricultural Sciences were published in these series in the period 1917 to 1937.

FORAGE CROPS

by

GILBERT H. AHLGREN

Professor of Farm Crops, Rutgers University
Research Specialist, New Jersey Agricultural Experiment Station
Chairman, Farm Crops Department, Rutgers University
The State University of New Jersey

FIRST EDITION
SECOND IMPRESSION

NEW YORK   TORONTO   LONDON

McGRAW-HILL BOOK COMPANY, INC.

1949

FORAGE CROPS

TO

MY WIFE, MILDRED W. AHLGREN

AND TO

FREDERIC, WISCONSIN

ITS SCHOOLS AND ITS PEOPLE

PREFACE

This book was written with the primary aim of fulfilling an important need for a modern textbook in forage crops—a need which has been keenly felt by many teachers in this field. It is hoped that the book will also prove valuable as a reference book for workers in the field of agronomy. The subject matter has been chosen and organized for classroom use based on many years of experience by the writer. The study of forage crops is intended to follow the basic courses in agronomy, botany, and soils.

In this text, the term "forage crops" has been used in its more restricted sense, referring to those crops harvested by man and later fed to livestock. However, since many of the crops and problems discussed are applicable to pastures, it is hoped that this book will find wide usage among teachers and workers in this closely allied field.

An effort has been made to embody in a comprehensive manner the facts and fundamentals associated with the production of hay and silage crops. Individual treatment of the most important legumes and grasses is intended to introduce the student to the characteristics and adaptations associated with each. Following the detailed species study, the latter part of the book is devoted to hay mixtures, soil treatments, seedbed preparation, making hay and silage, and other subjects that are common to all the forage crops.

The writer has drawn freely from hundreds of scientific and popular bulletins covering this important field. Data from these publications have been presented to substantiate the principles and fundamentals as discussed. The tables are meant for careful study and interpretation by students to acquaint them with the basic work from which the principles of forage-crop production have been evolved.

There are a great number of forage crops, and they are grown under many different conditions in America. The science of growing, handling, and processing these crops is extremely involved. The author is indebted for valuable assistance and suggestions to many associates and friends, but especially to Dr. E. A. Hollowell, Division of Forage Crops and Diseases, U.S. Department of Agriculture, for reading the entire manuscript. Also to J. A. Allison, M. E. Hein, R. E. McKee, W. J. Morse, and H. M. Tysdal, of the same division, for suggestions on certain chapters. For reviewing the chapters on Hay Standards and Quality Production grateful acknowledgment is made to W. H. Hosterman, Production and Marketing Branch, U.S. Department of Agriculture.

The author also wishes to acknowledge with grateful thanks the helpful suggestions made by many of his colleagues at Rutgers University. Thanks are due especially to Profs. J. C. Anderson, W. R. Battle, B. H. Davis, R. S. Filmer, C. M. Haenseler, E. R. Purvis, R. S. Snell, M. A. Sprague, and Dr. Alex Dotzenko.

The assistance of Dorothy M. Rule and Beatrice Valenti in preparing the manuscript has also been invaluable. The entire manuscript has been edited by Van Wie Ingham, Assistant to the Dean of the College of Agriculture, Rutgers University. Many suggestions made by Mr. Ingham concerning subject-matter arrangement and methods of presentation have been adopted. Without his help it would have been impossible to complete the manuscript in the time devoted to it. The author's wife, Mildred W. Ahlgren, has also given much help and encouragement in carrying this work through to completion.

NEW BRUNSWICK, N.J.   GILBERT H. AHLGREN
   October, 1949

CONTENTS

In the bitter wars between tribal groups and among the early nations of the earth, horses and camels played an important role. Hay became a necessity as nations gathered together their horse power with which to battle one another. Alfalfa was carried by the Persians into Greece with the invasion of Xerxes in 490 B.C. Then it was utilized by the Romans in their conquest of Greece and, according to history, carried back to Rome in 146 B.C. As far as is known, alfalfa was the first cultivated forage plant. It has been under cultivation in Italy ever since its introduction.

DEVELOPMENT IN ROME

The culture of forage crops, however, is a product for the most part of European and American civilization, and it has developed in close relationship to livestock husbandry. The first records of regular and systematic culture of hay crops are found in the old Roman literature. Pliny and other Roman writers praised alfalfa as a forage crop.

Columella described the growing of hay crops about A.D. 50 as follows:

The hay which grows naturally in a juicy soil, is reckoned better than that which is forced by constant watering. Land that shelves gently, if it is either flat or well watered, may be reduced into meadow. But level ground is most approved, which, having a very small gentle descent, does not suffer the showers nor the rivulets to flow into it, to abide long in it; or if any water comes upon it, it creeps off slowly. If any part be low and marshy, and the water stagnates upon it, it must be carried off in furrows. Either great abundance or scarcity of water, is equally pernicious to grass of all sorts.

Grazing Practices. The protection needed by young meadow seedlings was also described by Columella.

It is important that we neither allow a hog to feed therein, because with its snout, it digs up and raises the turf, nor larger cattle, unless the ground is exceedingly dry, because they sink their hoofs into it and bruise and cut the roots of the herbs. Nevertheless, the second year we will allow smaller cattle to be admitted, after the hay harvest is over, provided the dryness and condition of the place will suffer it. Then the third year when the meadow is become more hard and solid, it may receive greater cattle also. Moreover the leaner and pendant places must be assisted and refreshed with dung.

Curing Hay. The Romans were well aware of the significance of proper hay curing. Columella described this process as follows:

There is a measure to be observed in drying hay, that it be put together neither oven dry nor yet too green; for, in the first case, it is not a whit better than straw for it has lost its juice; and in the other, it rots in the loft if it retains too much of it; and after it is grown hot it breeds fire, and sets all in a flame. They do not put it up in mows, before that they suffer it to heat, and concoct itself, and then grow cool, after having thrown it loosely together for a few days.

From this description it is easy to agree that the Romans were well advanced in forage-crop husbandry regarding seeding, management, and haymaking practices. They might well be credited with being the fathers of forage culture.

LATER EUROPEAN CONTRIBUTIONS

Clover was known to the Saxons in 800, indicating that they must have thought it a valuable crop. Records show that red clover was grown in Spain in the fifteenth and sixteenth centuries. From Spain it was carried to Flanders, and in 1633 it was brought from Flanders to England. Here it became known and valued as a forage and hay crop. Cultivated meadows were not accepted readily at this early date in England. The first grass intentionally sown in England was ryegrass, there known as raygrass. Worlidge, writing in 1681, made first mention of its cultivation indicating that it was good for cold, sour, wet clay soils that were unfit for sainfoin and lucerne.

FORAGE CROPS IN NORTH AMERICA

In North America, the Indians kept no herbivorous animals, and so had no use for harvested forage. Their principal cultivated crop was corn, but they used it for food rather than forage. Domestic livestock was introduced to this continent by the earliest settlers. De Soto in 1539 brought horses and swine with his expedition. Horses, sheep, goats, swine, and chickens were brought into Jamestown, Virginia, by the John Smith expeditions of 1607 and 1609. The Pilgrims introduced livestock at an early date into what is now Massachusetts.

Cattle were highly valued property among the early colonists, since they afforded another source of food for a society which faced rugged and difficult conditions. But the plants which had supplied the requirements of the native animals soon proved inadequate to meet the needs of livestock introduced from abroad. Thus the first English settlers brought seeds of European forage plants with them. This process was continued with the passing years, so that most of the common forage plants used in North America today are not native, but have been introduced from Europe, Africa, and Asia.

Winter Feeding Problem. Forage for winter feeding was an urgent necessity in the New England colonies with their deep snow and extreme cold. For the most part in the early days it consisted of straw, cornstalks, and marsh hay. Haymaking soon became a regular occupation of the New Englanders, and it was in this area that forage culture got its real start in the New World. The early colonists intending to engage in livestock farming came equipped with scythes, forks, and rakes for haying. Placing meadow hay in stacks became the common method of storage.

The meadowlands in the colonies consisted at first mostly of open swampy areas unfit for cultivation. These nevertheless were highly valued and much sought after. Private ownership of land was practiced by the colonists, but meadows were so highly valued that they were kept part of the common property and yearly assigned to each family on the basis of the number of cattle owned.

This native vegetation of swamps and low-lying cleared areas generally was very disappointing. It was described by some of the colonists as inferior in value to the reeds and sedges harvested in England, being devoid of nutritive value and incapable of supporting livestock in a satisfactory manner. It apparently caused certain nutritional diseases in their livestock. Some colonists found a partial cure for this by burning the first crop when it was ripe and cutting the new second crop while it was still young and palatable.

Native American Grasses. Among the grasses found on the Atlantic Coast and in the Ohio Valley native to America was wild-rye (*Elymus* sp.). Its head resembled wheat and rye and was mistaken for these by many early settlers. Wild-rye occasionally was used for food but mostly for feeding cattle and horses.

Also found widely throughout the North Atlantic states was broomsedge (*Andropogon* sp.). It was described as being "rank, hard, and dry" and very unpalatable. It actually was used by the early colonists in making crude brooms. Very likely much of the American shore was covered by beachgrass (*Ammophola breviligulata*). This is a very unpalatable grass not suited for forage, but no doubt the colonists tried to use it for this purpose. Distributed in open places, in low, moist areas and along stream banks was switchgrass (*Panicum virgatum*). This grass was valued likely as feed since it is much finer than the beachgrass and not nearly so crude as broomsedge. Actually the salt marshes along the Atlantic Coast were the main source of hay for the early colonists. These areas grow many grasses, but especially black grass (*Juncus geravid*) and saltgrass (*Distichlis spicata*).

In the Southeast a species called wire grass was said to be plentiful. When interspread with the savannahs, it furnished more abundant and nutritious feed. It became tough as it matured, and the pioneers practiced burning to secure young palatable new growth.

Many strains and types of corn had been developed by the Indians to meet the varied climate and soil conditions under which it was grown. The colonists first used corn for food and fodder primarily, but with the development of the silo late in the nineteenth century, it became one of the leading forage crops. Nearly 6 million acres are grown for silage purposes today.

The indigenous sunflower was found growing wild over much of America. It is especially adapted to the prairie states, but the eastern Indians had used it at an early date to serve for food in soups and other preparations. Sunflowers were found by Hariot in 1585 on Roanoke Island. The sunflower today is grown for silage purposes especially in the northern Plains states.

The grasses of the range lands or great prairie regions of the United States are for the most part native. This western area comprising over 850 million acres of mountains, deserts, forests, and grazing land includes miles of rolling grasslands. Here herds of buffalo, elk, deer, and other animals roamed at will and garnered the rich grasses for feed. Such prairie hay grasses as western wheatgrass (*Agropyron smithii*) and needle-and-thread (*Stipa comata*) are found in the northern Great Plains, big bluestem (*Andropogon furcatus*) and little bluestem (*A. scoparius*) in the eastern Great Plains, and silver beardgrass (*A. saccharoides*) in Texas. In the middle Great Plains from Kansas to Texas the grama grasses (*Bouteloua* sp.), switchgrass (*Panicum virgatum*), and *Andropogon* species predominate as hay grasses. With the introduction of livestock much mismanagement of the Western range lands occurred. These areas are said to be in poorer condition today than they were when the Indians grazed and hunted the countless buffalo. The productive prairie then also supported great numbers of wild fowl such as golden plovers, prairie chickens, geese, and ducks.

Early Introductions from Europe. The growing of cultivated meadow crops received attention at an early date in America. When the weaknesses of the natural meadow flora were recognized, the new grasses and legumes were given a trial.

The introduction of tame forage crops into America occurred shortly after the early settlements, either by design or accidentally in the course of bringing hay for feeding cattle on the ocean voyages. Later settlers from England were often advised to bring grass and clover seed as well as harvesting equipment to their new homes.

The introduced grasses and legumes were described in those early days simply as English grass, English hay, or English clover. The first written record of such grass being used for hay was given by Denton in 1670. He described it as growing on Long Island, New York. Here excellent English grass was produced, the seed of which was brought out of England and which was sometimes mowed twice a year, according to Denton. Josselyn, in 1674, said that the English grass clover when sown in New England thrives very well. Hugh Jones reported clover and sainfoin growing in Virginia in 1724. Red clover was said by Kalan to be growing in New York State in 1749. It must have been highly valued, as Kalan further indicated that after mowing it was permitted to dry and then put under cover, to be carried away at the first opportunity. Jared Elliot, an early agricultural historian, published a paper in 1749 in which he urged the planting of timothy and fowl meadow grass, especially the latter. His enthusiasm for these grasses was the result of his earlier experience in the New England colonies. America took the lead in forage-crop and pasture work at that early date, but later both England and Scotland surpassed this country. Thomas Jefferson in 1782 indicated that the following plants were grown in Virginia: lucerne, sainfoin, burnet, timothy, ray and orchard grass; also red, white, and yellow clover, greensward, bluegrass, and crabgrass.

Timothy. The most important hay grass in America now is timothy. It was first grown by a man named Herd prior to 1720 near the Piscataqua River mouth in New Hampshire. It was introduced from England where it was found growing in waste places, and was known as cat's-tail grass. Early records indicated that it was known as herd's-grass in the New England area. Timothy seed was taken to New York, Maryland, Virginia, and North Carolina by a Timothy Hanson who lived near Portsmouth, New Hampshire. It was widely accepted in these states and became known as Timothy Hanson's grass, which was later shortened to timothy. Jared Elliot sent seed of it to Benjamin Franklin in 1747, and when it was planted and grown Franklin described it as "mere timothy." Large portions of the eastern part of the United States were planted to timothy by the colonists, and it has been the dominant hay grass in this region ever since.

Orchard Grass. Orchard grass also became popular in America at an early date. Cultivation started in Virginia sometime before 1760. George Washington had this to say about it: "Orchard grass of all others is in my opinion the best mixture with clover: it blooms precisely at the same time, rises quick again after cutting, stands thick, yields well, and both cattle and horses are fond of it green or in hay. Alone unless sown very thickly it is apt to form tussocks." It was grown in Kentucky in 1817 and widely used in the Eastern states during that early period. It was described as an early grass with vigorous growing habits, highly valued for both hay and pasture purposes.

Alfalfa. Alfalfa was brought to the West Indies by Columbus. Its first mention in English North America was by Moore in 1736 who indicated it was growing on St. Simons Island, Georgia. In 1739 it was reported to be growing rather unsuccessfully in South Carolina by Eliza Lucas, a plantation owner, in a letter to her father. George Washington, writing to Jefferson in 1795, presented his problem with it as follows: "Lucerne has not succeeded better with me than with you; but I will give it another and fairer trial before it is abandoned altogether." This phase of the Eastern introduction of alfalfa was very unsuccessful. Another Eastern introduction took place in the limestone section of central New York about 1791. The crop has been readily grown in this region ever since.

By far the most important introduction of alfalfa occurred in California. The seed was introduced from Chile by gold-rush adventurers about 1850. Its first recorded seeding in California was by W. E. Cameron near Marysville in the Sacramento Valley in 1851. By 1858 this man had 270 acres planted to alfalfa. For a while it was known as Chilean clover and later as alfalfa.

The Millets. The millets were used as food by Old World inhabitants, the seed being highly valued. Foxtail millet and broomcorn millet came from Asia. Pearl millet is probably a native of Africa. The people who settled America were not used to eating millet as food, and so it became a forage crop here. It was reported grown in Massachusetts in 1637. Jared Elliot tried it in Connecticut in 1747 and recommended it as a catch crop to use when clover failed. German millet (*Panicum germanicum*) was distributed in 1854 by the U.S. Patent Office. It is still cultivated in the West and Southwest.

The Sorghums. The sorghums were natives of Africa. Sorghum introduction into America probably was associated with the bringing of slaves to the West Indies, the seed being used for their food. Lawson found it being grown by the colonists in Carolina about 1700. Many sorghum varieties were described at an early date, and much variability was found in this crop. Sorghum became significant in America only after the opening up of the drier regions west of the Mississippi River following the Civil War. In the dry regions it competes with corn, over which it has a real advantage in drought resistance and early maturity.

Sudan Grass. Sudan grass was introduced into the United States from African Sudan in 1909. Only 8 ounces of seed are said to have been brought in at that time, but from this seed vast acreages have grown until Sudan grass has become the most important temporary hay grass grown in America today.

Johnson Grass. Johnson grass (*Sorghum halapense*), also a sorghum but a perennial form, was obtained as seed from Turkey by Governor Means of South Carolina in 1835. Later William Johnson of Alabama obtained seed of it and began advertising its good qualities—hence the name "Johnson grass."

Descriptions of grasses and legumes together with their introductions could be given here for nearly all the economically important hay crops of the humid northeastern, northwestern, and southeastern United States. Suffice it to say that these introductions began at an early date in the life of the American colonies and are still being continued by exploration and importation.

Improvement of Cultural Practices. Washington, Jefferson, and others recognized the need for sod crops in their farm-crop rotations. An early practice was to grow corn and wheat until the soil was exhausted and then to take a new piece of ground and do the same thing again. Under this system only the number of cattle that could be supported by the wild hay from lowland meadows and swamps, together with corn tops and blades, could be raised.

The weakness of the system was apparent to Washington, and he strongly advocated rotations in which fields would be periodically seeded down to grasses and clover and better fertilizer practices would be followed. In those early days without sod rotations, yields of wheat in Virginia fell in a short time from 30 bushels to 8 or 10 bushels per acre.

While tame forage crops were taken up rapidly by the early settlers, there has been a great lag in improvement of such crops and in knowledge of cultural methods to employ for the highest degree of success in their planting and harvest. Emphasis is being placed on the hay crops now in most of the agricultural colleges and state experiment stations, and information is accumulating at a rapid pace.

References

1. Beal, W. J.: Grasses of North America, Henry Holt and Company, Inc., New York, 1896.
2. Carrier, L.: Beginnings of Agriculture in America, McGraw-Hill Book Company, Inc., New York, 1923.
3. Carrier, L., and K. S. Bort: History of Kentucky bluegrass and white clover in the United States, *Jour. Amer. Soc. Agron.*, **8**: 256–266 (1916).
4. DeCandolle, A.: Origin of Cultivated Plants, Appleton-Century-Crofts, Inc., New York, 1895.
5. Piper, C. V., and K. S. Bort: The early agricultural history of timothy, *Jour. Amer. Soc. Agron.*, **7**:1–14 (1915).
6. Sampson, Arthur W.: Native American Forage Plants, John Wiley & Sons, Inc., New York, 1924.
7. Sanford, Albert H.: The Story of Agriculture in the United States, D. C. Heath and Company, Boston, 1916.
8. Vinall, H. N., J. C. Stephens, and J. H. Martin: Identification, history and distribution of common sorghum varieties, *U.S. Dept. Agr. Tech. Bul.* 506 (1936).
9. Wing, Joseph E.: Alfalfa in America, Sanders Publishing Co., Chicago, 1909.

CHAPTER 2

GEOGRAPHY AND PRODUCTION

In 1947 a total of 60.7 million acres of cultivated forage crops and 14.6 million acres of wild hay were grown in the United States. The total yield of both types combined amounted to over 102 million tons with a farm value of 1½ billion dollars. The hay acreages may be compared with the

TABLE 1. ACREAGE OF IMPORTANT CROPS IN THE UNITED STATES

Crop	Acreage harvested, thousands		
	1936–1945	1946	1947
Corn....................	90,083	88,489	83,981
Hay.....................	72,373	74,173	75,291
Wheat..................	57,036	67,075	74,186
Oats....................	37,101	43,205	38,648
Cotton.................	23,845	17,615	21,148
Soybeans...............	6,418	9,806	11,125
Barley.................	12,407	10,411	10,947
Truck..................	3,383	4,109	3,695
Others.................	33,906	30,048	29,334
Total..............	336,552	344,931	348,355

SOURCE: U.S. Department of Agriculture, Crop Reporting Service, 1947.

acreage of other important crops in Table 1. There were grown in 1947, 21 million acres of cotton, 38½ million acres of oats, and 84 million acres of corn. Hay ranked second only to corn on the basis of acreage grown. It occupied more than 22 per cent of the total crop acreage shown in Table 1. These figures give some idea of the important role that harvested forages play in American agriculture.

PRINCIPAL CROPS

Clover and timothy mixed occupied the largest acreage of any hay type in 1947—23,402,000. Alfalfa was second with 14,908,000 acres, followed closely by wild hay with 14,600,000. Although the alfalfa acreage was second, its total yield stands first, the crop having produced 33,475,000 tons while clover and timothy mixed produced 32,569,000 tons. Wild

10

hay is very inferior in productivity, since only 13,306,000 tons were harvested, or slightly less than 1 ton per acre. Further data on yield and acreages of the main forage crops are given in Table 2.

TABLE 2. HAY BY KINDS: ACREAGE AND PRODUCTION,
UNITED STATES, 1929–1947

Year	Acreage harvested of tame hay, thousands								
	Alfalfa	Clover and timothy	Sweet-clover	Lespe-deza	Soy-bean	Cow-pea	Peanut vine	Grains cut green for hay	Miscel-laneous
1929	11,529	29,867	952	349	1,774	953	1,252	3,208	5,857
1934	11,691	20,143	744	1,850	4,227	2,321	1,528	6,793	7,064
1939	13,234	18,543	984	4,731	4,590	1,896	1,859	3,913	7,296
1944	14,480	21,375	414	5,983	2,747	926	3,202	3,024	7,396
1947	14,908	23,402	332	6,545	1,372	449	3,142	2,454	8,087
	Production, thousand tons								
1929	23,787	38,139	1,098	380	2,051	805	574	3,433	5,751
1934	19,036	16,512	620	1,709	4,545	1,830	660	4,849	5,922
1939	26,894	22,253	1,144	5,049	6,772	1,621	845	4,056	7,741
1944	31,702	28,771	511	5,390	3,217	728	1,563	3,640	8,323
1947	33,475	32,569	395	6,768	1,666	617	1,421	3,058	9,476

SOURCES: U.S. Department of Agriculture, Agricultural Statistics, 1945; U.S. Department of Agriculture, Crop Reporting Board, 1947.

Table 2, giving data by 5-year intervals, shows the alfalfa acreage gradually increasing along with lespedeza, peanut vines, and miscellaneous tame hays such as orchard grass, redtop, and bromegrass. The acreages of soybeans, cowpeas, and grains have fluctuated. There is a decrease in sweetclover for hay and a very significant downward trend in clover and timothy mixed until 1944. This latter decline had been going on since 1910 and was in part the result of tractor replacement of horses on the farm so that less timothy is needed for feeding.

HAY REGIONS

The United States may be divided into a half dozen or more haymaking regions, using as a basis for such divisions the predominant plant species grown in any region. Soil and climate, especially moisture and temperature relations, determine to a large extent the type of plants suited to any locality. Since there are no sharp lines of division of climate or soil, species necessarily overlap from region to region and this may cause some confusion.   A broad viewpoint and an appreciation of dominating species as shown in a combination of yield and acreage records should overcome this difficulty.   In discussing these regions, accompanying tables are given which show the acreage and production of the five leading states for the prevailing hay type.

Timothy and Clover.   The most important haymaking section in America is often called the timothy-clover region.   This area lies generally north of Virginia and Kentucky.   It is east of the 96th meridian in Kansas and the 98th in Nebraska and the Dakotas.   Roughly, it consists of the North Atlantic and North Central states, including Maryland and West Virginia.   Almost 90 per cent of all timothy and clover hay grown in the United States is found in this region.   More than three times as much

TABLE 3.   ACREAGE AND PRODUCTION OF CLOVER AND TIMOTHY HAY

State	Acreage harvested, thousands			Production, thousand tons		
	Average 1936–1945	1946	1947	Average 1936 1945	1946	1947
Wisconsin............	2,405	2,963	2,815	3,713	4,296	4,222
New York............	2,806	2,834	2,721	3,920	4,676	4,490
Iowa.................	1,851	2,359	2,383	2,417	3,421	3,336
Pennsylvania.........	1,924	2,098	2,014	2,514	3,042	2,920
Ohio.................	1,771	1,994	1,994	2,267	2,891	2,592

SOURCE: U.S. Department of Agriculture, Crop Reporting Board, 1947.

clover and timothy is grown here as alfalfa.   Cold winters combined with shallow, poorly drained soils and lack of adapted alfalfa varieties are largely responsible for the dominance of clover and timothy.   The states of Wisconsin and New York lead in both the acreage and production of this type of hay.

Clover and timothy may be grown with success in other sections of the country; on the other hand, there are places within the region not suited to this crop.   Good crops of this type of hay are grown in Tennessee and Kentucky, in the moist valleys of the Rocky Mountains, and in the Pacific Northwest.   Areas within the clover-timothy belt that do not support the crop are the coastal plains of eastern Virginia and Maryland, the redtop region of southern Illinois, and the sandy soils of Wisconsin, Michigan, and Minnesota.

Annual Legumes.   The region of annual legumes lies to the south of the clover-timothy area, extending to the Gulf of Mexico and westward to Texas, being coincident with the cotton-growing region.   These legumes, which are predominantly southern, include cowpeas, peanut vines, crimson clover, the vetches, and lespedeza, as well as soybeans, which overlap strongly into the clover belt. The annual legumes fit into southern rotation practices in which cotton is the dominating influence. Also contributing to hay production in this region are grasses such as Sudan, Johnson, and Bermuda. Most hay grown for market purposes here comes from the rich, moist soils of the lower Mississippi Valley.

TABLE 4. ACREAGE AND PRODUCTION OF LESPEDEZA

State	Acreage harvested, thousands			Production, thousand tons		
	Average 1936–1945	1946	1947	Average 1936–1945	1946	1947
Missouri.............	1,012	1,261	1,450	1,031	1,261	1,450
Tennessee.............	1,172	1,166	1,119	1,231	1,399	1,231
Kentucky............	679	794	754	751	992	942
Arkansas.............	490	747	732	474	822	622
Virginia..............	381	479	460	396	527	437

SOURCE: U.S. Department of Agriculture, Crop Reporting Board, 1947.

Lespedeza is a new hay crop that has risen to a position of great importance in the annual legume area. There are three major types that contribute to its adaptability and usefulness in improving the soil, while it furnishes forage at the same time. In 1947 a band of five states across the southeastern section of the United States led all the others for this crop with the acreage and production in the same order. These states in order of their leadership were Missouri, Tennessee, Kentucky, Arkansas, and Virginia.

TABLE 5. ACREAGE AND PRODUCTION OF PEANUTS FOR HAY

State	Acreage harvested, thousands			Production, thousand tons		
	Average 1936–1945	1946	1947	Average 1936–1945	1946	1947
Georgia..............	768	1,008	998	292	393	379
Texas................	478	675	857	242	371	386
Alabama.............	372	434	420	181	195	189
Oklahoma............	118	217	319	64	119	160
North Carolina........	239	288	251	148	173	151

SOURCE: U.S. Department of Agriculture, Crop Reporting Board, 1947.

While peanuts are of lesser importance for hay than lespedeza, nevertheless they make an important contribution to the forage economy of the South. The acreage grown has increased in recent years because of the added emphasis placed on this crop, especially in Texas. Georgia is the leading state in the production of peanut hay, followed by Texas and Alabama. Actually the hay is a valuable by-product of the peanut crop, the crop seldom being planted solely for forage purposes.

The practice of harvesting soybeans for hay has decreased during recent years. This was due to the heavy industrial demand for the grain to be used in extracting oil and making many other commercial products. Soybeans are widely adapted in the United States. Evidence of this is the

TABLE 6. ACREAGE AND PRODUCTION OF SOYBEANS FOR HAY

State	Acreage harvested, thousands			Production, thousand tons		
	Average 1936–1945	1946	1947	Average 1936–1945	1946	1947
Illinois................	536	186	169	734	270	186
North Carolina.........	194	150	150	210	165	172
Mississippi............	238	143	130	278	179	169
Alabama..............	224	175	124	205	175	112
Indiana..............	358	136	108	480	190	151

SOURCE: U.S. Department of Agriculture, Crop Reporting Board, 1947.

fact that of the five leading states in soybean hay production, two are to be found in the clover-timothy region. In 1947, Illinois harvested 169,000 acres of this to lead all other states, and North Carolina was second with 150,000 acres.

Alfalfa. The largest hay region in the United States is an area in which alfalfa predominates. This region lies immediately to the west of and overlaps with the clover-timothy belt. Alfalfa is the chief hay crop throughout the subhumid area and on the irrigated lands of the whole western half of the United States. There are also areas in the clover-timothy region where alfalfa is prominent. It is grown extensively in Minnesota, Wisconsin, Michigan, and Iowa, to a lesser extent in the limestone regions of Indiana, Ohio, and New York State. Scattered acreages occur throughout the clover-timothy, annual legume, and other regions.

Alfalfa contributes more hay than any other crop species. The quality of the hay tends to improve from East to West, with the leafiest and greenest production coming from the Far West. The desirable properties are harder to obtain in the East, where the greater rainfall and humidity make haying more difficult.

TABLE 7. ACREAGE AND PRODUCTION OF ALFALFA FOR HAY

State	Acreage harvested, thousands			Production, thousand tons		
	Average 1936– 1945	1946	1947	Average 1936– 1945	1946	1947
Michigan..............	1,221	1,040	1,092	1,918	1,404	1,693
Kansas...............	653	826	1,016	1,209	1,569	1,981
California.............	845	1,005	1,005	3,650	4,623	4,623
Nebraska.............	797	913	1,004	1,308	1,735	2,058
Wisconsin.............	1,079	820	984	2,280	1,517	2,263

SOURCE: U.S. Department of Agriculture, Crop Reporting Board, 1947.

Even though California has not had the greatest acreage of alfalfa hay, it has led all other states in the tonnage produced. An ideal climate combined with irrigation and dry-land farming make this record possible. Four or more cuttings per year are not uncommon in that state. California's increasingly important dairy industry is largely responsible for an acreage of 1,005,000 in 1947. The decrease in alfalfa acreages from over a million per state in Wisconsin, Minnesota, and Michigan to less than a million, except in Michigan, is attributed to decreasing seed supplies of adapted varieties and to the incidence of bacterial wilt.

Prairie Hay. Of all the hay produced in this country in 1947, about 22 per cent was native forage, most of which came from the Great Plains east of the Rocky Mountains. The section may be called the prairie-hay region and extends from North Dakota and Minnesota south to Texas and westward to California. This area supports the most valuable native

TABLE 8. ACREAGE AND PRODUCTION OF WILD HAY*

State	Acreage harvested, thousands			Production, thousand tons		
	Average 1936– 1945	1946	1947	Average 1936– 1945	1946	1947
South Dakota..........	2,162	2,893	3,067	1,529	2,025	2,300
Nebraska..............	2,692	2,707	2,815	1,861	1,760	2,252
North Dakota..........	1,999	2,370	2,607	1,666	2,014	2,346
Minnesota.............	1,460	1,282	1,308	1,558	1,410	1,439
Montana..............	707	822	880	613	658	748

SOURCE: U.S. Department of Agriculture, Crop Reporting Board, 1947.
* Includes prairie, marsh, and salt grasses.

prairie grasses such as the bluestems and wheatgrasses. South Dakota has the largest harvested acreage of this type of hay, while Nebraska, North Dakota, and Minnesota are among the leaders. The yield, in general, is low, ranging from ¾ to 1 ton per acre, but the cost of producing such hay is very little, which accounts for its popularity.

Sorghum. In the Southwest is the sorghum region. The area of most intensive cultivation is in Texas, Kansas, and Oklahoma, but the region overlaps northward to the Dakotas. Sudan grass is the type used for hay and pasture, and the sweet sorghums are used for silage and fodder. For silage purposes, sorghum replaces corn to a large extent in this region.

TABLE 9.   ACREAGE AND PRODUCTION OF SORGHUMS FOR FORAGE

State	Acreage harvested, thousands			Production, thousand tons*		
	Average 1936– 1945	1946	1947	Average 1936– 1945	1946	1947
Texas................	3,257	2,390	1,750	3,970	2,920	1,925
Kansas...............	1,409	1,302	989	2,446	2,083	1,385
Oklahoma............	1,084	1,107	818	1,338	1,439	900
Colorado.............	475	350	304	491	385	395
Nebraska.............	698	316	273	1,114	521	410

SOURCE: U.S. Department of Agriculture, Crop Reporting Board, 1947.
* Dry weight.

Small Grains. The Pacific Northwest including northern California constitutes the region of small grains for hay. This section has a cool, moist climate which is ideal for such crops. The 732,000 acres harvested

TABLE 10.   ACREAGE AND PRODUCTION OF GRAINS CUT GREEN FOR HAY

State	Acreage harvested, thousands			Production, thousand tons		
	Average 1936– 1945	1946	1947	Average 1936– 1945	1946	1947
California.............	710	732	732	1,103	1,061	1,061
Oregon...............	244	219	226	322	318	282
Washington...........	274	170	153	377	230	191
Montana..............	184	135	142	149	128	142
Missouri..............	280	110	120	224	99	108

SOURCE: U.S. Department of Agriculture, Crop Reporting Board, 1947.

in California in 1947 represented about one-third of all the grain cut for hay in America and the most grown in any one state. The cereal grains are used for hay to some extent in every state.

Sweetclover. Sweetclover production is found mainly in the prairie-hay and clover-timothy regions. Montana led all other states in 1947 with 76,000 acres, followed by Minnesota with 31,000 acres. The Corn Belt states all grow small acreages of this crop. Its popularity is diminishing in the United States, with the acreage decreasing from a high of 1,118,000 in 1936 to only 332,000 in 1947.

Silage Corn. The silage corn region is about the same as the clover-timothy region. In 1947 Wisconsin produced more than 25 per cent of all the corn grown for this purpose, having 1,222,000 acres from which more than 9 million tons of silage were made. Minnesota and New York followed Wisconsin with 692 and 465 thousand acres, respectively. The fact that these three states are also the leading dairy states in America accounts for such large acreages in silage corn.

TABLE 11. UTILIZATION OF CORN FOR SILAGE, 1946 AND 1947

State	1946		1947	
	Acreage harvested, thousands	Production, thousand tons	Acreage harvested, thousands	Production, thousand tons
Wisconsin.............	1,222	9,409	1,185	9,598
Minnesota.............	692	5,744	680	4,896
New York.............	465	4,324	432	3,629
Michigan.............	289	1,734	289	1,763
Iowa.................	178	1,869	280	1,792

SOURCE: U.S. Department of Agriculture, Crop Reporting Board, 1947.

TOTAL ACREAGE AND PRODUCTION

The total acreage and production of hay crops in America are shown in Table 12. The leading states in total yield are Wisconsin with 6,918,000 tons, New York with 6,300,000 tons, and California with 6,098,000 tons. Florida and Rhode Island produced the smallest tonnages.

Over a period of years hay production has shown a steady upward trend, as indicated in Fig. 2. Tame hay has increased from 63 million tons in 1930 to over 89 million tons in 1947. Wild hay has increased by 4 million tons and corn silage by 6 million. The total increase in hay and silage production since 1930 totals 34 million tons, or nearly 32 per cent.

TABLE 12.   ACREAGE AND PRODUCTION OF ALL HAY IN THE UNITED STATES

State	Acreage harvested, thousands			Yield per acre, tons			Production, thousand tons		
	Average 1936–1945	1946	1947	Average 1936–1945	1946	1947	Average 1936–1945	1946	1947
Maine......	907	873	880	0.93	0.97	1.08	840	844	950
N.H.........	366	377	376	1.12	1.18	1.26	410	443	473
Vt...........	962	1,047	1,052	1.30	1.43	1.51	1,254	1,499	1,590
Mass........	368	381	372	1.47	1.71	1.62	541	650	602
R.I.........	36	37	36	1.32	1.43	1.58	48	53	57
Conn.......	294	296	296	1.44	1.62	1.68	424	480	496
N.Y.........	3,964	3,991	3,907	1.39	1.62	1.61	5,508	6,446	6,300
N.J.........	254	261	253	1.56	1.66	1.70	396	434	430
Pa..........	2,414	2,539	2,437	1.37	1.50	1.50	3,302	3,804	3,651
Ohio........	2,530	2,536	2,570	1.41	1.54	1.40	3,554	3,895	3,602
Ind.........	1,951	1,807	1,674	1.32	1.37	1.36	2,578	2,480	2,284
Ill..........	2,866	2,688	2,596	1.35	1.47	1.47	3,881	3,949	3,810
Mich........	2,699	2,798	2,830	1.38	1.24	1.32	3,718	3,464	3,730
Wis.........	4,009	4,106	4,134	1.66	1.51	1.67	6,672	6,220	6,918
Minn.......	4,484	4,032	4,009	1.43	1.46	1.42	6,419	5,897	5,687
Iowa........	3,514	3,244	3,317	1.54	1.63	1.55	5,411	5,273	5,154
Mo..........	3,276	3,545	3,804	1.08	1.19	1.15	3,586	4,214	4,392
N.Dak......	3,002	3,068	3,281	0.92	0.89	0.96	2,773	2,727	3,140
S.Dak.......	2,898	3,478	3,687	0.79	0.80	0.86	2,335	2,775	3,166
Nebr........	3,791	3,827	4,017	0.91	0.98	1.13	3,476	3,732	4,549
Kans........	1,536	1,721	2,027	1.39	1.35	1.54	2,151	2,327	3,116
Del.........	72	72	69	1.28	1.38	1.36	92	99	94
Md..........	423	448	449	1.27	1.41	1.36	537	631	611
Va..........	1,263	1,405	1,351	1.08	1.24	1.06	1,376	1,744	1,438
W.Va.......	753	812	810	1.14	1.30	1.16	864	1,059	940
N.C.........	1,178	1,253	1,225	0.96	1.02	0.99	1,130	1,283	1,207
S.C.........	596	501	490	0.74	0.90	0.78	441	449	382
Ga..........	1,312	1,402	1,373	0.55	0.52	0.51	714	728	696
Fla.........	114	120	123	0.55	0.48	0.51	63	57	63
Ky..........	1,591	1,827	1,865	1.19	1.41	1.44	1,937	2,583	2,678
Tenn.......	1,897	1,844	1,855	1.09	1.31	1.24	2,076	2,417	2,297
Ala.........	1,031	1,007	927	0.74	0.78	0.74	762	781	687
Miss........	896	854	806	1.19	1.38	1.22	1,064	1,182	980
Ark.........	1,301	1,351	1,370	1.08	1.20	1.01	1,413	1,623	1,382
La..........	321	335	327	1.22	1.28	1.17	390	429	381
Okla.......	1,185	1,322	1,545	1.16	1.13	1.18	1,386	1,490	1,819
Tex........	1,403	1,489	1,681	0.96	0.98	0.85	1,348	1,454	1,436
Mont.......	1,939	2,260	2,397	1.18	1.14	1.16	2,299	2,569	2,773
Idaho......	1,159	1,151	1,089	2.07	2.11	2.20	2,399	2,430	2,394
Wyo........	1,055	1,097	1,115	1.14	1.13	1.19	1,202	1,243	1,325
Colo.......	1,410	1,393	1,405	1.50	1.47	1.65	2,115	2,044	2,324
N.Mex......	203	224	229	2.02	2.29	2.23	410	514	510
Ariz........	253	310	273	2.24	2.39	2.19	568	740	598
Utah.......	577	575	559	1.99	1.94	2.10	1,149	1,118	1,172
Nev.........	400	436	430	1.44	1.53	1.55	577	666	666
Wash.......	937	876	824	1.90	2.04	1.96	1,780	1,787	1,617
Oreg.......	1,108	1,088	1,089	1.73	1.74	1.69	1,914	1,896	1,835
Calif.......	1,875	2,069	2,060	2.77	2.96	2.96	5,202	6,117	6,098
U.S........	72,373	74,173	75,291	1.30	1.36	1.36	94,490	100,739	102,500

SOURCE: U.S. Department of Agriculture, Crop Reporting Service, 1947.

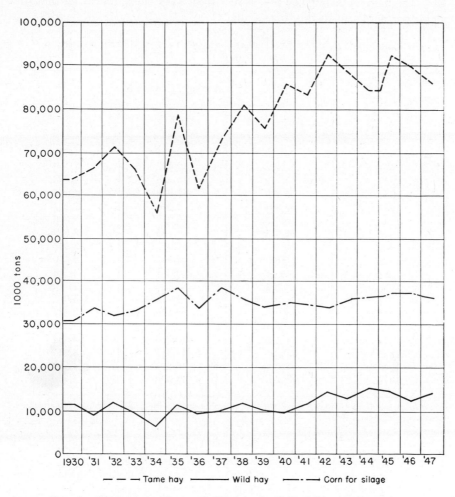

FIG. 2.   Production of hay and silage in the United States, 1930–1947.

During this same period the acreage in tame hay increased from 54 to 60½ million acres, wild hay by ¾ million acres. Data are given in Table 13. The increase in acreage thus is less than 9 per cent, indicating that the yields per acre are steadily increasing.

TABLE 13. ACREAGE OF HAY AND SILAGE IN THE UNITED STATES, 1930–1947

Year	Acreage, thousands		
	Tame hay	Wild hay	Corn for silage
1930	53,996	13,951	4,875
1931	56,103	12,057	4,710
1932	55,119	14,293	4,293
1933	55,810	12,629	4,864
1934	56,361	9,026	7,132
1935	55,614	12,948	5,309
1936	56,618	11,125	8,539
1937	53,943	12,072	5,543
1938	55,631	12,563	4,456
1939	57,046	12,051	4,513
1940	60,035	11,884	4,716
1941	59,317	12,459	4,091
1942	60,117	12,528	3,897
1943	60,880	13,464	4,370
1944	59,547	14,520	4,664
1945	59,905	14,311	4,641
1946	60,312	13,861	4,550
1947	60,691	14,600	4,640

SOURCES: U.S. Department of Agriculture, Agricultural Statistics, 1945; U.S. Department of Agriculture, Crop Reporting Board, 1947.

References

1. Agricultural Statistics, 1945, U.S. Department of Agriculture.
2. Crop Production, Annual Summary for 1945, U.S. Department of Agriculture, Bureau of Agricultural Economics, Crop Reporting Board.
3. Crop Production, Annual Summary for 1947, U.S. Department of Agriculture, Bureau of Agricultural Economics, Crop Reporting Board.
4. Johnson, Neil W.: Changes in Hay Production in War and Peace, U.S. Department of Agriculture, Bureau of Agricultural Economics, 1945.
5. Piper, C. V., *et al.*: Our forage resources, U.S. Department of Agriculture Yearbook, 1923, pp. 311–414.

CHAPTER 3

INFLUENCE OF CLIMATE AND SOIL

Crop production is an expression of the climatic and soil environment, together with the crop species or variety concerned. Thus such factors as rainfall, temperature, sunshine, and relative humidity have a profound influence on the type of crop that can be grown as well as on the efficiency of production. Similarly, each plant species is affected by the soil, whether it is deep or shallow, acid or alkaline, dry or wet, fertile or poor, sandy or clayey.

GENERAL CLIMATIC CONDITIONS

The development of various grass regions in the United States is due basically to the temperature and rainfall common to the region. In addition, adjustments in microclimate and the soil environment have been made

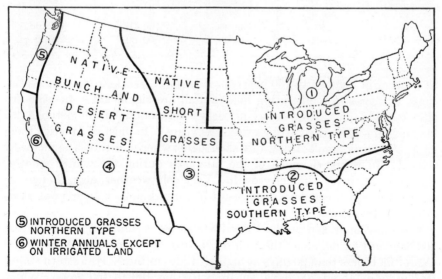

FIG. 3. Grasslands of the United States, showing dominant type of grasses in each region as determined by climate. (*U.S. Department of Agriculture.*)

to encourage the growing of our forage crops. Forests have been removed; soils have been limed, fertilized, drained, or irrigated; and competition from other species has been controlled through tillage methods. In the West,

21

undesirable physical properties such as heavy clays or light sands, presence of rocks and boulders, excessive dryness or wetness, soil depth, inadequate aeration, and low nutrient and lime content. Minor elements such as boron, zinc, and copper are deficient in some regions. The presence of excessive selenium in certain soils may prove toxic to livestock consuming herbage therefrom.

EXAMPLES OF CROP ADAPTATION

The influence of climate and soil is thus very marked in crop production. Fortunately, the 125 forage species (hay and pasture) have a wide range of requirements that permit the broad application of their culture. Varying degrees of resistance to cold and drought are found among the several species, and even among varieties. The same is true of adaptation to alkaline or acid soils. The length of day may stimulate vegetative growth or encourage flowering. Different degrees of root aeration are necessary for normal growth of the various plants, and this affects their adaptation to different types of soils.

RESPONSES TO CLIMATE

The response of crops to temperature, drought, day length, available moisture, and other factors has been measured for some of the forage species and varieties.

Temperature. In the humid region, grasses and legumes are adapted latitudinally, depending on temperature. In the prairie region, on the other hand, the grasses are less dependent on temperature, extending from North to South over a wide range of conditions.

Thus in the humid East red, alsike, and ladino clover of the legumes grow well in the Northeast, whereas the lespedezas and Kudzu vine are adapted to the Southeast. Of the grasses, brome, orchard, redtop, and timothy are adapted to the North and Bermuda and Johnson grass to the Southeast. Differences in cold resistance in the forage crops are particularly striking. Data from a test in which alfalfa, red clover, and several of the lespedezas were exposed to various freezing temperatures are given in Table 15. The plants were 6- and 7-week-old seedlings that were hardened for 6 to 10 days at 0 to 2° C. prior to exposure. In this test red clover and alfalfa survived completely. The lespedezas showed varying degrees of resistance to decreasing temperatures, with Korean the least hardy and sericea the most. Unhardened plants of the same species exposed to freezing temperatures at various stages of development respond similarly when they have attained a growth of 6 to 8 inches. Greatest seedling survival among the lespedezas occurs when the plants are 2 to 5 weeks old and decreases thereafter, except with sericea. Red clover and alfalfa are most susceptible to cold as young seedlings (2 to 5 weeks) and increase in hardiness with advancing age.

TABLE 15. PER CENT SURVIVAL OF ALFALFA, RED CLOVER, AND LESPEDEZAS AFTER EXPOSURE FOR 16 HOURS TO VARIOUS TEMPERATURES

Crop	Freezing temperature, °C.				
	−1.7	−2.5	−2.8	−4.1	Average
Alfalfa..................	100	100	100	100	100
Red clover...............	100	100	100	100	100
Lespedeza sericea..........	100	84	73	15	68
Common lespedeza.......	92	92	0	0	47
Kobe...................	100	36	4	0	35
Tennessee 76.............	89	48	0	0	34
Korean.................	67	25	0	0	23

SOURCE: *Jour. Amer. Soc. Agron.*, **26** (1934).

Variation in hardiness within a species has been recognized as an important factor in growing crops in the northern states. Some results from comparative hardiness tests conducted in Minnesota[3] with red clover strains showed a range in winterkilling of 7 to 92 per cent. American strains were far superior in hardiness to the European. Even seed produced in this country in milder climates such as Tennessee and Oregon was inferior to that grown under Minnesota conditions.

Alfalfa varies most strikingly in its adaptation to temperature conditions. As shown in Fig. 5, hardy types are essential in northern United States,

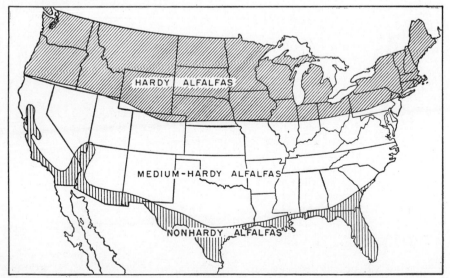

FIG. 5. Latitudinal adaptation of alfalfa in the United States. (*Bureau of Plant Industry, Soils and Agricultural Engineering, U.S. Department of Agriculture.*)

medium hardy in the central region, and the nonhardy group on the far-southern border. Variation in resistance to cold thus occurs among varieties and strains in this species. Certain varieties have been reported surviving in Siberia at −84°F., and other varieties withstood summer temperatures of 120°F.

Grasses also vary in their degree of resistance to cold. Studies conducted in North Dakota[22] on some 72-day-old seedlings of the prairie grasses show differences within and between the various species. Crested wheatgrass was more hardy than any of the other grasses, and the Fairway strain was best in this test. The range of survival was 27 to 100 per cent. Bromegrass of Kansas origin winterkilled most severely.

Drought Resistance. The need for drought resistance in forage crops is more critical in dry-land regions than in the humid sections. The ability of grasses and legumes to escape injury or even death in the seedling and sod stages is important, however, in all parts of America. Tests for drought resistance with various grasses and legumes by the Minnesota Station[23] showed a correlation between seedling and sod resistance to drought. Seedling resistance thus appears to be a guide or index to resistance of the mature sod. Data on seedling resistance to drought are given in Table 16. Russian wild ryegrass and crested wheatgrass were most resistant in Utah tests. In Minnesota crested wheatgrass was superior, and slender wheatgrass, orchard grass, and alsike clover were inferior. Drought resistance of

TABLE 16. PERCENTAGE SEEDLING SURVIVAL OF SPECIES OF GRASSES AND ALFALFA AND ALSIKE CLOVER FOLLOWING CONTROLLED SOIL DROUGHT TREATMENTS

Species	Average per cent survival	
	Utah*	Minnesota†
Alfalfa.................	....	42
Alsike clover...........	....	0
Crested wheatgrass......	73.6	59
Meadow foxtail..........	51.3	42
Orchard grass...........	67.9	2
Russian wild-rye.........	82.0	..
Slender wheatgrass.......	35.0	0
Tall oatgrass...........	68.3	..

Jour. Amer. Soc. Agron., **36** (1944).
†*Jour. Amer. Soc. Agron.*, **30** (1938).

a number of prairie grasses has also been investigated.[20] The grama grasses, buffalo grass, and *Sporobolus asper* were shown to be decidedly superior to the other species tested. *Bouteloua gracilis* is given credit for being most resistant to drought and *Agropyron smithii* the least in these studies.

Differences in resistance to drought also exist within species. Thus bromegrass was studied in detail in Utah,[8] and it was shown that a Nebraska selection H–1 survived by 70 per cent compared with only 19 per cent for the Washington selection L–4. The type and extent of the root system and the rate of development were shown to be significant in developing drought resistance in the case of this species.

Day Length. The time of flowering of grasses and legumes has a direct bearing on haymaking since the selection of compatible mixtures is guided in part by this natural phenomenon. Certain factors such as day length, temperature, and species or variety influence time of flowering. Plants grown in northern and southern areas would, therefore, be expected to differ in their flowering and heading dates. A comparison of a number of timothy strains grown at different latitudes gives evidence on this point.[7] The longer the day, or the farther north these timothy strains were grown, the later the date of heading. The earliest strain headed 21 days earlier in Washington, D.C., than it did at Guelph, Ontario. Early strains began to head and bloom in day lengths of 10 to 12 hours. Late strains required longer days before heading was initiated. The strains all matured during the month of June in Canada but were more widely spaced in the latitude of Washington.

Not all grasses and legumes respond in the same way to day length. Results of studies in which various grasses were exposed to different day lengths are given in Table 17. Orchard grass, reed canary, bromegrass,

TABLE 17. EFFECT OF PHOTOPERIOD ON TIME OF APPEARANCE
OF GRASS INFLORESCENCES

Daily light period, hr.	Orchard grass	Reed canary grass	Brome- grass	Huron timothy	Indian grass	Eastern gramagrass
10	None	None	None	None	None	June 2
14	May 8	May 20	May 23	None	Aug. 11	June 20
18	May 9	May 18	May 6	May 23	Oct. 27	June 23

SOURCE: *Jour. Agr. Res.*, **62** (1941).

timothy, and Indian grass failed to head at a 10-hour day but at longer day lengths normal flowering occurred. Indian grass was delayed in flowering by an 18-hour day. The eastern gamagrass flowered irrespective of the light interval tried, but the longer intervals delayed the flowering.

The lespedezas have been observed to respond markedly to day length. Some data for this character are given in Table 18. All the lespedezas

TABLE 18. RESPONSE OF LESPEDEZA VARIETIES TO LIGHT PERIODS

Variety	7-hr. period, seed set, days	Normal period, blooming, days	17-hr. period
L. stipulaceae.....	57	117	No blossoms at
L. striata........	62	121	end of 217 days
L. stipulaceae.....	57	136	
L. striata........	60	132	

SOURCE: *Jour. Am. Soc. Agron.*, **33** (1941).

produced seed at an early date under the short day length. Maturity was slower with the normal day and did not occur at all under the 17-hour period. The production of seed under a short day is all-important in the Southern states where natural reseeding occurs.

Water Requirement. The water requirements of various plants have been studied in an attempt to determine those most economical in their water demands. This is particularly significant in dry regions, but is also of value in growing crops throughout the United States. Many factors influence the quantity of water required to produce a certain weight of dry matter, and so results of experiments conducted in various parts of the country could not be expected to be in complete agreement.

Early work on the relative water requirements of plants was conducted in Colorado. Some of the data secured there are given in Table 19. The water requirement for bromegrass and western wheatgrass is thus more than 1,000 pounds per pound of dry matter produced. Sunflower, soybeans, alfalfa, and the clovers are intermediate in this respect and corn and

TABLE 19. POUNDS OF WATER REQUIRED TO PRODUCE ONE POUND OF DRY MATTER IN VARIOUS CROPS GROWN AT AKRON, COLORADO

Crop	Water requirement	Crop	Water requirement
Proso millet.............	208	Soybean................	672
German millet...........	248	Hairy vetch	690
Red Amber sorgo	298	Sunflower..............	705
Iowa Silvermine.........	302	Crested wheatgrass	705
Buffalo grass.............	308	Canada pea............	775
Sudan grass.............	359	Red clover.............	789
Cowpea.................	571	Crimson clover.........	805
Sweetclover.............	638	Bromegrass............	1,016
Alfalfa.................	659	Western wheatgrass......	1,076

SOURCE: *Jour. Agr. Res.*, **3** (1914).

the sorgos the more efficient users of water. Water requirement is not a measure of drought resistance. In Michigan[21] a study on rate of water usage by various forage crops showed that timothy was least demanding and bromegrass most during the growing season. Orchard grass, reed canary, and redtop were intermediate in this respect. The need for water is probably directly related to comparative growth rates of the different plants.

Response to Soil Factors

Conditions below the soil surface are often as important as the climate above. The soil, like the crops growing on it, is influenced strongly by the climatic conditions to which it has been subjected over long periods of time. On a climatic basis, the common major soils of the United States fall into four groups as follows: (1) the gray-brown soils of the Northeast, (2) the red-yellow soils of the Southeast, (3) the black prairie soils of the Central and prairie states, and (4) the soils of the arid West. The gray-brown soils are found in the northern half of that part of the United States lying east of the Mississippi River. Heavy rainfall over many centuries has leached out the lime and plant nutrients leaving an acid, infertile soil, low in humus content. The yellow-red soils have been leached even more strongly than the soils in the Northeast, and they have also been exposed to higher temperatures. They are, therefore, more acid and less fertile. This group of soils lies east of Texas and south of the Tennessee River. The third soil group, representing the prairie soils, extends from the Red River Valley on the north to the Rio Grande Valley in the south and eastward across the Corn Belt to Ohio. Some loss of nutrients and lime has occurred, but in general these soils are fertile and slightly acid to alkaline. Water is often a limiting factor in growing crops in this area. The fourth group is the desert soils. They are grayish-brown in color and extend over most of the area lying west of Kansas. Except for a thin strip along the Pacific Coast, rainfall is very limited, and thus there has been little loss of fertility from leaching. A high concentration of alkali is sometimes found, and if water can be supplied by irrigation these arid areas can be made highly productive.

The soils of the Northeast need lime, phosphoric acid, potash, and some nitrogen; the soils of the Southeast require lime, phosphoric acid, potash, and extra nitrogen; the black prairie soils need such minerals as phosphoric acid and potash; the desert soils need water primarily.

Moisture. Moisture content often determines the type of crop that can be grown on any particular soil. Thus the sweetclovers can be grown at low moisture where red clover would not persist. Alsike clover, reed canary grass, and redtop are adapted to fairly wet soils, but alfalfa requires a well-drained soil. Crested wheatgrass is known for its ability to grow and persist under very dry conditions in the northern prairie states.

Acidity. Crops that are very sensitive to soil acidity are alfalfa, sweet clover, and barley. Bermuda grass, corn, red clover, and the sorghums are more tolerant, and alsike clover, lespedeza, rye, and soybeans will stand considerable acidity and still grow well.

Type. Tall oatgrass and orchard grass grow satisfactorily on light soils, but timothy and bromegrass require moderately heavy soils. These and many other examples of adaptation to the soil are available.

Aeration. Most plants respond favorably to good soil aeration. Oxygen is related to the nitrogen and mineral absorption of plants, and so controlled studies have been conducted to determine the root oxygen needs of various crops. Data on soybeans given in Table 20 show that yields of soybeans

TABLE 20. COMPARATIVE DRY WEIGHT PRODUCTION OF SOYBEAN PLANTS GROWN AT DIFFERENT OXYGEN TENSIONS

Dry weight	Dissolved oxygen, p.p.m.			
	0	4	8	16
Top...............	11.0	12.8	12.4	13.4
Root.............	0.8	1.4	1.7	1.6
Total............	11.8	14.2	14.1	15.0

SOURCE: *Soil Sci.,* **53** (1942).

increased with increasing quantities of oxygen dissolved in the nutrient solutions. Increase in root growth was greater than proportional top growth and 4 p.p.m. of oxygen gave the superior response. Such lowland species as alsike clover, reed canary grass, and redtop probably have lower oxygen requirement than soybeans, alfalfa, or corn.

TABLE 21. CROP PLANTS MOST LIKELY TO SUCCEED IN THE PRESENCE OF DIFFERENT DEGREES OF SALINITY

0.1–0.4	0.4–0.6	0.6–0.8	0.8–1.0
Alfalfa	Sweetclover	Slender wheatgrass	Mangels
Vetch	Foxtail millet	Crested wheatgrass	Strawberry clover
Field peas	Wheat	Italian wheatgrass	Rhodes grass
Red clover	Oats	Meadow fescue	Bermuda grass
Corn	Sunflower	Kale	Western wheatgrass
Alsike clover	Cowpeas	Sorgo	Bromegrass
Timothy	Orchard grass	Barley hay	Tall oatgrass

SOURCES: *U.S. Dept. Agr. Cir.* 404 (1936); *Calif. Agr. Exp. Sta. Cir.* 292 (1925); *Utah Agr. Exp. Sta. Bul.* 168 (1919).

Alkali Tolerance. Grasses and legumes have been classified on the basis of resistance to alkalinity, as shown in Table 21. The forage grasses appear to be among the most resistant species to alkaline conditions. Mixtures of western grasses are suggested for alkaline soils. Alfalfa is difficult to start in saline soils, but once established it is quite resistant.

A Crop for Each Situation

Grasses and legumes used for forage are thus numerous and of diverse adaptation. For any given combination of soil regions, latitude, altitude, and climatic conditions, there are grasses or legumes that can be grown for livestock feed. In the several regions a most impressive fact is apparent. In all soil regions except the chernozem and desert the climax vegetation would be other than grass. For the successful culture of forage crops in these regions where grass does not flourish naturally, constant alertness to soil improvements is essential. Protection against the climax vegetation must be afforded or else alfalfa, red clover, timothy, and other such species would be destroyed by natural competition.

References

1. Aamodt, O. S.: Climate and Forage Crops, U.S. Department of Agriculture Yearbook, 1941, pp. 439–458.
2. Allard, H. A., and Morgan W. Evans: Growth and flowering of some tame and wild grasses in response to different photoperiods, *Jour. Agr. Res.*, **62**: 193–228 (1941).
3. Arny, A. C.: Winter hardiness of medium red clover strains, *Jour. Amer. Soc. Agron.*, **16**: 268–278 (1924).
4. Benedict, H. M.: Effect of day length and temperature on the flowering and growth of four species of grasses, *Jour. Agr. Res.*, **61**: 661–671 (1940).
5. Briggs, Lyman J., and H. L. Shantz: Relative water requirement of plants, *Jour. Agr. Res.*, **3**: 1–64 (1914).
6. Cook, C. W.: A study of the roots of *Bromus inermis* in relation to drought resistance, *Ecology*, **24**: 169–182 (1943).
7. Evans, Morgan W., H. A. Allard, and O. McConkey: Time of heading and flowering of early, medium and late timothy plants at different latitudes, *Sci. Agr.*, **15**: 573–579 (1934).
8. Gilbert, S. G., and J. W. Shive: The significance of oxygen in nutrient substrates for plants: I. The oxgyen requirement, *Soil Sci.*, **53**: 143–152 (1942).
9. Harris, F. S., and D. W. Pittman: Relative resistance of various crops to alkali, *Utah Agr. Expt. Sta. Bul.* 168 (1919).
10. Hibbard, P. L.: Alkali soil–origin, examination, and management, *Calif. Agr. Expt. Sta. Cir.* 292 (1925).
11. Kearney, T. R., and C. S. Scofield: The choice of crops for saline land, *U.S. Dept. Agr. Cir.* 404 (1936).
12. Khankhoje, Pandurang: Some factors which influence the water requirements of plants, *Jour. Amer. Soc. Agron.*, **6**: 1–23 (1914).
13. Klages, K. H. W.: Ecological Crop Geography, The Macmillan Company, New York, 1942.

14. McAlister, Dean F.: Determination of soil drought resistance in grass seedlings, *Jour. Amer. Soc. Agron.*, **36**:324–336 (1944).
15. Mark, J. J.: The relation of reserves to cold resistance in alfalfa, *Iowa Agr. Expt. Sta. Res. Bul.* 208 (1936).
16. Miller, E. C.: Relative water requirements of corn and sorghum, *Kans. Agr. Expt. Sta. Tech. Bul.* 12 (1923).
17. Mueller, Irene M., and J. E. Weaver: Relative drought resistance of seedlings of dominant-prairie grasses, *Ecology*, **23**:387–398 (1942).
18. Partridge, N. L.: Comparative water usage and depth of rooting of some species of grass, *Proc. Amer. Soc. Hort. Sci.*, **39**:426–432 (1941).
19. Rogler, George A.: Response of geographical strains of grasses to low temperatures, *Jour. Amer. Soc. Agron.*, **35**:547–580 (1943).
20. Schultz, H. K., and H. K. Hayes: Artificial drought tests of some hay and pasture grasses and legumes in sod and seedling stages of growth, *Jour. Amer. Soc. Agron.*, **30**: 676–682 (1938).
21. Smith, George E.: The effect of photoperiod on the growth of lespedeza, *Jour. Amer. Soc. Agron.*, **33**:231–236 (1941).
22. Smith, T. Jackson: Responses of biennial sweet clover to moisture, temperature, and length of day, *Jour. Amer. Soc. Agron.*, **34**:865–876 (1942).
23. Tysdal, H. M., and A. J. Pieters: Cold resistance of three species of lespedeza compared to that of alfalfa, red clover, and crown vetch, *Jour. Amer. Soc. Agron.*, **26**: 923–928 (1934).

CHAPTER 4

EXPANSION OF ALFALFA

Alfalfa is the oldest of all crops grown solely for forage. It is a native of southwestern Asia in the mountainous areas east of the Mediterranean Sea, as indicated by the many wild types still to be found in the Caucasian region of southern Russia and in the mountainous regions of Iran, Afghanistan, and adjacent localities.

Early historical records show that alfalfa was grown by the Persians, Arabians, Greeks, and Romans. The Arabians called green alfalfa *ratba* and the dried forage, *quatt*. The word alfalfa was later derived by the Arabs from the Iranian *aspasti*, which translated essentially means "horse fodder." Alfalfa is said to have been grown for many centuries in Arabia where it became acclimated to the aridity of the region. It probably reached Egypt at an early date, but records of such introduction have not been found.

Introduction into Greece. The Medes and Persians invaded Greece in 490 B.C. and are recognized as having introduced alfalfa into that country. Following the defeat of Xerxes at Platea in 479 B.C., the invaders withdrew, and the Greeks discovered healthy patches of alfalfa which had been established behind the lines to feed the war horses and camels of their enemies. The plant was named "medic" by the Greeks, indicating its Median origin. It became known as *medica* in Latin writings and *medicago* in modern botanical taxonomy.

Appearance in Italy. The Romans acquired alfalfa from the Greeks in about the second century before the Christian Era. Many of their writers, including Pliny, Virgil, Cato, Varro, and Columella, describe the crop in some detail, thus indicating more than a passing acquaintance with it. Columella's description of planting and managing the crop in the first century of Christendom shows that the Romans were well aware of its value and recognized many of the principles of good husbandry associated with the growing of it:

It can bear to cut down four times, sometimes also six times, in a year because it dungs the land. All emaciated cattle whatsoever grow fat with it because it is a remedy for sick cattle, and a jugerum of it is abundantly sufficient for three horses the whole year. It is sown as we shall hereafter direct. About the beginning of October cut up the field wherein you sow medic next spring and let it lie all winter to

33

rot and grow crumbly. Then about the first of February plow it carefully a second time and carry all the stones out of it and break all clods. After about the month of March plow it the third time and harrow it. When you have thus manured the ground, make it in the manner of a garden, into beds and divisions ten feet broad and fifty feet long, so that it may be supplied by water with paths and there may be an open access for weeders on both sides. Then throw old dung upon it and sow in the latter end of April. Sow it in such a proportion that a cyathus of seed may take up a place ten feet long and five feet broad. After you have done this, let the seeds that are thrown into the ground be presently covered with earth with wooden rakes. This is a very great advantage to them because they are very quickly burnt up with the sun. After sowing, the place ought not to be touched with an iron tool, but as I said it must be raked with wooden rakes and weeded from time to time lest any other kind of herb destroy the feeble medic. You must cut the first crop of it somewhat later, after it has put forth some of its seeds. Afterwards you are at liberty to cut it down as tender and as young as you please after it has sprung up and to give it to horses, but at first you must give it to them more sparingly until they be accustomed to it, lest the novelty of the fodder be hurtful to them, for it blows them and creates much blood. Water it very often after you have cut it. Then after a few days when it shall begin to sprout weed out of it all plants of a different kind. When cultivated in this manner it may be cut down six times in a year and it will last ten years.

Introduction into China. At about the same time that alfalfa was introduced into Italy, there was a dissemination of it eastward. The Chinese emperor Wu sent an expedition to Russian Turkestan in 126 B.C. to obtain some of the superior Iranian horses found there. This expedition brought back not only the horses but also some of the precious alfalfa seed. The crop soon appeared in gardens about the imperial palaces of China. It spread gradually throughout northern China and for a long time was the only crop cultivated entirely for forage purposes there.

Spread in Europe. The Romans introduced alfalfa into what is now France, Spain, Germany, and Switzerland. Columella, for example, planted it in Andalusia in southern Spain in the first century A.D. At the same time its culture was adopted in the Lake Lucerne region of what is now central Switzerland. It became so popular in this region that in later distributions in Europe it was known as lucerne and is still popularly called by that name.

The Arabs and Moors may also have introduced it into Spain from Morocco in Africa at the time of their invasion in A.D. 711. This is partially substantiated by the fact that the crop was later known there by its Arabic name *alfalfa*. The crop became widely grown in southern and western Europe wherever soil and climatic conditions favored it. It spread as far north as Germany and across the channel to the British Isles. From the sixth to the sixteenth centuries Europe was enshrouded by public war and private brawl which blighted scientific advancement. About the middle of the fifteenth century, learning began to awaken again. Soon the discovery of America followed, and alfalfa resumed its world-wide march.

ALFALFA IN THE NEW WORLD

Spanish Introductions. The Spaniards in quest of gold introduced alfalfa into Central and South America. Records of its presence appeared following the conquests of Mexico and Peru by Cortez and Pizarro. In the fertile, limestone-rich, and semiarid soils of Mexico and Peru the crop prospered and spread both northward and southward. It ultimately became very prominent in Chile and Argentina. While the records are silent, many think that the Spanish missions carried it northward to the Rio Grande and finally late in the eighteenth century into Texas, New Mexico, Arizona, and California.

On the Atlantic Seaboard. European colonists brought alfalfa to the Atlantic Seaboard under the name "lucerne." It was reported in Georgia in 1736 and 3 years later in South Carolina. By 1795 such outstanding farmers as Washington and Jefferson were attempting to grow the crop, but their efforts were relatively unfruitful. Records indicate that Robert Livingston experimented with it from 1791 to 1800 in Jefferson County, New York, and his work met with some considerable success. It became established in the limestone sections of New York State and has prospered there ever since.

Alfalfa was early recognized as a valuable addition to America's forage-crop assets, as evidenced by a letter written in the *New Brunswick Times* by a "New Jersey Farmer" in 1823. The letter follows:

It may materially promote the interests of agriculture to offer through the medium of your paper a few remarks on the culture of lucerne. This article (frequently denominated French clover) I have found by experience to be not only one of the most convenient but also the most profitable of any grass which can be cultivated. It vegetates quicker in the spring than any other grass, it resists the effect of drouths, it may be cut four or five times in the course of the season, and it will endure for at least twelve years without being renewed. Of all other grass it is the most profitable for soiling. I am of the opinion that one acre properly got in would be sufficient to maintain six head of cattle, from the first of May until November, for before it can be cut down in this way the first part of it will be ready for the scythe. English writers have recommended the drill system for this article, but in this climate I have found this to be entirely fallacious. The proper mode to be adopted is to have your land in good order, to sow it broadcast, and to get the seed in during the month of April or May. The plan I would recommend would be to sow fall rye at the rate of 15 to 20 pounds to the acre with it. The effect of this is that the rye vegetates quickly and serves as a nurse to the young grass against the heat of the scorching sun, and by the time the grass attains sufficient strength to protect itself, say in four or five weeks, the rye withers and apparently dies. In

the spring, however, the rye will again come forth mixed with lucerne, will add much
to the quantity on the ground, and prove a most excellent feed for cattle.   The rye
cut green in this way and before getting into seed will admit of being cut two or
three times in the course of the season, with the lucerne before it decays.

The kind of soil most suitable for this culture is a dry mellow loam, but a sandy
or clay loam will also answer, provided it is not wet.   In a favorable season you
may generally begin to cut green for cattle by the first of May, which saves your
young pasture and is in every respect a very great convenience, as hogs and every
description of animals devour it with equal avidity.   Backward as this season has
been, I have been furnishing a copious supply every day to seven cattle, since the
5th of May.   The seed can be procured at Rhorburn's or other seed stores in New
York at 40 to 50¢ a pound.

Many problems faced the Eastern growers, however, and the extensive
culture of alfalfa was delayed for many years until the application of accumulated scientific information made the crop more certain.

In California.   California became the promised land with the discovery
of gold at Sutter's Mill.   Overland and sea routes were followed by adventurers in the mad rush across the continent.   Among the routes was the
hazardous ocean trip "around the Horn."   Some one of the California-
bound boats that docked in Chile for fresh food supplies and a day ashore
presumably carried samples of alfalfa seed from there to California.   The
exact time of this introduction is unknown, but it is believed to have been
prior to 1850.   W. E. Cameron made the first recorded planting of the crop
in 1851, at Marysville in the Sacramento Valley.   By 1858 he had increased
his acreage to 270 and undoubtedly had stimulated considerable interest
in alfalfa because of his marked success with the crop.   This Western
introduction proved to be a most significant one.   In the early years the
crop was known as Chilean clover, after the country from which it was
obtained.

Through the West.   Alfalfa spread from California throughout the
Western states as they became settled.   In time it became known as Spanish alfalfa instead of Chilean clover, probably because of its Spanish origin
when introduced into the New World and possibly also because the Spanish
missions may have introduced it northward of the Rio Grande.   Emigrants
from California to Utah brought seed into the fertile valleys of that state
and there, true to English custom, it became known as "lucerne."   Seed
production in Utah was a marked success, and this state soon became a
primary seed source for much of the West.   Alfalfa was recorded in Colorado by 1885 and in Montana in 1890.   It became an important crop in
Kansas by 1894, and thence it spread into Nebraska along the Platte River.
By 1900 it had crossed the Missouri River and had become important on
some of the well-drained soils of Missouri and Iowa.   Its success in America
was assured.

Development of Strains and Varieties

During this period of Western expansion many changes occurred in the alfalfa crop. The original strains of Spanish alfalfa brought into California were not very winter hardy. As the crop extended its borders northward it was subjected to natural selection, only the more hardy plants surviving.

Common Alfalfa. Marked differences in winter survival resulted in the development of regional strains of the Common alfalfa designated by the states in which the seed was produced. Strains like the northern Common have developed with the ability to become relatively dormant in the fall and to resist cold. The common strains of southern alfalfa, on the other hand, grow rapidly late in the fall, failing to respond to the shortening day lengths.

Regional strains of Common alfalfa have been tested for winter hardiness at many of the experiment stations. A general summary of results gives the following classification on the basis of hardiness. It is clear that the northern strains have proved superior in this respect.

TABLE 22. RANKING OF REGIONAL COMMON ALFALFA STRAINS REGARDING WINTER HARDINESS

Strain	Hardiness ranking	Strain	Hardiness ranking
Montana...............	Good	Oklahoma...............	Fair
South Dakota...........	Good	Texas..................	Poor
Nebraska...............	Good	New Mexico............	Poor
Kansas.................	Fair	Arizona................	Poor
Utah...................	Fair	Southern California......	Poor

Recent Introductions. Aside from the natural selections described above, early improvement in alfalfa varieties came about through the introduction of new lots of seed by immigrants and later by plant explorers. New varieties better adapted than the available Common strains provided a second impetus to the spread of alfalfa eastward in the United States.

In 1857, Wendelin Grimm came from the Grand Duchy of Baden, Germany, and settled in Carver County, Minnesota. He brought with him 20 pounds of seed of *ewiger Klee*, or everlasting clover, which he seeded in the spring of 1858. This alfalfa later became known as Grimm alfalfa, and it proved to be generally winter hardy enough to survive adverse conditions in the humid Northern states. Not until after 1900, however, was its superiority in this respect fully recognized. Today, Grimm alfalfa is the most widely grown winter-hardy variety in America, although its popularity is declining because of its susceptibility to the alfalfa wilt disease.

In 1871, Nathaniel Bethel obtained some alfalfa seed from Alsace-Lorraine and introduced it into Ontario, Canada. A Dr. Colver also brought seed from Baden, Germany, into the same part of Canada in 1875. These introductions were eventually given the name of Canadian Variegated and subsequently proved to be very similar to Grimm. The Turkistan alfalfa became important commercially about 1898 when seed was imported into America through normal trade channels. Other strains and types of alfalfa were later introduced by plant explorers of the U.S. Department of Agriculture and the state experiment stations.

Principal Types Classified. The introduction of alfalfa seed from many different sources has given rise to a number of recognized types. These are usually classified into five groups on the basis of their flower color, point of origin, and winter hardiness.

Common. Common alfalfa (*Medicago sativa*) includes all the purple-flowered, nonpubescent or smooth varieties. These include mainly the regional strains developed in the western part of the United States, the seed of which can be traced to the introduction from Chile into California about 1850. Varying climatic conditions in the Western states have produced strains differing in hardiness and in growth habits. This important group includes Montana Common, Utah Common, and many other strains named according to point of origin.

Variegated. Variegated alfalfa (*M. media*) originated from natural hybrids between the purple- and yellow-flowered species, *M. sativa* and *M. falcata*. These varieties range in flower color from yellow to purple and are characterized by being more cold-resistant than the Common group. Variegated varieties are Grimm, Baltic, Hardigan, Cossack, Ladak, and Canadian Variegated.

Turkistan. Turkistan alfalfa includes all alfalfas produced from seed originating in Turkistan. They are characterized by a shorter flower and more spreading habit of growth than the Common and a high degree of resistance to cold, drought, and the alfalfa wilt disease. They are generally susceptible to leaf spot diseases. The flowers are often uniformly purple-colored. Named varieties include Hardistan, Kaw, and Orestan.

Nonhardy. Nonhardy alfalfa refers to varieties of southern origin. They are very susceptible to winter injury and thus are grown principally in the southern United States. This group is characterized by long periods of growth together with quick recovery following cutting. The varieties of significance are Peruvian, African, Indian, and Arizona Chilean.

Yellow-flowered. Yellow-flowered alfalfa includes several perennial species of *Medicago* of which *M. falcata* is most important. These are generally cold- and drought-resistant. They usually produce a large first cutting followed by a slow recovery. It is hard to produce seed from them, as the pods open readily upon maturity, resulting in severe loss from shattering. This group of alfalfas has been used primarily for breeding work. No varieties are grown commercially in the United States.

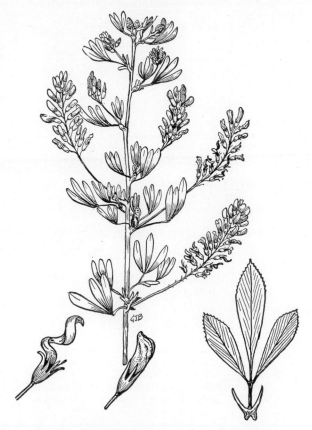

Fig. 6. General appearance of the alfalfa plant.

Breeding. The spread of the Common alfalfa, the increase in acreage of Grimm, and the introduction of new types and strains set the stage for alfalfa breeding work. New varieties were produced from time to time in different localities of the United States, and these possessed certain superior characteristics for the respective states and regions. A summary is given in Table 23. These varieties have helped to extend the alfalfa frontiers so that the crop is now grown in every state with at least some degree of success.

SIGNIFICANCE OF THE CROP

The expansion of the alfalfa acreage in the West was not difficult. The soils were generally high in mineral nutrients, deep, and well drained, especially in terms of the limited rainfall. Climatic conditions were and are

TABLE 23. HISTORICAL SUMMARY OF THE DEVELOPMENT OF IMPROVED VARIETIES OF ALFALFA IN THE UNITED STATES AND CANADA

Variety or strain	Year introduced	Name and location of breeder	Superior characters
Grimm...........	1905	Wendelin Grimm, Minnesota	Yield, quality, winter hardiness
Cossack..........	1907	N. E. Hansen, South Dakota	Winter hardiness, productivity
Baltic............	1908	Wheeler, South Dakota	Cold resistance, productivity
Grimm 19A.......	1909	Wheeler, South Dakota	Winter hardiness, productivity
Ladak...........	1910	H. L. Westover, Samuel Garver, U.S.D.A.	Yield, cold and drought resistance. More resistant to bacterial wilt than Grimm
Ontario Variegated	1910	C. A. Zavitz and coworkers, Ontario	Winter hardiness, productivity
Hardigan.........	1920	F. A. Spragg, E. E. Down, Michigan	Yield of hay and seed
Meeker Baltic....	1920	P. K. Blinn, Colorado	Yield, cold resistance, hay quality
Grimm 451.......	1921	J. Bracken, L. E. Kirk, Saskatchewan	Hardiness, yield
Grimm 666.......	1925	M. Champlin, L. E. Kirk, Saskatchewan	Seed yield
Hardistan........	1930	A. Hecht, T. A. Kiesselbach, A. Anderson, G. L. Peltier, Nebraska	Bacterial wilt resistance
Grimm, M. C.....	1931	J. N. Bird, Quebec	Winter hardiness
Kaw.............	1932	S. C. Salmon, C. O. Grandfield, Kansas	Resistance to wilt and cold
Ranger..........	1943	H. M. Tysdal, G. L. Peltier, T. A. Kiesselbach, Nebraska	Wilt and cold resistance, seed production
Nemastan........	1945	H. L. Westover, G. Thorne, R. J. Evans, and O. F. Smith	Resistant to stem nematode. Adapted to Western region
Buffalo..........	1945	C. O. Grandfield, Kansas	Wilt resistance and high yield
Atlantic..........	1946	H. B. Sprague, Glenn Burton, New Jersey	Adaptation, production, and seed yield
Williamsburg.....	1947	R. P. Cocke, Virginia	Sclerotinia resistant, Southern adaptation
Narragansett.....	1948	T. E. Odland, Rhode Island	Superior yield, Northeastern adaptation

SOURCE: U.S. Department of Agriculture Yearbook, 1937.

ideal for alfalfa, offering an abundance of sunshine, a dry atmosphere, and moderate winters. Ideal weather also facilitates handling and curing the crop throughout most of the Western states, whether it is raised for hay or for seed.

Yields. Early recognition of superiority in yield and quality perform-ance did much to stimulate interest in alfalfa as a hay crop. A study of average yields for a number of hay crops is given in Table 24. Alfalfa invariably outproduces all others under conditions to which it is adapted.

TABLE 24. AVERAGE YIELD OF VARIOUS HAY CROPS, TONS PER ACRE

Crop	1899	1909	1919	1929	1939
Alfalfa.................	2.49	2.52	2.13	2.04	2.00
Clover and timothy.......	....	1.27	1.31	1.28	1.14
Grain hay..............	1.28	1.24	0.96	1.09	1.00
Wild hay..............	....	1.07	0.93	0.82	0.80

SOURCES: U.S. Department of Agriculture: Agricultural Statistics, 1941; Agricultural Statistics, 1944; *U.S. Dept. Agr. Statistical Bul.* 11 (1925).

Its high feeding value was soon recognized, and livestock producers the country over attempted to grow the crop wherever conditions were reason-ably favorable.

Acreage. The national acreage of alfalfa has grown steadily since it was first reported in census figures for 1899. These data are given in Table 25.

TABLE 25. ALFALFA PRODUCTION IN THE UNITED STATES, 1899–1939

Year	Acres, thousands	Total yields, thousand tons	Average yield, tons per acre
1899	2,094	5,221	2.49
1909	4,707	11,860	2.52
1919	8,647	19,380	2.13
1929	11,515	23,494	2.04
1939	13,421	26,888	2.00

SOURCES: Data for 1899 from *U.S. Dept. Agr. Statistical Bul.* 11 (1925); 1909 from *U.S. Dept. Agr. Statistical Bul.* 11 (1925); 1919 from U.S. Department of Agriculture: Agricultural Statistics, 1941; 1929 from U.S. Department of Agriculture: General Report, vol. III, 1935; 1939 from U.S. Department of Agriculture: Agricultural Statistics, 1941.

Further expansion is indicated, but the rate of increase is definitely lessen-ing. Alfalfa is now the most important hay crop grown in the United States, and it is also the most widely adapted.

Problems and Prospects. Most general increases in acreage have been made east of the Mississippi River since 1919. The Corn Belt and Great Lakes states especially have recently increased their acreages tremendously. Data on changes in acreage in the individual states are given in Table 26. A fairly stable condition in acreage is found by 1919 in most states west of the Mississippi River except Minnesota. In the Northeastern states only

TABLE 26. PROPORTIONAL CHANGES IN ALFALFA ACREAGE BASED ON PERCENTAGE
INTERPRETATION

State	Per cent of 1939 acreage				Acreage, 1939, thousands
	1899	1909	1919	1929	
Maine...................	..	...	...	150	6
New Hampshire..........	..	...	...	100	3
Vermont.................	..	...	...	54	13
Massachusetts...........	..	...	...	50	8
Rhode Island...........	..	...	...	...	1
Connecticut.............	..	...	...	38	16
New York...............	2	12	41	65	292
New Jersey.............	..	2	31	54	48
Pennsylvania............	..	2	14	43	215
Ohio....................	1	6	18	37	516
Indiana.................	..	4	14	35	474
Illinois.................	2	4	19	43	471
Michigan................	0	1	7	48	1,100
Wisconsin...............	..	2	6	3	1,127
Minnesota..............	0	0	4	57	1,212
Iowa...................	0	3	20	53	879
Missouri...............	1	18	78	75	210
North Dakota...........	..	4	54	266	114
South Dakota...........	5	27	193	365	241
Nebraska...............	19	113	200	187	608
Kansas.................	65	157	321	178	410
Delaware...............	..	...	...	100	5
Maryland...............	..	9	34	60	35
Virginia................	..	5	37	65	65
West Virginia..........	..	...	...	35	27
North Carolina..........	..	...	...	66	9
South Carolina.........	..	...	...	66	3
Georgia................	..	...	...	66	6
Florida................	..	...	...	...	.....
Kentucky...............	1	11	32	56	176
Tennessee..............	1	7	24	31	72
Alabama................	..	233	333	133	3
Mississippi.............	..	14	46	35	65
Arkansas...............	2	...	...	60	82
Louisiana..............	9	...	...	54	22
Oklahoma...............	6	78	132	69	264
Texas..................	18	51	54	46	108
Montana...............	11	34	56	112	662
Idaho..................	21	41	86	101	773
Wyoming...............	20	46	90	108	367
Colorado...............	71	79	122	126	641
New Mexico............	61	113	129	112	91
Arizona................	39	41	68	59	156
Utah..................	60	64	81	123	447
Nevada................	71	66	86	108	136
Washington............	12	32	76	76	300
Oregon................	20	45	80	95	264
California..............	40	64	96	106	751

SOURCE: U.S. Department of Agriculture: Agricultural Statistics, 1940.

14 per cent of the hay acreage was in alfalfa in 1944. There is ample room for expansion here in association with the important livestock industry found in the same region.

Expansion of the alfalfa acreage in the Northeastern and North Central regions can be characterized as relatively slow and more difficult of attainment than in the West. The soils in general are of an acid nature, lacking in the basic lime and mineral nutrients. Severe winter losses often occur because the high moisture content of the soil favors heaving and ice-sheet formations. The soils are relatively shallow and often poorly drained.

This means that the environment must be adjusted for alfalfa to be grown successfully in most Eastern regions. The soil must be limed, adequate mineral fertilizer added and maintained, and surface and underdrainage provided in many areas. The best alfalfa varieties must be combined with good management and careful selection of planting site. These conditions can be attained, as has been demonstrated in the Lake states. Similar adjustments made in the Northeastern states will permit substantial increases in the acreage of alfalfa grown there.

Alfalfa has expanded from a crop of no significance in 1850 to a point where it is the most important forage crop in America. This expansion was made possible by man's ingenuity in solving the cultural problems associated with the crop and in developing varieties to fit the new environments as the crop moved eastward. Scientific work with this crop is not completed. Important problems of disease resistance, seed production, good-quality hay production, and many others lie ahead. Their solution will further stimulate the expansion of this greatest of all forages.

References

1. Coburn, F. D.: The Book of Alfalfa, Orange Judd Publishing Co., Inc., New York, 1906.
2. Henry, George W.: Alfalfa in history, *Jour. Amer. Soc. Agron.*, **15**:171–176 (1923).
3. Tysdal, H. M., and H. L. Westover: Alfalfa Improvement, U.S. Department of Agriculture Yearbook, 1937, pp. 1122–1153.
4. U.S. Department of Agriculture: Agricultural Statistics, 1941.
5. U.S. Department of Agriculture: Agricultural Statistics, 1944.
6. U.S. Department of Agriculture: *General Report*, vol. III (1935).
7. *U.S. Department of Agriculture Bureau of Agricultural Economics: Statis. Bul.* 11 (1925).
8. U.S. Department of Agriculture Yearbook, 1937.
9. Westover, H. L.: Alfalfa varieties in the United States, *U.S. Dept. Agr. Farmers' Bul.* 1731 (1934).
10. Wing, Joseph E.: Alfalfa Farming in America, Sanders Publishing Co., Chicago, 1912.

CHAPTER 5

GROWING ALFALFA

Wherever alfalfa thrives in America it is an outstandingly productive crop of profitable and consistent performance. From a livestock standpoint, it is unsurpassed for general feeding. It is useful not only for hay, but for pasture and grass silage as well. It is a valuable soil improver and usually produces a stimulating effect on the succeeding crop. Many Western growers produce seed and often find this a profitable enterprise.

Aside from the soil improvement, seedbed, and seeding problems discussed in other chapters, certain phases of production deserve special consideration. Alfalfa is highly sensitive to climatic conditions and management treatments. The degree of success with this crop is closely related to the wisdom and judgment exercised in its culture.

SELECTION OF VARIETIES

An early choice which all producers must make is the variety to plant. This is obviously an important consideration, and success or failure of the project hinges directly on the choice. No amount of good management can make up for weaknesses in an unadapted variety. Some generally desirable variety characteristics follow: (1) high yielding capacity, (2) strong disease resistance and survival value, (3) hay of good quality indicating leafiness and fine stems, (4) good seed production, (5) superior competitive capacity and drought resistance, especially during the first season, (6) distinctive identifying characteristics either of seed or vegetative and floral morphology. Not all these characteristics are found in any single variety. The realization of degrees of perfection for each character is dependent on varietal adaptation and management by the grower. The last character is not found in any present variety but would serve a real purpose agriculturally could it be accomplished.

Variety Tests. Alfalfa variety tests serve as the basis for securing fundamental information in evaluating the varieties. Most of the agricultural experiment stations conduct such tests and make their data available for public use. Table 27 presents a portion of such information from several selected states as it relates to varietal productiveness. The differences given in yields in this table may not seem pronounced to the student. This is true, but actually the data are incomplete because as soon as

44

TABLE 27. COMPARATIVE HAY YIELDS FOR VARIOUS ALFALFA VARIETIES, TONS

Variety	Colorado, 4-year ave.	New Mexico, 2-year ave.	Nebraska 5-year ave.	New Jersey, 3-year ave.	Delaware, 4-year ave.
Grimm	4.81	....	3.22	....	4.22
Ladak	5.12	....	3.14	....	....
Baltic	4.66	....	....	....	....
Common	4.63	7.42	3.03	3.41	3.83
Hardistan	4.29	6.57	2.90	3.24	....
Ranger	....	7.43	....	3.62	....
Buffalo	....	7.55	....	3.52	....
Atlantic	....	7.60	....	3.94	....

stands begin to thin out variety tests are often abandoned and, therefore, the real significance of varietal productive capacity is lost.

An indication of the need for better interpretation of variety tests is given in Fig. 7, constructed for two varieties, the data being taken from a Nebraska test. The average yield for Hardistan for this 6-year period was 4.38 tons per acre and for Nebraska Common, 3.20 tons. At the end of the sixth year, however, Hardistan produced 2.82 tons and Nebraska

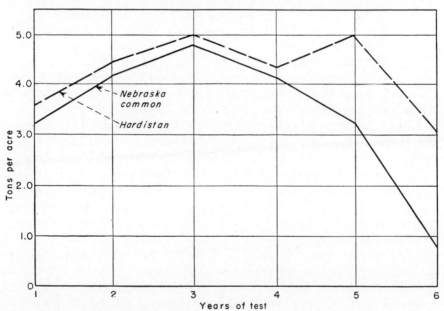

FIG. 7. Yield performance of two selected alfalfa varieties in Nebraska. (*Nebraska Agricultural Experiment Station.*)

Common only 0.58 ton per acre. The reduction in yield was due to loss of stand, only 25 per cent of the Common surviving at the end of the sixth year compared with a 98 per cent survival of the Hardistan. In the first four years of the test, as given in the graph for these two varieties, they were essentially equivalent in yield performance, but in the last two years the superiority of Hardistan became pronounced.

WINTERKILLING

The loss of stand experienced in many of the variety tests is due primarily to winterkilling or to the wilt disease. Studies on winter survival and cold hardiness of alfalfa varieties, especially in the Northern states, cast some light on the former factor. Thus in Ohio, Grimm alfalfa was found to

TABLE 28. PER CENT WINTER SURVIVAL OF ALFALFA VARIETIES AT VARIOUS STATIONS

Variety	Ohio 4-season ave.	Nebraska controlled tests	Wisconsin rating
Cossack.................	....	105	Hardy
Hardistan..............	....	100	Hardy
Ladak..................	....	83	Hardy
Hardigan...............	....	82	Hardy
Grimm.................	82.1	72	Hardy
Kansas Common........	74.3	55	Medium
Arizona Common........	....	22	Nonhardy
Argentine..............	....	17	

survive better than Kansas Common. In these Wisconsin tests, Arizona Common winterkilled severely, whereas all other varieties were considered hardy excepting Kansas Common. Controlled cold-chamber tests conducted in Nebraska give the most reliable index for varietal resistance to this factor. In these tests Cossack and Hardistan proved the most cold hardy and Argentine and Arizona Common the least.

Hardiness is an important factor in winterkilling and is often considered to be the capacity of plants to survive the various hazards of winter. Many plants require a prehardening period to adjust their physiologic responses to lower temperatures. A hardy alfalfa plant growing vigorously in midsummer would be severely injured if suddenly subjected to strong freezing temperatures. By the end of the fall season, however, it suffers no real injury from low temperatures. No exact explanation is available for this phenomenon, but it is known that the hardening process involves a slowing down of plant metabolism and a lowered respiration rate. The storage of plant food has an important bearing on the ability of plant protoplasm to adjust itself to withstand low temperatures.

Fig. 8. Differences in persistence of alfalfa varieties are easily detected in variety trials. (*Nebraska Agricultural Experiment Station.*)

Winter hardiness is associated with early fall dormancy or slow recovery following the last cutting. The variegated group of alfalfas appear most winter hardy, and they make the least regrowth in the fall. Evidence on the growth characters is found in Table 29. The nonhardy varieties tested

TABLE 29. YIELD OF HAY AND HEIGHT OF GROWTH AFTER LAST CUTTING, ALFALFA VARIETIES, 5-YEAR AVERAGE

Variety	Yield of hay per acre, lb.	Height of plants, in.
Turkistan..............	560	6.2
Ladak.................	640	6.6
Other variegated.......	1,050	9.9
Adapted common........	1,150	11.4
Nonhardy common.......	1,180	13.5

SOURCE: *Ohio Agr. Expt. Sta. Bul.* 540 (1934).

in Ohio made the most fall growth, indicating inability of these strains to prepare for winter conditions.

Fall Cutting. Aside from variety, the organic food reserves are known to influence winter survival, and it is here that management becomes particularly significant. Cutting during the critical fall period, as studied in

Michigan,[7] showed that the strongest reduction in yields occurred from the Sept. 15 cutting. Earlier or later cuttings were less damaging, although some reduction in vigor did occur.

TABLE 30. EFFECT OF DIFFERENTIAL FALL CUTTINGS ON 3-YEAR-OLD ALFALFA IN 1936 ON THE STANDS AND YIELDS IN 1937

Date of third cutting, 1936	Days since second cutting on Aug. 4	Decrease in stands between August, 1936, and May, 1937, %	Yields of dry matter June 18, 1937, lb. per acre	Reductions in yields due to third cutting, %
Sept. 1	28	87	2,979	29
Sept. 15	42	65	3,439	18
Sept. 30	57	45	3,772	10
Oct. 15	72	29	3,883	8
Oct. 29	86	18	3,915	7
None	..	2	4,212	..

SOURCE: *Conn. Agr. Expt. Sta. Bul.* 242 (1942).

Further data on fall cutting as affecting winter survival is found in some Connecticut studies, as given in Table 30. Early September cutting resulted in a severe loss of stand and in a strong reduction in yield the succeeding year. The later in the fall the hay was cut, the less the injurious effect on the stand.

Frequency of Cutting. The effect of stage and frequency of cutting was studied in Wisconsin, the following data being secured (see Table 31). Two cuttings a year made at the full-bloom stage appeared to be most satisfactory for stand maintenance. Three cuttings annually made at the

TABLE 31. WINTERKILLING AS AFFECTED BY STAGE AND FREQUENCY OF CUTTING ALFALFA

Cutting treatment	Per cent of dead plants in plots on Apr. 22, 1922				Date of last cutting, 1921
	Grimm	Imported Turkistan	Kansas Common	Average	
Bud stage, three cuttings	13	22	34	23	Aug. 22
Tenth bloom, three cuttings	18	25	74	39	Sept. 8
Full bloom, two cuttings	8	14	24	15	Aug. 8
Seed stage, two cuttings	9	21	43	24	Sept. 22

SOURCE: *Wis. Agr. Expt. Sta. Res. Bul.* 80 (1927).

bud or tenth-bloom stage reduced the stand by 23 and 39 per cent compared with only 15 per cent at the full-bloom stage and two cuttings.

Starch Reserves. Winter hardiness is closely related to starch reserves found in the roots during the winter season. These reserves build up in the fall as the alfalfa plant regrows provided that it is not cut during the critical fall period. New growth the succeeding spring or following any cutting comes from these stored root reserves. The reserves are stored primarily as starch during any period that alfalfa is growing satisfactorily.

When the crop is cut, there is a heavy drain on the stored-starch supply as the new top growth is initiated and stimulated. Late fall cuttings then might create a condition where much of the starch reserves were used by starting new top growth without adequate time for starch to be again synthesized and stored. Under such conditions the plant is very susceptible to winterkilling. Data showing this type of response are given in Table 32. Thus alfalfa plots cut Sept. 15 and Oct. 1 contained almost no insoluble starch at all.

The effect of the number of cuttings made per season on stand maintenance was studied in Arkansas, and the data are given in Table 33. Early

TABLE 32. INFLUENCE OF FALL CUTTING TREATMENT ON DRY MATTER AND INSOLUBLE STARCH IN ROOTS COLLECTED THE FOLLOWING FEB. 21

Fall treatment	Dry matter, %	Insoluble starch (dry-weight basis), %	Actual weight of insoluble starch in 100 grams of fresh tissue, grams	Total carbo-hydrates in 100 grams of fresh tissue, grams
Cut Sept. 1	36.5	2.03	0.74	9.18
Cut Sept. 15	32.6	0.07	....	7.67
Cut Oct. 1	32.9	0.03	....	8.26
Cut Oct. 15	32.5	0.73	0.24	8.56
Cut Oct. 31	33.7	1.72	0.58	9.90
No cutting	34.8	2.10	0.73	9.22

SOURCE: *Mich. Agr. Expt. Sta. Spec. Bul.* 292 (1938).

TABLE 33. CONDITION OF STANDS FOLLOWING CUTTING AT DIFFERENT STAGES

Time of cutting	Condition of stands, %					
	1921	1922	1923	1924	1925	1926
Early or frequent cutting	100	100	94	84	80	58
Normal cutting	100	100	95	85	75	65
Delayed cutting	100	100	100	82	88	85

SOURCE: *Ark. Agr. Expt. Sta. Bul.* 242 (1929).

cuttings long continued resulted in the most severe stand losses. Delayed cuttings were most effective in maintaining stands.

Heaving. Certain external factors of the environment are also associated with winterkilling of alfalfa. Extreme low temperatures may result in death of the plant. Alternate freezing and thawing may result in heaving the plant out of the soil and thus in its subsequent death. Ice sheets have a smothering effect on the plants by "sealing" them with the soil and preventing the natural movement of air.

Heaving is particularly serious on wet heavy soils. There are two types of heaving. In the first, ice crystals form around and on the underside of the crown and expansion heaves the entire plant partially out of the ground. The second type consists of crystals forming below a layer of frozen soil and around the plant root. Expansion of the ice crystals snaps the root below the soil surface.

Prevention of winter heaving is best accomplished by planting alfalfa on well-drained soils or by providing good surface and underdrainage as may be needed. Associated grass helps maintain more uniformity in soil temperatures; so does a snow cover. Heaving is much less serious in fields where the plants are permitted to store sufficient food reserves.

ALFALFA WILT

The second significant factor in alfalfa stand maintenance is alfalfa wilt (*Corynebacterium insidiosum*). It is probably just as important as winterkilling. A summary of controlled artificial wilt-resistance tests as conducted in Nebraska is given in Table 34. A wide range in resistance

TABLE 34. COMPARATIVE RESISTANCE OF ALFALFA VARIETIES TO BACTERIAL WILT. 10 YEARS' DATA

Variety	Per cent resistance	Variety	Per cent resistance
Turkistan	85	Peruvian	6
Orestan	62	Grimm	5
Hardistan	56	Hardigan	5
Ladak	47	Baltic	3
Cossack	12	North Dakota Common	3
Kansas Common	10	Arizona Common	1

SOURCE: *Nebr. Agr. Expt. Sta. Bul.* 331 (1941).

to this disease thus appears evident. Release of the Buffalo and Ranger varieties makes available material possessing a high degree of resistance to bacterial wilt. Long-time stands will depend on the selection of wilt-resistant varieties in most of the humid and irrigated sections of the United States.

TABLE 35. FIELD TESTS INDICATING DIFFERENCES IN WILT RESISTANCE OF ALFALFA VARIETIES. PERCENTAGE STAND BASIS AT END OF GROWTH PERIOD

Variety	Kansas, 4-year	New Jersey, 4-year	New Mexico, 3-year
Buffalo................	95	85	62
Ranger................	..	86	50
Kansas Common.......	25	48	27
Grimm................	12	..	23

Bacterial wilt is widespread throughout the United States wherever moisture conditions favor rapid growth of alfalfa. Symptoms of infection are stunted plants with yellowish leaves that wilt severely during hot weather. A cross section of the root indicates a yellowish to brownish ring underneath the bark and permeating the woody tissue. Control measures appear impractical except through the growing of disease-resistant varieties.

HAY YIELDS

The stage at which alfalfa is cut for hay obviously affects the hay yields. The question of whether to make two or three cuttings or even more a season is difficult and can be determined best from long-time studies. Such a study was conducted in Wisconsin, where winter conditions are severe. Data are given in Table 36. The full-bloom stage of harvesting appears

TABLE 36. YIELDS OF ALFALFA HAY ACCORDING TO CUTTING TREATMENT, TONS PER ACRE

Cutting treatment	Wisconsin, 5-year ave.	Kansas, 8-year ave.	New Mexico, 4-year ave.
Bud stage............	0.73	2.65	8.88
Tenth bloom..........	1.14	3.21	8.90
Full bloom...........	2.04	3.43	8.79
Seed stage...........	1.66	2.91	8.18

SOURCES: *Wis. Agri. Expt. Sta. Res. Bul.* 80 (1927); *Kans. Agr. Expt. Sta. Bul.* 242 (1927); *N.Mex. Agr. Expt. Sta. Bul.* 323 (1945).

most practical from these studies. Actually harvesting somewhat earlier may be even more advantageous. In Kansas neither early nor late cutting seems satisfactory, but the intermediate stages were not only productive but also of good feed value.

In New Mexico climatic conditions are relatively mild. Pronounced winter losses from early cutting apparently do not occur. Early cutting did reduce yields somewhat in the fourth year of this experiment, but no large differences are found in the average results such as the Kansas and Wisconsin investigators report.

In the East the Delaware Station reports data[5] showing that two cuttings a year are most profitable there.   Average yields per acre per year with

Fig. 9.   More hay is made from alfalfa than from any other crop.   (*Allis Chalmers Manufacturing Co.*)

two cuttings were over 5 tons of cured hay; with three cuttings, over 4 tons; and with 4 cuttings, about 3½ tons.   Stands were strongly reduced in the third year of the study where three and four cuttings were made annually, as indicated by the lowered yield.

CHEMICAL COMPOSITION

The chemical composition of alfalfa has been studied at several stations. Extensive data on all three alfalfa crops are given in Table 37.   The leaves were considerably higher than the stems in protein and in ash content. Data from Kansas given in Table 38 are very similar, indicating the need to save the leaves in the production of high-quality hay.

The increase in fiber content and decrease in protein is shown graphically in Fig. 79.   As the plant increases in age the protein content decreases and the percentage of fiber increases.   Thus when cuttings are delayed until full bloom or later, the life of the stand is increased but the quality of the hay is reduced.

TABLE 37. RELATIVE COMPOSITION OF LEAVES AND STALKS OF ALFALFA AT EARLY BLOOM, PER CENT

Crop and plant part	Water in total green weight	Starch	Crude fiber	Fat	Crude protein (total)	Ash
First crop:						
Whole plant*......	78.6	39.2	30.5	2.9	16.3	11.1
Leaves............	76.1	41.8	13.8	6.0	24.1	14.3
Stalks............	79.7	37.1	42.2	0.9	10.7	9.0
Second crop:						
Whole plant*......	79.8	38.8	32.2	1.9	17.9	9.2
Leaves............	75.2	43.8	13.7	3.0	27.9	11.7
Stalks............	76.8	34.3	47.6	1.0	9.9	7.2
Third crop:						
Whole plant*......	77.5	40.5	35.5	1.9	12.9	9.3
Leaves............	83.7	49.6	14.5	3.3	20.7	12.1
Stalks............	....	33.3	52.4	0.8	6.5	7.0

SOURCE: *N.Dak. Agr. Expt. Sta. Cir.* 86 (1929).
* Aboveground portion.

TABLE 38. PER CENT OF FEED CONSTITUENTS IN LEAVES AND STEMS OF ALFALFA

Plant part	Ash	Crude protein	Crude fiber	Nitrogen-free extract	Ether extract
Leaves..........	11.07	25.45	15.47	44.50	3.18
Stems..........	8.17	12.42	38.78	41.09	1.36

SOURCE: *Kans. Agr. Expt. Sta. Bul.* 242 (1927).

CULTIVATION

Cultivation of established alfalfa fields does not appear to have any real beneficial effects. Most investigators report no effect or actually an injurious one. This is especially true where alfalfa wilt is present and can be readily spread by machinery. At the Ohio Station the following treatments and results were obtained in a 1931 study: spring tooth after first cutting, 7,478 pounds dry matter per acre; spring tooth after first and second cutting, 7,450 pounds; disk after first cutting, 7,053 pounds; disk after first and second cutting, 7,355 pounds; and untreated, 8,001 pounds. Cultivation in this test actually resulted in reduced yields.

In the West cultivation of old stands often improves the quality of the hay by destroying weeds and grasses. Total yields, especially from the first cutting, are reduced, as shown in Table 39. In general, it appears that cultivation is not profitable except in a few areas of America where weeds in alfalfa are a special problem. For seed production, cultivation is often practiced with good success.

TABLE 39. COMPARATIVE YIELDS OF ALFALFA HAY FROM CULTIVATED AND UNCULTIVATED FIELDS FOR THREE YEARS, 1923–1925

Treatment	Yields in field-dry hay per acre, tons			
	First cutting	Second cutting	Third cutting	Total yields
Cultivated..........	2.90	1.24	0.34	4.46
Uncultivated........	3.28	1.27	0.30	4.85

SOURCE: *Oreg. Agr. Expt. Sta. Bul.* 246 (1929).

References

1. Ahlgren, Gilbert H., Howard B. Sprague, and Firman E. Bear: Growing alfalfa in New Jersey, *N.J. Agr. Expt. Sta. Bul.* 718 (1945).
2. Booth, E. G.: Alfalfa: The best fodder crop, *N.Dak. Agr. Ext. Cir.* 86 (1929).
3. Brown, B. A., and R. I. Munsell: The effects of cutting systems on alfalfa, *Conn. Agr. Expt. Sta. Bul.* 242 (1922).
4. Graber, L. F., N. T. Nelson, W. A. Luckel, and W. B. Albert: Organic food reserves in relation to the growth of alfalfa and other perennial herbaceous plants, *Wis. Agr. Expt. Sta. Res. Bul.* 80 (1927).
5. Harris, Henry C., and C. E. Phillips: Alfalfa production in Delaware, *Del. Agr. Ext. Bul.* 18 (1933).
6. Nelson, Martin: Experiments with alfalfa, *Ark. Agr. Expt. Sta. Bul.* 242 (1929).
7. Rather, H. C., and C. M. Harrison: Alfalfa management with special reference to fall treatment, *Mich. Agr. Expt. Sta. Spec. Bul.* 292 (1938).
8. Schoth, Harry A., and George R. Hyslop: Alfalfa in Western Oregon, *Oreg. Agr. Expt. Sta. Bul.* 246 (1929).
9. Staten, Glen, R. S. Stroud, and John Carter: Alfalfa production investigations in New Mexico, *N. Mex. Agr. Expt. Sta. Bul.* 323 (1945).
10. Throckmorton, R. I., and S. C. Salmon: Alfalfa production in Kansas, *Kans. Agr. Expt. Sta. Bul.* 242 (1927).
11. Tysdal, H. M., and T. A. Kiesselbach: Alfalfa in Nebraska, *Nebr. Agr. Expt. Sta. Bul.* 331 (1941).
12. Weihing, R. M., D. W. Robertson, O. H. Coleman, and R. Gardner: Growing alfalfa in Colorado, *Colo. Agr. Expt. Sta. Bul.* 480 (1943).
13. Westover, H. L., and W. H. Hosterman: The uses of alfalfa, *U.S. Dept. Agr. Farmers' Bul.* 1830 (1940).
14. Willard, C. J., L. E. Thatcher, and J. S. Cutler: Alfalfa in Ohio, *Ohio Agr. Expt. Sta. Bul.* 540 (1934).

CHAPTER 6

RED CLOVER PRODUCTION

Red clover is grown most extensively in the North Central and North-eastern states. It is an important crop as far south as Tennessee and Virginia and also in the irrigated valleys of the Western states, especially Idaho, Oregon, and Washington.

ADAPTATION

It is best adapted to regions with moderate rainfall and is capable of withstanding winter and summer temperatures of considerable magnitude. Soils that are rich in lime, high in organic matter, fairly heavy in texture, deep and well-drained are most satisfactory but not essential since it will tolerate poorer soils than alfalfa. It does not thrive on open dry soils. Essentially, red clover will grow on almost any soil that will produce good crops of corn.

This legume is widely used with short rotations in regions where various other crops are grown for livestock feed. Thus corn, a small grain, and clover are common crops in the 3- and 4-year livestock-farm rotations. In most of the clover belt the crop is used for hay and pasture. Some growers, after harvesting hay from the first crop, grow the second for seed or plow it under for soil improvement. Stands of red clover are somewhat easier to produce than those of alfalfa, and this, together with its high feed and soil-improvement value, accounts for its prominent position in North-eastern agriculture.

Effects of Climate. The borders of red clover culture are determined primarily by moisture supplies. Red clover is replaced in the prairie states by sweetclover and in the arid West by alfalfa. In the irrigated valleys of the West both red clover and alfalfa are grown, but red clover is important only in the northern states, where the shorter growing season enables it to compete with alfalfa. Little is known as to the effect of varying climatic conditions on the productivity and health of the red clover crops. A long-time study in Ohio, however, permitted the following conclusions:

1. Increase in yields generally occurred with an increase in total rainfall for the months of April, May, and June.
2. An increase in cloudiness during April, May, and June resulted in greater production.

3. Higher total snowfall increased yields.

4. An increase in temperature for March and April and a decrease for May and June improved the yields.

It is usually recognized that red clover makes a more vigorous vegetative growth under the conditions described above than when the season is dry, sunny, and warm.

In addition to the effect on yields, climatic conditions have been shown to affect the feeding value of this crop. Such a study conducted in Wisconsin[6] compared red clover grown at Madison with that grown at Ashland, in northern Wisconsin, where the growing season is about 65 days shorter and the temperature averages 6°F. less than at Madison. The clover grown farther north was 10 per cent lower in protein content on the average than that grown in southern Wisconsin. These results were explained on the basis of greater carbohydrate formation at the lower temperatures of Ashland and also by the possibility of cooler soils in early spring retarding symbiotic nitrogen fixation. Thus clover hay grown in northern latitudes may have a lower protein content than that grown southward.

Fig. 10. The general characteristics of the red clover plant.

TYPES OF RED CLOVER

There are essentially two types of red clover, namely, the medium red (*Trifolium pratense*) and the mammoth red (*T. pratense perenne*). Medium red clover is usually considered a biennial, although many strains or plants within a strain persist as short-lived perennials. Mammoth clover is sometimes considered to have a longer life expectancy. The medium red clover group is often known as "double-cut" because two cuttings a season can be harvested from varieties within this group. The mammoth clover group may be called "single-cut," as these varieties yield only one cutting a season. It blooms 10 days to 2 weeks later than medium red, is somewhat taller, and produces a larger first cutting than the double-cut clovers. Several varieties are found within each clover group, but those of the medium red type are by far the most popular in America.

In northern latitudes mammoth red clover yields about the same total amount of hay as medium red. Since it is a one-cut clover, the quality of the hay is probably poorer than the medium red. Comparative yields in Ohio and West Virginia are given in Table 40. Mammoth clover has yielded well in variety tests, yet its coarseness and one-cut habit has reduced its chances for popularity in the clover belt.

TABLE 40. COMPARATIVE YIELDS PER ACRE OF MEDIUM AND MAMMOTH RED CLOVER, TONS

Type	Wooster, Ohio, 10-year ave.	Columbus, Ohio, 3-year ave.	Morgantown, W.Va., 4-year ave.
Medium red............	2.02	2.61	1.42
Mammoth red..........	2.29	2.25	1.66

SOURCES: Ohio State University, Timely Soil Topics 69; *W.Va. Agr. Expt. Sta. Bul.* 250 (1932).

ACREAGE

The culture of red clover spread rapidly following its introduction into America. For a long time it was the leading legume hay crop, but recently it has been surpassed by alfalfa. The acreage in red clover in the United States is given in Table 41. Considerable variations have occurred, indicating that certain problems have arisen in growing the crop.

TABLE 41. ACREAGE IN RED CLOVER AND RED CLOVER–TIMOTHY MIXTURES, THOUSANDS

Crop	1899	1909	1919	1929	1939
Red clover.....................	3,456	1,875	3,160	4,202*	....
Clover and timothy..............	....	36,672	33,451	29,750	17,273

* Includes red clover with alsike.

The acreage in red clover decreased significantly during the early part of the twentieth century. This was not caused by a lessened demand for the hay, but by difficulties experienced in growing it and also a decline in the timothy acreage. Crops were reduced in quantity, and there was less certainty of getting a good stand. Part of this difficulty in the clover belt was an inadequate understanding of the lime and mineral requirements of the crop, but the main difficulty was the use of unadapted seed and the resultant increase in disease and insect injury.

Cultural Problems

Frequent shortages of domestic red clover seed resulted in large importations of foreign seeds, both prior to and immediately following the First World War. Concurrent with these introductions arose difficulties in growing satisfactory crops. Intensive work by state and Federal agronomists soon indicated a number of primary causes that were strongly associated with the foreign shipments of seed.

Winterkilling. One of the chief difficulties encountered in growing this crop proved to be winterkilling, especially in the Northern states. Here winter-hardy varieties are essential for survival, and to a lesser extent this is true in the central and southern part of the clover belt. Tests conducted in Minnesota as given in Table 42 show the relative rating of clover

TABLE 42. COMPARISON OF WINTER HARDINESS OF RED CLOVER STRAINS AT ST. PAUL, MINNESOTA

Sources of seed	Loss in stand, %	Yields, lb. per acre on a 15% moisture basis	Yields (Northern-grown native strains = 100), %
Native strains:			
Northern grown.............	18.1	3,983	100.0
Central, Southern, and Western grown....................	27.3	3,673	92.2
Foreign strains:			
Western and Central continental Europe...................	21.3	3,244	81.4
Southern continental Europe, England, Wales, and Chile...	85.4	744	18.7

SOURCE: *Jour. Amer. Soc. Agron.*, **20** (1928).

strains from various parts of the world in this characteristic. Northern-grown strains of red clover were most hardy. Loss of stand was directly related to loss of productiveness. A similar test[1] conducted in Wisconsin gave results of like nature.

While winters are less severe in the latitude of Iowa and Ohio than in more northern latitudes, winterkilling is still a factor of importance. During a mild winter in Ohio, winterkilling was most severe in the case of red clover from Italy,[19] but losses occurred with all foreign strains. During a severe winter in Iowa,[16] the least winterkilling occurred with the local strains, whereas plots planted with Italian and French seed were almost completely destroyed. Thus in the central latitudes winterkilling may be severe when unadapted nonhardy strains are used.

Even in the southern section of the clover belt winterkilling has proved to be a factor. This problem was studied in Kentucky,[17] using red clover

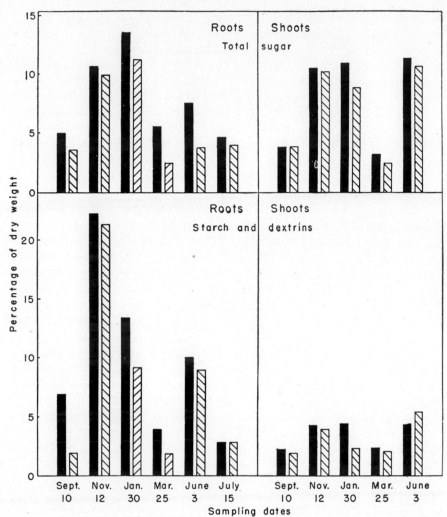

Fig. 11. Total sugar, and starch and dextrins in clover roots and shoots. Solid black bars represent the Ohio variety and hatched columns the French variety. (*Maryland Agricultural Experiment Station.*)

strains from many parts of this country as well as foreign countries. Foreign strains for the most part were completely destroyed, whereas adapted seed from Kentucky, Tennessee, and other Central states maintained the best stands. A similar test conducted in West Virginia[8] gave further proof of the need to consider winter hardiness in red clover the country over. Here the Northern strains proved more hardy; European strains and the one from Chile were the least hardy.

Efforts have been made to explain the reason for differences in hardiness between red clover varieties. An intensive study on an Ohio variety compared with a French variety was conducted in Maryland. Considerable variation in percentage of carbohydrate was found at different seasons of the year, as shown in Fig. 11. The French variety was consistently lower in starch, dextrins, and total sugar content. The Ohio variety contained slightly more nonprotein nitrogen and about the same total nitrogen as the French strain. It was somewhat lower in pentosans and hemicellulose. In view of previous work with alfalfa carbohydrate reserves, this would appear to be highly significant with red clover. The Maryland investigators indicate that the ability of hardy clover plants to maintain a high level of reserves, especially sugar, is important in the prevention of protein precipitation by extreme cold weather.

Diseases. A second very important factor in growing red clover is disease. While there are a number of significant diseases, anthracnose has been most thoroughly studied. There are two kinds, namely, the northern (*Kabatiella caulivora*) and southern (*Colletotrichum trifolii*). These diseases became recognized as severe problems in clover culture between 1920 and 1930, and they have been responsible for extensive testing and breeding work. As in the case of winter hardiness, their ravages are primarily associated with foreign and unadapted seed, but local varieties are also attacked.

Early data on these diseases indicated wide differences in varietal susceptibility. However, varieties developed and adapted within a given region were similar in their ability to resist the diseases. Data on southern anthracnose from a Kentucky study are given in Table 43. Local varieties were most resistant followed by southern, central, and northern varieties.

TABLE 43. EFFECT OF *Colletotrichum trifolii* ON PER CENT STANDS SURVIVING OF RED CLOVER

Clover	Per cent stand	
	First test	Second test
Kentucky 101	90	95
Tennessee	90	60
Southern	64	67
Central	50	56
Northern	23	42
Northwestern	10	31
Russian	..	45
German	..	40
French	..	38

SOURCE: *Ky. Agr. Expt. Sta. Bul.* 324 (1931).

Northwestern and foreign varieties proved most susceptible. Even earlier tests were conducted in Virginia[23] with varieties from many sources, and here it was also shown that foreign varieties were more susceptible to the southern anthracnose disease.

Little comparative data have been published on varietal resistance to the northern anthracnose. The results on one test conducted in Kentucky[7] show the local variety, Kentucky 101, was more resistant to this disease than other strains tested. The disease is of greatest importance through the central part of the clover belt.

VARIETY IMPROVEMENT

This early work, as described above, indicated the need for adapted varieties in three general regions within the Northeast. They are shown in Fig. 12. The chief limiting factor to the production of red clover in the

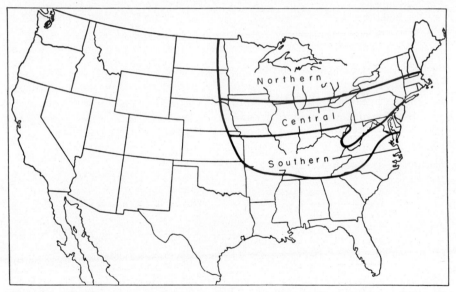

FIG. 12. The three main red clover regions. (*Bureau of Plant Industry, Soils and Agricultural Engineering, U.S. Department of Agriculture.*)

southern region is anthracnose, although winterkilling cannot be completely ignored. In the central region disease resistance and winter hardiness must be combined in suitable varieties. Winters of low temperature and little snow protection often prevail here. Diseases appear to be less serious in the northern region, but winter-hardy strains possessing a long period of dormancy are essential.

Cumberland. The U.S. Department of Agriculture recognized these general regions of clover needs in 1928 and set out in cooperation with certain of the experiment stations to develop adapted varieties. Thus three disease-resistant strains—one each from Virginia, Tennessee, and Kentucky—were composited and called Cumberland. The Cumberland variety is widely adapted over this region, as shown from the data given in Table 44. It is a vigorous grower, somewhat resistant to southern anthracnose, and in some instances a short-lived perennial. A new variety, Kenland, appears superior to Cumberland in this southern region.

TABLE 44. PERFORMANCE OF CUMBERLAND RED CLOVER, TONS OF CURED HAY PER ACRE

Variety	Kentucky, 4-year ave.	New Jersey, 3-year ave.	Virginia, 2-year ave.
Cumberland..............	2.29	3.1	2.55
Midland.................	2.11	2.5	2.48
Idaho...................	1.61	2.3	...

SOURCE: *Jour. Amer. Soc. Agron.*, **35** (1943).

Midland. Old strains of red clover that had proved to be good hay producers and to have some resistance to northern anthracnose were collected and studied in the central region. One strain was chosen from each of the states of Iowa, Indiana, Illinois, and Ohio, and these were composited into a new variety called Midland. Performance data for this variety are given in Table 45. Local strains in this region gave equivalent performance, as would be expected.

TABLE 45. HAY PRODUCTION OF MIDLAND RED CLOVER (ACRE BASIS)

Variety	Illinois, 2-year ave., tons	Ohio, 5-year ave., %	Iowa, tons
Midland.................	1.76	104	2.87
Cumberland.............	1.51	106	2.47*
Illinois.................	1.74	95	2.81†
Ohio....................	....	100	...

SOURCE: *Jour. Amer. Soc. Agron.*, **35** (1943).
* Oregon strain.   † Iowa strain.

The Cumberland and Midland varieties were produced from local strains which had developed some resistance to the anthracnose diseases. American strains long subjected to natural selection have developed resistance capable of partially combating these two serious diseases. Further breeding work will undoubtedly give even better strains.

Leaf Hopper Resistance. The leaf hopper (*Empoasca fabae*) has been found to do considerable damage to certain red clover varieties. Hopper injury is characterized by dwarfing and leaf discoloration particularly of a reddish or brownish nature, and it often results in death to young plants. It appears commonly on the second and third cutting of alfalfa, causing the plants to be stunted and yellowish in appearance.

It soon became apparent to a number of investigators that this was another problem in the growing of red clover to which the varieties showed great differences in resistance. The Kentucky Agricultural Experiment Station attacked the problem early and found that some of the same general principles applied in this case as with the anthracnose disease and winter hardiness. Their studies[12] showed that all the European strains were highly susceptible to attacks by the leaf hopper, whereas the local strains were resistant. Varieties of the Kentucky area were affected the least; Michigan and Minnesota strains were also resistant to attack. In comparing alfalfa and the clovers, it was found that alfalfa is more severely injured when attacked by the leaf hopper.

Close observation of the strains showed the American selections to be very hairy in contrast to the European ones, which were smooth or nearly so or in which the hairs were appressed. American red clover is not only hairy, but the hairs project at right angles to the stems. Data showing degrees of hairiness appear in Table 46. Thus a Kentucky selection was found to be about four times as hairy as an Italian strain. Apparently the amount and type of hairiness reduces hopper injury. The difference in hairiness between a Kentucky and French strain is shown in Fig. 13.

TABLE 46. THE NUMBER OF HAIRS ON 2 SQUARE MILLIMETERS OF SURFACE ON PETIOLES

Kind of clover	One petiole from each of 30 mature plants		Kind of clover	One petiole from each of 10 young plants	
	Ave. no. hairs	Range		Ave. no. hairs	Range
Kentucky 1	91.8	36–170	Kentucky 1	38.3	20–49
Wisconsin 4	75.4	25–142	Wisconsin 4	27.6	12–33
Oregon 6	69.3	39–165	Tennessee 6	27.2	12–42
Oregon 1	67.3	24–206	French	26.5	15–41
Wisconsin 7	63.0	24–160	Oregon 1	26.3	18–32
Wisconsin 3	61.4	30–201	Oregon 2	26.1	16–29
Oregon 2	59.7	28–100	Italian	23.1	15–34
Oregon 3	58.6	30–115	Wisconsin 3	22.5	16–80

SOURCE: *Ky. Agr. Expt. Sta. Bul.* 329 (1932).

Another reason hairy American strains of red clover escape the degree of severe injury from leaf hopper soon became apparent to investigators. Of the total nymphs that were hatched from plants of both Ohio and Italian

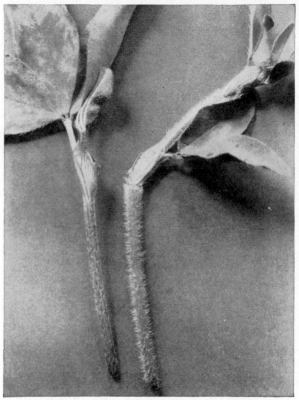

Fig. 13.   Stems of two red clover plants showing the character and amount of hairiness of each.   (*Kentucky Agricultural Experiment Station.*)

TABLE 47.   Comparison of Ohio and Italian Red Clover as Source Plants for Nymph Hatching of the Leaf Hopper

Plant type	Experiments				Per cent of grand total
	1st	2d	3d	Total	
Italian............	590	358	583	1,531	74.6
Ohio.............	264	112	145	521	25.4
Grand total.....	...	...	...	2,052	

Source: *Jour. Econ. Ent.,* **29** (1936).

strains, only 25.4 per cent of them came from the Ohio plants while 74.6 per cent came from the foreign plants (see Table 47). This indicates that the leaf hopper prefers the smooth, glabrous type of clover for oviposition. Thus the pubescent American strains are more likely to escape damage from leaf hopper and in this respect are superior to the smooth European types.

CULTURAL PRACTICES

The most important consideration in growing red clover is the use of a locally adapted variety that is resistant to winterkilling and disease. Some attention should be given also to fundamental cultural practices, such as seeding rate and time for cutting. The most favorable seeding rate for red clover was studied in Illinois. Obviously high seeding rates ensure a stand, whereas low seeding rates require extra care in seedbed preparation if a good stand is to be obtained. Nevertheless, the data given in Table 48

TABLE 48. EFFECT OF RATE OF PLANTING ON WEED-FREE HAY YIELDS OF OHIO, OREGON, AND FRENCH RED CLOVER

Seed source	Seeding rate per acre, lb.			
	5	10	15	20
	Moisture-free hay per acre, tons			
Ohio...............	1.68	1.78	1.73	1.70
France............	1.11	1.30	1.35	1.29
Oregon...........	1.08	1.15	1.19	1.25

SOURCE: *Jour. Amer. Soc. Agron.*, **33** (1941).

indicate that the seeding rate makes little difference in the yield compared with the difference due to the variety sown. High seeding rates of unadapted varieties will not compensate for the lack of adaptation.

Time of Cutting. The best time for cutting red clover in order to obtain the greatest yields of good-quality hay has been studied at a number of stations. Harvesting at the full-bloom stage is reported to give the highest yields[17] in Illinois and Pennsylvania, while cutting at later stages gave superior results in Connecticut. Yields and protein content of medium and mammoth red clover hay cut at various stages of maturity are reported in Table 49 from studies conducted in Ohio. For both types, the best stage for harvesting seems to be from one-third to full bloom in order to get the highest yields of protein and total dry matter.

TABLE 49. EFFECT OF TIME OF CUTTING ON AVERAGE HAY AND PROTEIN YIELDS, HOLGATE, OHIO

Date of maturity and stage of cutting	Yield of hay per acre, 1st cutting, lb.	Protein, in hay, 1st cutting, %	Protein per acre, 1st cutting, lb.	Yield per acre, 2d cutting, lb.
Medium Red Clover				
May 19—buds................	1,530	22.4	343	960
May 26—first flowers.........	1,980	21.1	418	1,080
June 2—30% bloom...........	2,580	18.7	482	1,020
June 9—65% bloom...........	3,010	15.9	478	980
June 16—full bloom...........	3,100	14.9	462	910
Mammoth Red Clover				
May 5......................	1,200	24.0	288	2,620
May 19.....................	1,570	23.8	374	1,140
June 2—buds................	2,790	18.8	524	640
June 9—first flowers..........	3,070	17.3	531	580
June 16—30% bloom..........	3,460	15.9	550	150
June 23—full bloom...........	3,800	14.4	547	.....

SOURCE: *Ohio Agr. Expt. Sta. Bimo. Bul.* 19 (1934).

FEEDING VALUE

Alfalfa is often considered to be higher in protein content than red clover. This has not been borne out by careful experiments. In a series of 17 comparisons between red clover and alfalfa in Ohio,[21] the average protein content of red clover hay was found to be 16.6 per cent and that of alfalfa 16.7 per cent. These carefully controlled tests show that the two hay species have almost equal protein content at all the various stages of development. Red clover and alfalfa hay harvested at similar stages and treated alike should be equally valuable.

The proportion of the various constituents of the red clover plant is given in Table 50. The stems make up the major weight of the plant. The proportion of leaves to other organs decreases with advancing age. The feeding value of these various organs is given in Table 51. The leaves and heads are highest in protein content and the leaves and leaf stalks in percentage of ash. The stems have high fiber content and are low in feeding value compared with the other parts of the plant.

The spread of red clover and the development of its culture in America has been truly remarkable. It attests to the ingenuity of growers throughout the present clover belt and in the scattered valleys of the Northwest.

TABLE 50. RELATIVE WEIGHT OF LEAVES, STEMS, AND FLOWER HEADS AT DIFFERENT AGES, PER CENT

Plant parts	Mar. 31, leaves forming	Apr. 26, stems forming	May 19, buds forming	June 1, first flowers	June 16, full bloom	Flowering finished
Leaves..............	40	41	24	24	19	18
Leaf stalks............	60	29	14	12	11	10
Stems................	..	30	58	58	59	60
Flower heads.........	..	..	4	6	11	12

SOURCE: From Piper, "Forage Plants and Their Culture," rev. ed., copyright, 1924, by The Macmillan Company and used with their permission.

TABLE 51. RESULTS OF ANALYSES OF THE DIFFERENT PARTS OF A DRY RED CLOVER PLANT, PER CENT

Constituents	Heads	Stems	Leaves	Leaf stalks
Protein.....................	18.25	8.06	24.63	11.16
Moisture...................	9.99	8.02	8.70	8.88
Ash.......................	7.20	5.67	8.39	8.02
Ether extract (fat)...........	2.86	1.25	5.00	2.18
Crude fiber.................	10.29	34.94	13.36	13.08
Nitrogen-free extract.........	51.41	42.06	39.92	56.68

SOURCE: *U.S. Dept. Agr. Farmers' Bul.* 1339 (1923).

The solution of major problems by red clover breeders has contributed no small part to the remarkable position of this crop in the short rotations of the Northeast.

References

1. Aamodt, O. S., J. H. Torrie, and O. F. Smith: Strain tests of red and white clovers, *Jour. Amer. Soc. Agron.*, **31**: 1029–1037 (1939).
2. Arny, A. C.: The adaptation of medium red clover strains, *Jour. Amer. Soc. Agron.*, **20**: 557–568 (1928).
3. Bear, F. E.: Mammoth red clover, Timely Soil Topics 69, Ohio State University, Columbus, Ohio, 1924.
4. Brown, B. A., and R. I. Munsell: Effects of cutting systems on alfalfa, *Conn. (Storrs) Agr. Expt. Sta. Bul.* 242 (1942).
5. Burke, Edmund: Studies on the composition and nutritive value of clover hay and clover silage in Montana, *Mont. Agr. Expt. Sta. Bul.* 117 (1917).
6. Delwiche, E. J., and W. E. Tottingham: Effect of climate on nitrogen content of maize, barley and red clover, *Jour. Amer. Soc. Agron.*, **22**: 681–688 (1930).
7. Fergus, E. N.: An analysis of clover failure in Kentucky, *Ky. Agr. Expt. Sta. Res. Bul.* 324 (1931).
8. Garber, R. J., and T. E. Odland: Varietal experiments with red clover and alfalfa, and field tests with meadow mixtures, *W.Va. Agr. Expt. Sta. Bul.* 250 (1932).

9. Greathouse, Glenn A., and Neil W. Stuart: The relation of physical properties and chemical composition of red clover plants to winterhardiness, *Md. Agr. Expt. Sta. Bul.* 391 (1936).

10. Hollowell, E. A.: Registration of varieties and strains of red clover, *Jour. Amer. Soc. Agron.*, **35**:830–833 (1943).

11. Hollowell, E. A., and David Hensinkveld: The effect of rate of planting on yields of adapted and unadapted red clover, *Jour. Amer. Soc. Agron.*, **33**:569–571 (1941).

12. Jewett, H. H.: The resistance of certain red clovers and alfalfas to leafhopper injury, *Ky. Agr. Expt. Sta. Res. Bul.* 329 (1932).

13. Pieters, A. J.: The proper binomial or varietal trinomial for American mammoth red clover, *Jour. Amer. Soc. Agron.*, **20**:686–702 (1928).

14. Pieters, A. J.: Red clover culture, *U.S. Dept. Agr. Farmers' Bul.* 1339 (1923).

15. Pieters, A. J., and E. A. Hollowell: Clover Improvement, U.S. Department of Agriculture Yearbook, 1937, pp. 1190–1214.

16. Pieters, A. J., and R. L. Morgan: Field tests of imported red clover seed, *U.S. Dept. Agr. Cir.* 210 (1932).

17. Piper, C. V.: Forage Plants and Their Culture, The Macmillan Company, New York, 1927.

18. Poos, F. W., and H. W. Johnson: Injury to alfalfa and red clover by the potato leaf hopper, *Jour. Econ. Ent.*, **29**:325–331 (1936).

19. Thatcher, L. E.: Homegrown vs. foreign red clover seed, *Ohio Agr. Expt. Sta. Bimo. Bul.* 9: 187–191 (1924).

20. Welton, F. A., and V. H. Morris: Climate and the clover crop, *Jour. Amer. Soc. Agron.*, **17**:790–800 (1925).

21. Willard, C. J.: The comparative protein content of alfalfa and red clover, *Jour. Amer. Soc. Agron.*, **23**:754–756 (1931).

22. Willard, C. J., J. S. Cutler, and J. B. McLaughlin: The time of cutting the true clovers, *Ohio Agr. Expt. Sta. Bimo. Bul.* 19: 39–43 (1934).

23. Wilsie, Carroll P., and E. A. Hollowell: Effect of time of cutting red clover on forage yields, seed setting and chemical composition, *Iowa Agr. Expt. Sta. Res. Bul.* 357 (1948).

24. Wolfe, T. K., and M. S. Kipps: Red clover experiments, *Va. Agr. Expt. Sta. Bul.* 252 (1926).

CHAPTER 7

ALSIKE CLOVER

Alsike clover came to America more than a century later than red clover. The first reported introduction was made from England into New York State in 1839. Records indicate that alsike was grown in Sweden as early

Fig. 14.   The general appearance of alsike clover.

as the tenth century and was introduced to England from that country in 1834. Although it is widely utilized in the clover belt, very little scientific data concerning its culture is available.

Unlike red clover, there is no problem of regional adaptation of strains. Alsike seed from one source appears to be as good as that from other sources, although this may be apparent only, because of the lack of careful scientific study. Apparently, this clover is attacked by certain disease and insect pests, but the severity of such injury is not known. It is classified botanically as a perennial, but it usually acts as a biennial in hayfields.

The biggest drawbacks of alsike are its marked tendency to lodge because of weak stems and its early maturity, which makes it ready to cut for hay prior to the advent of best haying weather. It also is essentially a "single-cut" clover, producing little aftermath. These characters are responsible for its relative unpopularity. They also point the way for improvement work, provided that the species possesses a degree of variability.

ADAPTATION

Alsike is adapted to cool climates, as is indicated by its Scandinavian origin. It appears to be at least as hardy as red clover and probably less subject to winter heaving. Cool summers favor optimum growth and hay yields. Its general region of adaptation is shown in Fig. 15.

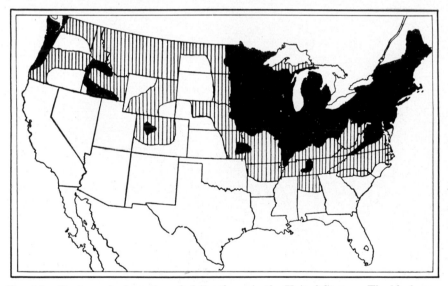

Fig. 15. Regions of adaptation of alsike clover in the United States. The black area shows where it is regularly used as a forage or seed crop; the hatched area shows where it is rarely grown or only in special places. (*Bureau of Plant Industry, Soils and Agricultural Engineering, U.S. Department of Agriculture.*)

A heavy soil well supplied with moisture appears most suited to the growth of this clover. It will endure poorly drained soils better than any other hay legume, including ladino clover. It is less sensitive to soil acidity than red clover and thus is especially valuable on lime-poor soils.

TABLE 52. RESPONSE OF ALSIKE CLOVER TO INCREASING SOIL FERTILITY

Season	Low		Medium		High	
	Stand, %	Height, in.	Stand, %	Height, in.	Stand, %	Height, in.
Winter...............	52	1	84	5	76	4
Late summer...........	15	1	14	3	58	2
Harvest...............	..	3	..	13	..	16

SOURCE: *Ky. Agr. Expt. Sta. Bul.* 269 (1926).

That it responds to fertility is evident from Table 52. The crop was planted in Kentucky in early spring, and data were collected the following winter and summer. Increasing fertility increased the height and reduced the percentage of stand losses.

Yield comparisons of alsike with red clover have been made at several experiment stations. Thus data from Ohio and West Virginia show that alsike clover has yielded about as well as red clover. Unfortunately, most of this yield is made in the first cutting when the best haying weather does not always prevail.

TABLE 53. COMPARATIVE YIELDS OF ALSIKE AND MEDIUM RED CLOVER, TONS

Type	Wooster, Ohio, 10-year ave.	Columbus, Ohio, 3-year ave.	West Virginia, 3-year ave.
Medium red...........	2.02	2.61	1.71
Alsike................	2.64	1.88	1.70

SOURCES: *Ohio Agr. Expt. Sta. Bimo. Bul.* 11 (1926); *W.Va. Agr. Expt. Sta. Bul.* 250 (1932).

QUALITY OF HAY

As with all legumes, the leaves of alsike clover are the most valuable part of the hay. The proportion of leaves to stems and the protein content of each are given in Table 54. In this table the leaves also include the flowers and seeds. The proportion of leaves is thus shown to run between 50 and 67 per cent, although the investigator points out that the study was made in a dry season and this may have affected the ratios. The proportion of leaves to stems increased with advancing age of the plants. The leaves are about twice as high in crude protein as the stems, and average protein content for the entire plant tops indicates a most acceptable hay for live-stock feeding.

TABLE 54. PERCENTAGE OF LEAVES AND STEMS AND OF PROTEIN IN ALSIKE CLOVER

Date of harvesting	Leaves	Stems	Crude protein in		
			Leaves	Stems	Total hay
May 20..........	55.9	44.1	24.0	14.3	19.7
May 31..........	50.7	49.3	19.6	13.5	16.6
June 2..........	56.7	43.3	....	....	....
June 10..........	62.3	37.7	20.2	9.2	16.1
June 15..........	56.6	43.4	18.6	8.6	14.3
June 25..........	67.7	32.3	17.7	8.0	14.6

SOURCE: *Ohio Agr. Expt. Sta. Bimo. Bul.* 19 (1934).

Alsike makes a finer quality hay than red clover because it is finer stemmed, and since it is not hairy it is freer of dust. Cattle tend to consume it more completely, seldom leaving stems in the manger.

The best time of cutting and the effect of stage of maturity on protein content are given in Table 55. The protein content decreased rapidly with

TABLE 55. INFLUENCE OF TIME OF CUTTING ALSIKE CLOVER ON AVERAGE YIELDS AND PROTEIN CONTENT

Date of first cutting	Stage	First cutting			
		Yield of hay per acre, lb.	Protein in hay, %	Protein per acre, lb.	Yield per acre, 2d cutting, lb.
May 19.............	Buds	1,220	23.7	289	230
May 26.............	15% bloom	1,650	21.6	356	220
June 2.............	50% bloom	2,160	18.2	393	250
June 9.............	Full bloom	2,810	16.0	450	200
June 16.............	Many brown	3,250	14.8	481	...
June 23.............	Mostly brown	3,360	13.4	450	...
June 30.............	Nearly ripe	3,320	13.4	445	...

SOURCE: *Ohio Agr. Expt. Sta. Bimo. Bul.* 19 (1934).

advancing maturity, although total yields of dry matter increased up to the "mostly brown" stage and total yields of protein up to the "many brown" stage. Cutting this clover at the full-bloom or later stage is indicated for a good yield and a high-quality product.

Comparisons with Red Clover and Sweetclover. A comprehensive study together with a comparison of alsike with red clover and sweetclover is given in Tables 56 and 57. Alsike is conspicuous for its earliness here and also for its favorable yields and nitrogen content in comparison with red clover or sweetclover.

TABLE 56. COMPARATIVE YIELD AND NITROGEN CONTENT OF ALSIKE AND RED CLOVER SEEDED IN OATS ON APR. 6 AND HARVESTED THE FOLLOWING YEAR

Date of harvesting	Pounds per acre, air-dry tops		Per cent of nitrogen in tops	
	Red	Alsike	Red	Alsike
Apr. 1–7	600	1,090	3.40	3.55
Apr. 24–26	1,800	1,900	3.16	2.83
May 10–17	3,810	3,310	....	....
May 24–31	5,600	5,650	2.89	2.71
June 14–16	4,320	.....	....	....
July 2–7	4,580	4,480	....	....

SOURCE: *Ohio Agr. Expt. Sta. Bimo. Bul.* 19 (1934).

TABLE 57. COMPARATIVE YIELD AND NITROGEN CONTENT OF ALSIKE CLOVER AND SWEETCLOVER SEEDED ALONE ON JULY 28 AND HARVESTED THE FOLLOWING YEAR

Date of harvesting	Pounds per acre, air-dry tops		Per cent of nitrogen in tops	
	Sweet	Alsike	Sweet	Alsike
Apr. 12	140	450	4.50	4.00
May 1	630	1,070	4.53	3.54
May 19	1,850	2,320	3.32	3.30
June 2	3,710	4,620	2.78	2.41
June 23	6,390	6,130	....	....
July 12	4,810	4,810	....	....

SOURCE: *Ohio Agr. Expt. Sta. Bimo. Bul.* 19 (1934).

Feeding Value. From a feeding standpoint, analyses show that there is little difference between red and alsike clover hay (Table 58). Actually alsike seems to be somewhat superior. Thus in feeding trials it has been higher in digestible dry matter, protein, and carbohydrates than red clover but lower in fat.

Red clover hay and alsike hay and silage were compared at the Montana Station; data are given in Table 59. Again alsike compares very favorably with red clover, being higher in protein and lower in fiber content. Feeding tests with sheep at the Montana Station showed that each pound of gain

TABLE 58. QUANTITIES OF DIGESTIBLE MATERIALS IN 100 POUNDS EACH OF ALSIKE AND RED CLOVER HAY

Kind of hay	Dry matter, %	Protein, %	Carbohy-drates, %	Fat, %	Fuel value, calories
Red clover.............	84.7	7.38	38.15	1.81	92,324
Alsike clover............	90.3	8.15	41.70	1.36	98,460

SOURCE: *U.S. Dept. Agr. Farmers' Bul.* 1151 (1920).

TABLE 59. COMPARISON OF ANALYSES OF ALSIKE CLOVER HAY AND SILAGE WITH RED CLOVER, PER CENT ON DRY-MATTER BASIS

Source	Material analyzed	Ash	Crude protein	Crude fiber	Ether extract	Nitrogen-free extract
Maine.........	Alsike clover hay	9.1	15.0	31.4	1.9	42.6
Maine.........	Alsike clover silage	10.4	12.1	37.2	3.9	36.5
Utah.........	Red clover hay	8.8	14.0	34.6	2.6	40.0

SOURCE: *Mont. Agr. Expt. Sta. Bul.* 117 (1917).

required 6.32 pounds of alsike hay, 6.43 pounds of red clover, and 6.58 pounds of alfalfa.

Alsike clover has many good points in its favor, such as adaptation to wet and acid soils and the ability to produce high-quality hay of good feeding value. It nevertheless appears to be a much neglected clover with no recorded attempts to improve the species and few significant studies concerning superior management techniques. While ladino clover appears to be adapted to similar environments, it cannot replace alsike because of the different management needs of the two species.

References

1. Burke, Edmund: Studies on the composition and nutritive value of clover hay and clover silage in Montana, *Mont. Agr. Expt. Sta. Bul.* 117 (1917).
2. Fergus, E. N., and W. D. Valleau: A study of clover failure in Kentucky, *Ky. Agr. Expt. Sta. Bul.* 269 (1926).
3. Garber, R. J., and T. E. Odland: Varietal experiments with red clover and alfalfa, and field tests with meadow mixtures, *W. Va. Agr. Expt. Sta. Bul.* 250 (1932).
4. Pieters, A. J.: Alsike clover, *U.S. Dept. Agr. Farmers' Bul.* 1151 (1920).
5. Willard, C. J.: Alsike clover, *Ohio Agr. Expt. Sta. Bimo. Bul.* 11: 43–46 (1926).
6. Willard, C. J.: The time of cutting the true clovers, *Ohio Agr. Expt. Sta. Bimo. Bul.* 19: 39–43 (1934).

CHAPTER 8

LADINO CLOVER

Ladino clover (*Trifolium repens*) is a large type of the common white clover. It spreads vigorously under favorable conditions by means of creeping fleshy stolons that root at the nodes. Single plants are known to occupy several square feet of area within one season after planting. In markings, shape, and color it is similar to white clover except for the increased size of all plant organs except seed. Under favorable soil and

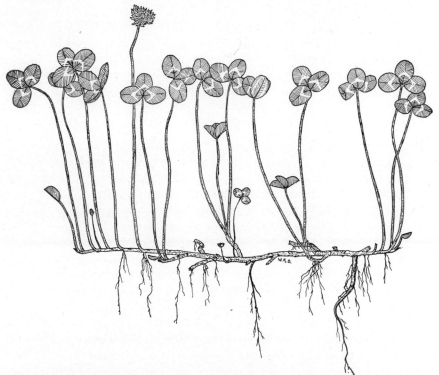

FIG. 16. Ladino clover is a giant form of white clover spreading vigorously by means of stolons.

climatic conditions ladino often attains a height of 15 to 20 inches or more, thus making it valuable as a component in some hay and silage mixtures. The plant is a perennial where conditions permit it to persist.

History and Adaptation

First records of its being grown in America date back to 1903 when the U.S. Department of Agriculture secured seed from the Po Valley in Italy for trial in the Northeastern states. The tests were unsuccessful, for the most part, but new lots of seed were obtained in 1911 and this time tried in Idaho with considerable success. The crop soon spread to the three Pacific states and in a short time became recognized there as a crop of real economic value. Beginning in 1930, interest in the crop was renewed in the Northeast, and since then ladino has become the most important pasture legume in that region.

Ladino clover is generally grown from Maine to Virginia and westward to Ohio. It is increasing in popularity in North Carolina, Tennessee, and Kentucky and in the dairy states of Michigan and Wisconsin. It is widely grown in the Northwestern states and in California wherever adequate moisture supplies are available. Ladino is best adapted to regions possessing a relatively cool summer climate together with a good supply of rainfall uniformly distributed. It is capable of surviving extreme cold winter temperatures provided that it is adequately fertilized, carefully managed, and grown in a grass association. Hot dry periods during the summer season reduce its growth but do not usually destroy the plants.

Culture

Heavy moist soils of high fertility are best suited for growing this crop, although it has been grown with considerable success even under upland conditions provided that the soil is fertile. In the West frequent irrigations are required to keep the plants in a healthy state of growth.

Only a few carefully controlled studies have been reported for ladino, due no doubt to the relative newness of this crop. Since this legume possesses stolons that root at the nodes, surface applications of lime and fertilizer should result in ready response. Because ladino is a very productive species, it requires a high level of fertility for maximum yields.

Response to pH. Most legumes grow best where adequate lime is available. Ladino clover is no exception. Studies of this nature made in Connecticut are given in Table 60. Ground limestone, added at the rates of 4 to 8.5 tons per acre during the period 1914 to 1920 resulted in soil pH values of 5.64 to 5.96 in 1939. The yields of alfalfa and ladino clover harvested from these plots show a positive correlation with the pH value, other factors being equal. Thus ladino clover produced 2,290 pounds of dry matter at pH 5.64 and 3,160 pounds at pH 5.96. Almost an extra ½ ton of hay was secured from ladino due to a pH difference of 0.32. Ladino appears to be about as responsive as alfalfa to lime, although it is known to be more tolerant of acid soils. In farm practice a ton of lime per acre is

Extension Folder 159   June 1951

Build Your Own
Terraces

Harold E. Jones—D. M. Ryan

MAINTAIN
fertility

CONSERVE
soil

RETAIN
water

PREVENT
gullies

and you can
use your own
FARM EQUIPMENT

UNIVERSITY OF MINNESOTA
Agricultural Extension Service
U. S. DEPARTMENT OF AGRICULTURE

> A TERRACE is a combined earth ridge and channe[l]
> not run off the land. Terraces are an aid to erosion
> farming, strip cropping, and building grass waterway[s]
> tices. Properly constructed terraces reduce soil and w[ater]

Equipment

One of the first subjects to consider before building terraces is this: what kind of equipment can you use?

Terraces can be efficiently constructed with equipment available on the farm. The most commonly available implement that can be used is the moldboard plow, but if you have only a disk plow available, you may use the same general method if you make some adjustment in the number of rounds. Base this adjustment on the amount of soil moved in comparison with the plow.

Other farm equipment such as the one-way disk and the rotary scraper have also been used effectively, or if you contract for your terrace construction, whirlwind terracers, bulldozers, and road graders can be used. The road grader can be used on a greater variety of soils and more irregular slopes than the moldboard or disk plow.

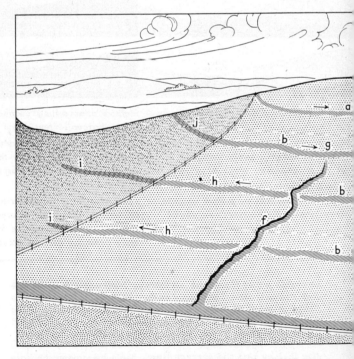

A TERRACED FIELD. The base terrace (a) should be no more than
(b) carry excess water into a grassed natural outlet (c) which drain
be terraced across but water should be diverted from deeper gul[lies]
discharge into permanent pasture (i). Outlet ends of these two terr[ace]
terrace (j) extends through pasture to protect steep slope.

built across a slope to catch water and make it walk
control practices such as good crop rotation, contour
but terracing cannot be substituted for these prac-
water losses and protect crop seedings.

Steps in Building the Terraces

1. **Determine whether the land is suitable for terracing.** An important factor is slope, for it governs the amount
of runoff from a field. A second factor is a suitable outlet which
will carry water to a place which is fairly flat and washing
won't occur.

Uniformity, steepness, and length of slope determine
whether terracing should be done.

DO construct terraces on long gentle slopes where
there is a large amount of runoff water. The
graded terrace is not expensive and performs successfully on slopes up to 12 per cent.

DO NOT construct terraces on short steep slopes and
irregular slopes with deep gullies or isolated knolls.
This includes slopes over 12 per cent.

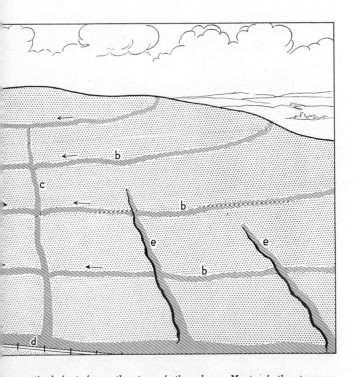

ve vertical feet from the top of the slope. Most of the terraces
into a permanently protected waterway (d). Small gullies (e) may
(f) by a terrace at their head (g). Terraces at left of deep gully
s are staggered to spread the water and prevent gullying. Second

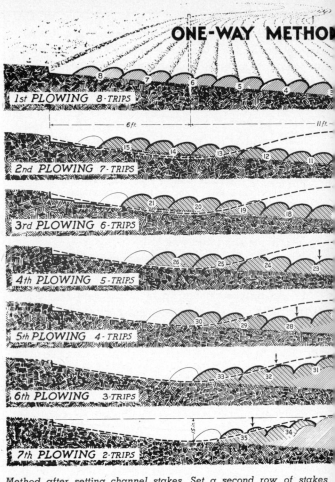

ONE-WAY METHOD

1st PLOWING 8-TRIPS

8 7 6 5 4

⟵ 6 ft. ⟶   ⟵ 11 ft. ⟶

2nd PLOWING 7-TRIPS

15 14 13 12 11

3rd PLOWING 6-TRIPS

21 20 19 18

4th PLOWING 5-TRIPS

26 25 24 23

5th PLOWING 4-TRIPS

30 29 28

6th PLOWING 3-TRIPS

33 32 31

7th PLOWING 2-TRIPS

15 in. 35 34

Method after setting channel stakes. Set a second row of stakes
curves) a distance of 11 feet below channel stakes. This row mark

This drawing is based on use of a two-bottom, 12-, 14-, or 16-inch
be left on. Use sharp shares. Maintain enough speed to turn fur
crop residues and disk heavy sod well before plowing.

Start first plowing by throwing furrow slice against lower stake
unless adjoining land is to be plowed. Start each successive plow
the third furrow slice (marked with arrow) of the previous plowi
to form a smooth backslope. If terrace ridge is not 15 inches abc
necessary.

Hand levels are accurate enough to determine whether a
field can be terraced, but it takes a surveyor's level in the
hands of an experienced operator to lay out the terrace lines.

If the soil is too shallow or the subsoil is too rocky for
terracing, possibly you can use diversion ditches instead of
terraces. This is only on long, gentle slopes, however.

If you live in a dry section and have a fairly permeable
soil, you may use level terraces—those with no grade. Level
terraces detain runoff water until it can be absorbed.

2. Locate the terrace outlets. First look for an existing
outlet—either a natural water course or a sodded area which
will spread the water. If natural outlets aren't available a

soil. You may find it necessary to rearrange fields and fence lines in setting up the terrace system.

Terraces which are not laid out or built correctly are often very troublesome. Before laying out your terrace, inspect others in your community and if possible watch an experienced operator. You can also get technical help and advice from your county agent or the farm planner of your conservation district.

4. Prepare for plowing. Remove all trash and obstacles such as rocks and stumps from the terrace area before beginning work. Be sure that the moisture content of the soil is right for best scouring of the plow.

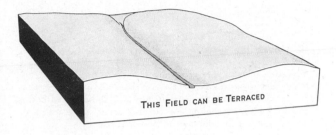

THIS FIELD CAN BE TERRACED

5. Construct the terraces. The two-way method for constructing terraces is best adapted to gentle slopes and soil that scours well. The one-way method is best where the slope is steep and it is difficult to turn the furrow uphill.

You may have to make some adjustment of rounds to make the methods work well with your equipment and the soil conditions of your farm. For instance, you may have to do more work than is shown in the charts to make the terrace the right height.

If you have taken out sharp curves it may be necessary to fill across gullies and cut down high spots with a dirt mover or a rotary scraper. Do not use rocks or any material other than soil as part of the fill or it will not hold.

Your terrace should approach these standard requirements:

>   Back slope of channel—6 feet
>   Bottom width of channel—6 feet
>   Front slope of terrace—8 feet
>   Back slope of terrace—16 feet
>   Vertical distance between channel and ridge—
>   1½ feet
>   Two-foot wide rounded top on ridge
>   No low spots in ridge and no high spots in
>   channel

THIS FIELD CANNOT BE TERRACED

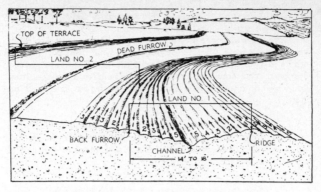

Follow this method in plowing a terraced field.

6. Check the terraces. The finished terrace should have all slopes long and gentle enough so that any piece of farm equipment can be easily operated on them. After checking the channel and ridge grades with a surveyor's level, cut all high spots in the channel grade and fill low spots in the ridge grade to the proper height. Be careful not to have too much grade in the terrace channel or it will erode.

Follow These Maintenance Rules

1. **Make** all farming operations parallel to the terrace.
2. **Lay out** headlands for plowing on the terrace ridge.
3. **Use** the terrace as the starting point for strip cropping.
4. **Check** after each rain. . . . .
   - the ridge for low spots.
   - the channel for high spots.
   - the upper end for any water by-passing the terrace.
5. **Repair** terraces as soon as possible.
6. **Maintain** the grass cover on the terrace outlet to prevent gullies. Apply fertilizer at seeding time and at least every second year.

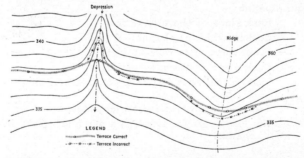

Redline the terrace line by straightening sharp curves through low places and over high places.

UNIVERSITY FARM, ST. PAUL 1, MINNESOTA

Cooperative Extension Work in Agriculture and Home Economics, University of Minnesota, Agricultural Extension Service and United States Department of Agriculture Co-operating. Paul E. Miller, Director. Published in furtherance of Agricultural Extension Acts of May 8 and June 30, 1914.
7500—6-51

TABLE 60. EFFECTS OF RATE OF LIMING ON YIELDS OF ALFALFA AND LADINO CLOVER

Limestone applied 1914–1920, tons per acre	Number of plots in group	pH of soil in 1939	Dry matter in 1940, lb. per acre	
			Alfalfa	Ladino
4.0	4	5.64	1,326	2,290
5.5	4	5.77	1,640	2,624
7.0	8	5.82	2,024	2,953
8.5	4	5.96	2,382	3,160

SOURCE: *Conn. (Storrs) Agr. Expt. Sta. Bul.* 235 (1941).

applied every 3 or 4 years to keep the soil pH in a satisfactory state for ladino.

Lime and Fertilizer Together. The use of mineral fertilizers appears to increase yields. The amounts to use and the ratios are not always the same for various climatic and soil conditions, as would be expected. It is generally agreed that the fertilizers should be used in conjunction with lime, and this is borne out by the data in Table 61. In this study the

TABLE 61. LADINO AND RED CLOVER YIELDS ON VARIOUSLY FERTILIZED PLOTS

Fertilizer treatment*	Dry matter, lb. per acre	
	Red	Ladino
L	1,332	987
LP	2,992	2,284
LPK	3,714	2,883
LNPK	3,699	1,992
PK	2,235	1,483
P	973	385

SOURCE: *Conn. (Storrs) Agr. Expt. Sta. Bul.* 235 (1941).

* Limestone at 2,000 lb.; superphosphate (16%) at 500 lb.; muriate of potash at 100 lb.; and nitrogen at 30 lb. per acre.

response of red clover and ladino to six soil amendments was measured. It can be noted that red clover gave somewhat higher hay yields than ladino, but this would be expected where ladino is handled as a hay crop. Best response from ladino was secured with lime and phosphate and potash fertilizer. Inferior growth resulted from the use of lime alone or mineral fertilizers without lime.

Importance of Potash. Evidence is increasing showing the significance of adequate quantities of potash fertilizer in stimulating yields and lengthening the life of ladino stands. A greenhouse study (see Table 62) in which

TABLE 62. YIELDS OF LADINO CLOVER AS AFFECTED BY POTASSIUM SUPPLY

Solution	Potassium, p.p.m.	Green weight of tops, grams	Dry weight of tops, grams
1	1	23.7	5.0
2	4	60.6	10.8
3	16	171.3	29.3
4	64	252.0	33.5
5	256	339.3	45.8

SOURCE: *Soil Sci.*, **52** (1941).

potassium was added at 1, 4, 16, 64 and 256 p.p.m. shows a direct yield increase as the available potassium was increased. Thus at 4 p.p.m. only 10.8 grams of dry matter was produced but at 256 p.p.m., 45.8 grams. This would indicate that ladino clover responds strongly to potash fertilizer provided that no other factor is limiting growth.

A field test conducted in New Jersey gives further evidence of the significance of this element. A ladino clover field was treated with varying amounts of potash (see Table 63) over a 6-year period, and records were

TABLE 63. THE EFFECT OF POTASH FERTILIZER ON PER CENT STAND OF LADINO CLOVER

Plant species	Pounds K$_2$O per acre annually			
	0	50	100	200
Ladino clover..........................	20.6	37.3	47.8	60.0
Kentucky bluegrass..................	45.3	38.2	29.3	24.3
Timothy.............................	1.6	3.4	4.8	4.4
Orchard grass.......................	2.1	3.9	2.5	4.5
Quackgrass.........................	5.4	2.8	2.3	...
Weeds..............................	21.0	12.4	12.3	5.8

SOURCE: *N.J. Agr. Expt. Sta. Bul.* 736 (1948).

kept on the per cent stand of ladino. The data given in Table 63 give the plant counts at the end of the sixth year. Where no potash was supplied, there was a stand of only 20.6 per cent; with 100 pounds, 47.8 per cent; and with 200 pounds, 60 per cent. This type of data strongly suggests that potash is very effective in maintaining good stands of ladino.

Seeding Mixtures. Ladino clover is seldom sown alone except when it is used for seed or poultry and bee-pasture purposes. Mixing with other legumes or with certain grasses normally gives better yields and tends to lengthen the productive life of the planting. Mowing and curing are also easier when the mixture contains some grass.

In a Connecticut study ladino clover was seeded alone and with orchard grass, variable seeding rates of both being tried (see Table 64). Mixing ladino with orchard grass increased the yields irrespective of seeding rates, but the 3 pounds of ladino and 5 pounds of orchard grass seed per acre was the superior seeding rate. Actually ladino is seldom seeded at more than 1 or 2 pounds per acre, especially if sown in a mixture.

TABLE 64. EFFECTS OF VARYING THE SEEDING RATES OF ORCHARD GRASS AND LADINO CLOVER

Seed mixture, lb. per acre	Yields of air-dry matter, lb. per acre			
	1933	1934	1935	Ave.
Ladino 6.0 alone....................	2,063	4,078	2,237	2,793
Ladino 4.5 + orchard grass 2.5......	2,064	4,198	3,565	3,276
Ladino 3.0 + orchard grass 5.0......	2,286	4,861	3,357	3,501
Ladino 1.5 + orchard grass 7.5......	1,346	4,048	3,124	2,839

SOURCE: *Conn. (Storrs) Agr. Expt. Sta. Bul.* 235 (1941).

A small quantity of ladino seed (½ pound per acre) is often mixed with red clover–timothy or alfalfa–timothy hay plantings. The advantage of such a practice is that the ladino fills in bare spots and often replaces the red clover or alfalfa as they thin out, thus substantially contributing to hay yields or making the mixture better adapted for pasture purposes. Other mixtures are also used, as ladino with bromegrass, orchard grass, or reed canary grass. Under these conditions the mixture is considered primarily for pasture purposes but also as a potential hay or silage crop. Under such conditions the first cutting may be cured for hay or made into grass silage and later growth pastured.

Cutting Treatments. One of the greatest problems in growing ladino is to maintain good stands over a period of years. Losses of stand from winter injury and summer killing occur regularly, but these can be kept at a minimum by careful management. Severe shading of the ladino by associated grass or legume companions is known to be a factor in loss of stand, and this is one reason why ladino makes a better pasture than hay plant.

In an extensive cutting-treatment study in Connecticut it was found that ladino maintained itself best when cut back to a height of 4 inches as compared with 2 inches (see Table 65). Cutting back to 2 inches tended to reduce the stand whether it was grown with timothy or orchard grass. The

TABLE 65.   EFFECTS OF CUTTING SYSTEMS ON MAINTAINING STANDS OF LADINO

System of cutting	Area occupied by ladino, %		Dry matter, lb. per acre	
	May 9, 1940, with timothy	Sept. 3, 1940, with orchard	With timothy	With orchard
When 6–2 in..............	14	43	2,637	2,936
When 6–4 in..............	51	60	2,844	3,370
When 8–2 in..............	18	43	2,922	3,025
When 8–4 in..............	52	69	2,603	3,288
When 10–2 in..............	23	51	2,878	3,305
When 10–4 in..............	40	68	3,054	3,413

SOURCE: *Conn. (Storrs) Agr. Expt. Sta. Bul.* 235 (1941).

4-inch height of cut also resulted in the highest yields.   These data were collected from plots which had been treated in a similar manner the year previously and in which yields favored the 2-inch cut.   One can only conclude from such evidence that more information is needed on cutting systems before final evaluations can be made.

Feeding Value.   The feeding value of ladino is changed very little from the young to the bloom stage of growth.   Protein ranges from 23 to 28 per cent of dry weight of the very young growth and seldom drops below 18 to 20 per cent as the plant begins to bloom.   It is relatively low in fiber content, and the calcium and phosphorus are usually high compared with other forages.   From a silage standpoint, ladino preserves well provided that it is adequately wilted or that preservatives are added.

Other Uses.   Horticulturists are using ladino in orchards as a cover and green-manure crop.   It is especially valuable in apple orchards on soils of good moisture-holding capacity.   It is usually mowed during the summer, and the clippings are left under the trees to improve the soil.   Beekeepers consider ladino an excellent plant for honey production.   The bees show a preference for it over many other flowers and find a good supply of nectar in the blooms.   Its continued growth throughout the season makes it a dependable source for the bees.

CONCLUSIONS

Ladino appears to make a high-quality hay containing ample quantities of protein, minerals, and vitamins.   All classes of livestock relish the hay, but it is most valuable for dairy cattle and sheep.   It is somewhat more difficult to mow because of its high moisture content and its succulent, tangled mass of stems.   Preliminary trials indicate that it makes a good quality of silage when properly ensiled.

There appear to be many advantages associated with the growing of this crop where it is adapted. A few of these follow:

1 It acts as a medium-lived perennial with fair management practices.
2. It will increase hay yields quite often when sown with other clovers and grasses in mixtures.
3. It possesses a high feeding value.
4. It tolerates moist and poorly drained soils where alfalfa cannot survive.
5. It can be used for hay, pasture, or silage.

Some limitations in using this crop for forage are also evident:

1. It is difficult to mow and cure for hay especially if grown without other legumes or grasses.
2. Its use is somewhat restricted to moist fertile soils, being unadapted to droughty and unfertile areas.
3. Careful management regarding mowing, grazing, and fertilizing is required or the stand may be winterkilled or summer killed.
4. It is not so productive as alfalfa on good alfalfa soils.

Much more information is needed on ladino regarding the best farm practices to employ in the culture of this crop. It has now earned a secure position in American agriculture, and it is bound to contribute even more significantly in the years ahead. Fundamentally, ladino is a pasture legume, but it does contribute both yield and quality in certain hay mixtures in those regions where it is adapted. It also plays a significant role in "multiple-purpose" mixtures where the crop may be used for pasture, hay, silage, or occasionally seed production.

References

1. Ahlgren, Gilbert H.: Some effects on volume rate of solution supply and of potassium concentration on the growth of white clover, *Soil Sc.*, **52**: 229–235 (1941).
2. Ahlgren, H. L., and F. V. Burcalow: Ladino clover, *Wis. Agr. Ext. Cir.* 367 (1946).
3. Brown, B. A., and R. I. Munsell: Ladino clover experiments, 1930 to 1940, *Conn. (Storrs) Agr. Expt. Sta. Bul.* 235 (1941).
4. Eby, Claude: Ladino clover, *N.J. Agr. Expt. Sta. Cir.* 408 (1941).
5. Haddock, J. L.: Ladino clover for New Hampshire, *N.H. Agr. Ext. Cir.* 254 (1943).
6. Hollowell, E. A.: Ladino white clover for the Northeastern states, *U.S. Dept. Agr. Farmers' Bul.* 1910 (1942).
7. Madson, B. A., and J. Earl Coke: Ladino clover, *Calif. Agr. Ext. Cir.* 81 (1937).
8. Sprague, M. A., and Claude Eby: Growing ladino clover in New Jersey, *N.J. Agr. Expt. Sta. Bul.* 736 (1948).

CHAPTER 9

THE SWEETCLOVERS

Up until 1912, sweetclover was generally considered a weed, commonly occurring along roadsides and in many waste areas, being at that time of no significant value to agriculture. Its elevation to a position of importance

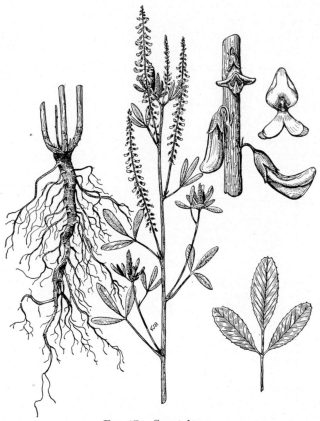

Fig. 17. Sweetclover.

among American forage crops is a most remarkable achievement. In 1947 there were 332 thousand acres and 421 thousand tons of sweetclover harvested for hay in the United States. During the 10-year period from 1936 to 1945 the average was 756 thousand acres and 906 thousand tons.

Along with its production for hay are extensive plantings for pasture, soil improvement, and seed harvesting. The assimilation of nitrogen together with extensive top and root growth make it well qualified for pasture and soil improvement, and it is considered of greater importance for these purposes than it is for hay.

History and Spread

The sweetclovers were introduced into America from their habitat, western Asia. White sweetclover was present in Virginia as early as 1739 and was reported in New England in 1785. Seed was extensively distributed in Alabama sometime after 1856, and it became used as a hay crop on the black limestone soils of Alabama and Mississippi. Much seed was scattered about in waste places and other areas by beekeepers, since sweetclover proved to be a good honey crop. The center of sweetclover production today is in the Corn Belt and the northern and central Great Plains states, but it is grown to some extent over most of the United States.

Species and Varieties

Only two species of sweetclover have attained a significant status in America. These are *Melilotus alba*, the common biennial white-flowered sweetclover, and *M. officinalis*, the common biennial yellow-flowered sweetclover. Of lesser importance are *M. alba annua*, an annual white-flowered sweetclover; *M. indica*, an annual yellow-flowered species common

Fig. 18. Sweetclover varieties showing a wide range of maturity in the second year after planting. *Left*, Evergreen, bud stage; *center*, Spanish, full bloom; *right*, Madrid, seed-formation stage. (*U.S. Department of Agriculture and the Nebraska Agricultural Experiment Station.*)

in the South; and *M. suaveolens*, a yellow biennial sweetclover adapted primarily to the northern Great Plains.

The biennial sweetclovers do not bloom or set seed until the second year of growth. The first season's growth is leafy, and its hay quality approaches that of alfalfa. The second year's crop grows rapidly in early spring and becomes quite coarse with advancing maturity. Annual sweetclover blooms and produces seed in the first year from a spring planting.

In general, the yellow biennial sweetclover is 10 to 14 days earlier in maturing than the biennial white, has finer stems, and is leafier, but produces less top growth. It is also more sensitive to drought and to acid soil conditions. There is little difference between the white and yellow sweetclovers from the standpoint of number of stems per plant and the size of the root system. In an Ohio study[8] individual plants of the white type averaged 9.8 stems and the yellow type 9.3 stems. The roots were about 2 inches longer and slightly thicker in the white type.

Classification of Varieties. There are many commercial varieties of sweetclover available, each having superior characters for certain regions. Classification of the varieties according to species is given in Table 66.

TABLE 66. SWEETCLOVER VARIETIES CLASSIFIED AS TO SPECIES

M. alba		*M. officinalis*
Alpha	Pioneer	Albotrea
Common White	Sangamon	Common Yellow
Evergreen	Spanish	Erector
Grundy County	Willamette	Madrid
Iowa Late	Wisconsin Late	Switzer

White sweetclover thus has 10 important varieties, whereas yellow sweetclover has only five. The only important variety of *M. suaveolens* is Redfield and of *M. alba annua* the Hubam.

Varietal Characteristics. A detailed study of variety characteristics was made in Nebraska. Data are given in Table 67. The diversity in growth, maturity, coarseness of stems, and seedling vigor permits ample opportunity for the selection of varieties adapted to the farm needs. The variation in characters influences the time of harvest, the quality of hay produced, and the ease with which stands can be obtained.

Height and Leafiness. Sweetclover varieties vary in growth and percentage of leaves, as is indicated by data in Table 68. Thus Grundy County, with more than 60 per cent leaves, was the most leafy variety in the first cutting, and Albotrea, averaging 42 per cent, was the most leafy in the second season. In this study Spanish was the tallest variety in both first and second season. Ranges in height for the first season were from 18 inches for Alpha 3 to 33 inches for Spanish and in the second year from 34 inches for Alpha 1 to 67 inches for Spanish.

TABLE 67. DESCRIPTIONS OF VARIETIES OF SWEETCLOVER AS GROWN IN NEBRASKA

Variety	Vegetative characters				
	Flower color	Time of maturity in 2d year	Plant height at maturity, 1941	Coarseness of stem	Relative seedling vigor
Common White............	White	Midseason	Tall	Coarse	Medium
Common Yellow..........	Yellow	Early	Medium	Medium	Medium
Grundy County...........	White	Early	Medium	Medium	Medium
Madrid...................	Yellow	Early	Medium	Medium	Strong
Spanish..................	White	Midseason	Tall	Coarse	Strong
Evergreen................	White	Late	Tall	Coarse	Strong
Willamette...............	White	Midseason	Tall	Coarse	Strong
Sangamon................	White	Mid-late	Tall	Coarse	Medium
Iowa Late White..........	White	Mid-late	Tall	Coarse	Strong
Wisconsin Late White.......	White	Late	Tall	Coarse	Medium
Redfield..................	Yellow	Late	Tall	Coarse	Medium
Pioneer..................	White	Midseason	Short	Medium	Weak
Alpha....................	White	Midseason	Short	Fine	Weak
Switzer..................	Yellow	Early	Medium	Medium	Medium
Albotrea.................	Yellow	Early	Medium	Medium	Medium

SOURCE: *Nebr. Agr. Expt. Sta. Bul.* 352 (1943).

TABLE 68. HEIGHTS AND LEAF PERCENTAGES OF FIRST- AND SECOND-SEASON HAY CROPS FROM VARIOUS SWEETCLOVER VARIETIES

Variety	First-season heights, in.	Second-season heights, in.	First-season leaf, %	Second-season leaf, %
Albotrea.....................	22	40	48.1	41.8
Alpha 1.....................	21	34	51.6	31.9
Alpha 3.....................	18	40	53.3	28.8
Arctic......................	27	58	47.7	26.4
Common White...............	29	60	47.0	....
Grundy County...............	21	51	60.3	29.9
Spanish.....................	33	67	49.3	24.5
Madrid.....................	31	55	42.5	34.0
Redfield Yellow..............	28	57	52.0	23.4
Willamette White.............	31	64	44.2	21.3
Zouave Yellow...............	29	46	53.4	35.1

SOURCE: *Wash. Agr. Expt. Sta. Bul.* 365 (1938).

Hay Yields. Varietal influence is most strongly felt in yields of hay. Data selected from yield trials in Nebraska and Washington are given in Table 69. There is obviously a wide range among varieties in yield performance. This varies with the crop and the environment and should be considered in planting sweetclover for hay.

TABLE 69. COMPARATIVE HAY YIELDS OF SWEETCLOVER VARIETIES AT TWO EXPERIMENT STATIONS, TONS

Variety	First-season yields		Second-season yields	
	Washington	Nebraska	Washington	Nebraska
Common White..............	1.46	1.22	3.74	2.56
Grundy County..............	1.13	0.87	3.05	2.00
Madrid.....................	1.71	1.85	3.40	2.21
Redfield....................	1.37	1.23	2.90	1.82
Willamette..................	1.72	1.95	4.49	2.58

SOURCES: *Wash. Agr. Expt. Sta. Bul.* 365 (1938); *Nebr. Agr. Expt. Sta. Bul.* 352 (1943).

MOWING TREATMENTS

Most sweetclover growers prefer to cut the first-year crop for hay in late summer. This cutting makes an excellent hay when properly cured. In the northern Great Plains a hay crop is not always possible in the first year because the growth is not large enough. In the second year, the first cutting is best mowed just before blooming begins and before the plants become woody and unpalatable. In the drier regions this crop is often cut when it is 2½ to 3 feet tall.

Height of Cutting. In the fall of the first year regular mowing heights may be safely employed in cutting the crop. The first crop in the second year comes from the crown buds but the second crop from the axils of the leaves or the lower portions of the stems. Thus in the second year, if the first crop is cut too close so that most of the lower parts of the stems are removed, there will be no second crop.

When cutting the first crop in the second year, a stubble of about 12 inches should generally be left if a heavy loss of stand is to be avoided. Many growers recognize the difficulties associated with using the second year's growth for hay since the position of the stem buds results in the destruction of many of the plants unless good judgment is exercised. The height of the buds on the stems varies, but generally speaking the thicker the stand, the higher the bud locations.

An experiment on the effect of height of cut is reported in Table 70. When a height of 4 inches was employed, there was no second growth at all. At 8 inches only a 10 per cent crop resulted in the first test, and in the

TABLE 70. EFFECT ON THE GROWTH OF THE SECOND CROP OF CUTTING WHITE
SWEETCLOVER 4, 8, AND 12 INCHES LONG

First test		Second test	
Cutting treatment, in.	Second growth	Cutting treatment, in.	Second growth
4	None	4	None
8	10% crop	8	None
12	Full crop	12	Full crop

SOURCE: *Jour. Amer. Soc. Agron.*, **26** (1934).

second no growth was recorded. Cutting at 12 inches permitted a normal
second growth. It is obvious that close cutting of the second crop will
result in heavy loss of stand.

Time of Cutting. The effect of time of cutting for hay in the first and
second year on stand survival and growth is shown in Table 71. That

TABLE 71. EFFECT OF FIRST- AND SECOND-YEAR FIELD TREATMENT ON THE STAND
SURVIVAL AND GROWTH OF SWEETCLOVER (COMMON YELLOW)

First-year treatment	Survival in spring, %	Second year, first cutting	Stem survival after first cutting, %	Height of second crop, in.
Hay, Oct. 1..........	71	Hay, early bud	80	22
Hay, Oct. 1..........	79	Hay, full flower	19	13
Pasture.............	90	Hay, early bud	80	22

SOURCE: *Nebr. Agr. Expt. Sta. Bul.* 352 (1943).

mowed close for hay on Oct. 1 survived the winter 75 per cent, and when
pasturing was simulated survival was 90 per cent. In the second year,
mowing the first crop in the full flower stage resulted in severe loss of stand
and in reduced growth, whereas harvesting at the early bud stages gave
an average survival of 80 per cent.

QUALITY AND FEEDING VALUE

A better quality of hay can be obtained from early mowing in the second
year, but at great sacrifices in yield, as shown in Table 72. Yields increase
rapidly in early spring, and a week to 10 days' delay in cutting may result
in ¼ ton of hay more per acre. In addition, early cutting reduces the
speed of curing because of less favorable weather. The later cutting, on
the other hand, results in a coarser quality product.

TABLE 72.   EFFECT OF DATE OF CUTTING ON ACRE YIELDS OF SWEETCLOVER, TONS

Date of cutting	Yield	Date of cutting	Yield
May 23...........	0.48	May 23..........	1.02
May 26...........	0.72	May 27..........	1.18
May 29...........	0.78	May 29..........	1.56
June 1............	1.03	June 3...........	1.27
June 7............	1.51	June 7...........	1.43

SOURCE: *Ill. Agr. Expt. Sta. Bul.* 394 (1933).

Coarseness. Objections to sweetclover for hay are related to its early growth in the second year. This is often coarse and stemmy, cures slowly, and does not make a high-quality hay. Early spring clipping may delay the first crop, bringing it on 3 to 4 weeks later and thus making a better hay with more leaves and finer stems. Briefly, the second year first crop matures for hay when the weather is still unsettled. The stems cure much more slowly than the leaves, thus resulting in heavy losses of the latter in the haymaking process. Because of the heavy stems the growth is too rank and coarse for best quality hay.

Curing. Unless sweetclover hay is well cured, there is danger in feeding it. The stems are high in moisture content and dry out slowly, thus making a good medium for molds and other organisms to develop. Improperly cured hay fed to livestock has resulted in poisoning in a few instances in the Middle West. The difficulty is attributed to the decomposition of coumarin, a material common in sweetclover hay. The blood of affected animals loses its ability to clot, and eventually internal hemorrhages cause death. Attempts are being made to eliminate this problem through plant breeding.

Leaves and Stems. The percentage of leaves to stems and the nitrogen content of each are dependent on a number of factors. The proportion of leaves to stems in the fall growth of the first crop does not change much with the advancing season (see Table 73). The nitrogen content of the leaves and stems is also relatively constant. In the second year's growth there was a decrease in percentage of leaves from 61 to 33 per cent as the plants matured. The drop in percentage of nitrogen was more rapid and significant in the stems than in the leaves. Highest percentage of leaves and protein content occurs early in the spring, and both decrease consistently thereafter until harvest time.

The influence of time and height of cutting on the proportion of coarse and fine stems and on the leaves has been studied in Illinois.[5] In general, the earlier the mowing and the higher the height of cut, the better the quality of the hay, curing excluded. Another study on time of cutting as

TABLE 73. PERCENTAGE OF LEAVES IN SWEETCLOVER HAY AND OF NITROGEN IN
THE LEAVES AND STEMS

Date	Leaves in the hay	Nitrogen in	
		Leaves	Stems
First year:			
Aug. 11	62.2	3.99	2.26
Aug. 25	60.7	3.39	2.20
Sept. 15	59.1	3.84	2.32
Sept. 28	63.4	3.97	2.07
Sept. 30	64.2	4.05	2.02
Oct. 17	64.0	3.94	2.14
Second year:			
May 10	61.0	....	....
May 24	55.8	5.38	2.46
May 31	47.0	5.32	2.51
June 18	40.6	5.21	1.82
June 30	28.4	4.90	1.46
July 18	33.2	4.11	1.48

SOURCE: *Ohio Agr. Expt. Sta. Bul.* 405 (1927).

TABLE 74. EFFECT OF THE TIME OF FIRST CUTTING FOR HAY IN THE SECOND YEAR
ON THE YIELD AND QUALITY OF THE SECOND CUTTING OF SWEETCLOVER
(COMMON YELLOW)

	First cutting			
	May 26	June 1	June 11	June 23
Stem height, in.	29	41	45	47
Hay yield, tons per acre	1.63	1.86	2.21	2.71
Stem diameter*	M	M–C	C	C
Quality of hay	Good	Fair	Poor	Poor

	Second cutting			
	July 6	July 15	July 23	Aug. 1
Stem recovery, %	80	65	18	7
Stem height, in.	24	17	10	8
Hay yield, tons per acre	0.53	0.25	0.04	Trace
Stem diameter	M	F	F	F
Quality of hay	Good	Good	Good	Good

SOURCE: *Nebr. Agr. Expt. Sta. Bul.* 352 (1943).
* Coarse (C), medium (M), or fine (F).

conducted in Nebraska gives further information on hay quality (see Table 74). The early cutting favored large returns from the second crop, which invariably made good hay, climatic factors being satisfactory.

Feeding Value. The feeding value of sweetclover hay varies with the crop harvested. The first-year crop is considerably superior to that of the second year. Comparative data are given in Table 75. The first-year

TABLE 75. PER CENT COMPOSITION OF WHITE AND YELLOW SWEETCLOVER HAY

Crop	Moisture	Ash	Crude protein	Fiber	Nitrogen-free extract	Ether extract
White sweetclover						
Sept. 30.......	4.86	8.29	20.8	16.4	47.1	2.58
June 16.......	5.45	8.56	12.8	37.7	33.3	2.30
Yellow sweetclover						
Sept. 28.......	5.43	9.42	20.3	22.0	38.3	4.55
June 6........	6.19	12.19	16.4	35.0	26.4	3.89

SOURCE: *Ohio Agr. Expt. Sta. Bul.* 405 (1927).

crop is about equal to alfalfa in feeding value, but the second-year hay is much inferior. The ash content is high in both years and should be very valuable in livestock feeding.

Feeding Tests. Some results of feeding experiments with sweetclover hay seem worth examining. Data on a lamb-feeding experiment conducted in South Dakota are given in Table 76. Sweetclover hay proved

TABLE 76. FEEDING EXPERIMENTS WITH LAMBS IN SOUTH DAKOTA, SHOWING THE COMPARATIVE VALUE OF DIFFERENT KINDS OF HAY AS ROUGHAGE

Roughage fed	Average weight, lb.		Required for 1 lb. of gain		Average daily gain per head, lb.
	At beginning	At end	Grain	Hay	
Prairie hay..............	83.6	107.9	5.09	2.35	0.36
Pea-vine hay............	83.6	107.3	5.40	3.15	0.35
Alfalfa hay..............	81.4	119.4	3.36	3.02	0.56
Sweetclover hay..........	84.7	113.6	4.42	3.19	0.43

SOURCE: *U.S. Dept. Agr. Farmers' Bul.* 820 (1917).

superior in this test to prairie and pea-vine hay but inferior to alfalfa. In a feeding experiment with steers in South Dakota,[1] sweetclover again proved second to alfalfa and red clover but surpassed prairie hay. Sweetclover thus appears to be almost equal to alfalfa and red clover from a feeding standpoint.

Silage. Sweetclover makes a high-quality silage when properly ensiled. The first crop of the second season is well suited to this purpose since it matures too early for making best-quality hay. The analysis of sweetclover silage[1] compared with corn shows that the first-year crop is superior to that from corn in protein content. The first crop of the second year is about equal to corn in crude protein and superior in ash, but it contains less carbohydrates and more fiber.

References

1. Coe, H. S.: Sweet clover: utilization, *U.S. Dept. Agr. Farmers' Bul.* 820 (1917).
2. Crosby, M. A., and L. W. Kephart: Sweet clover in corn belt farming, *U.S. Dept. Agr. Farmers' Bul.* 1653 (1939).
3. Garver, S., J. M. Slatensek, and T. A. Kiesselbach: Sweet clover in Nebraska, *Nebr. Agr. Expt. Sta. Bul.* 352 (1943).
4. Hermann, Wilford: Comparison of heights, yields, and leaf percentages of certain sweet clover varieties, *Wash. Agr. Expt. Sta. Bul.* 365 (1938).
5. Sears, O. H., J. J. Pieper, and W. L. Burlison: Sweet clover in Illinois, *Ill. Agr. Expt. Sta. Bul.* 394 (1933).
6. Stewart, George: Height of cutting sweet clover and influence of sweet clover on succeeding oat yields, *Jour. Amer. Soc. Agron.*, **26**: 248–249 (1934).
7. Walster, H. L.: Sweet clover as a hay crop, *Jour. Amer. Soc. Agron.*, **16**: 182–186 (1924).
8. Willard, C. J.: An experimental study of sweet clover, *Ohio Agr. Expt. Sta. Bul.* 405 (1927).

CHAPTER 10

THE LESPEDEZAS

The lespedezas, which are relative newcomers among the crops of this country, are filling a most important role in the agriculture of the Southeastern part of the United States. It is there that they are demonstrating their superiority as soil-conserving crops in rebuilding the worn-out, continuously cultivated corn and cotton soils. At the same time they provide a fine crop of forage in the form of hay or pasture, or they may be grown for seed. The adaptability of the lespedezas to soils of a lower fertility level than the clovers and alfalfa makes for them a place unchallenged by these legumes. Although the plants are quite drought-resistant, they are not adapted to dry-land farming because they cannot take full advantage of early spring moisture supplies. They are hot-weather plants that bloom and seed in southern latitudes, where the days are relatively short.

SPECIES AND VARIETIES

There are three species of lespedeza which have become significant in forage-crop production in America. These are *Lespedeza sericea, striata,* and *stipulacea.* The *sericea* is the perennial type of which at present there are no named varieties. Each of the annual species has three commonly recognized varieties. Under the *L. striata* these are the Common, Kobe, and Tennessee 76; and for *L. stipulacea* they are Korean, Harbin, and Early Korean; a recent addition to the latter species is Climax.

The earliest introduction of any lespedeza into the United States was some time prior to 1846, at which time the Common variety was recorded in Georgia, apparently having come from Japan. It spread throughout much of the Southeast in the wild state and became known as Japanese clover or Common lespedeza. Soon it was recognized as an acid-tolerant plant for poor, run-down soils. Tennessee 76 is a superior strain selected out of Common at the Tennessee Experiment Station in 1915. This is a taller and later strain than Common, producing more hay. The Kobe variety was grown in South Carolina in 1919 from seed obtained near Kobe, Japan. It is somewhat earlier than Common, and it grows larger and coarser.

Lespedeza stipulacea was introduced in 1919 by the U.S. Department of Agriculture. The Korean variety matures about a month earlier than the

92

Common, and thus it is better suited to extend lespedeza culture northward.   Harbin is a strain of Korean brought to this country by the Department of Agriculture from Harbin, Manchuria, in 1929.   It is the earliest strain of lespedeza in the United States, but unfortunately it is very small and therefore lacking in productiveness.   Early Korean is much like the standard variety, but it matures about 2 weeks earlier.

As long ago as 1896, attempts were made to introduce the perennial lespedeza, *sericea*, into North Carolina.   It grew well in these plantings, but nevertheless sericea did not become established commercially.   It was finally recognized as a valuable species after the U.S. Department of Agriculture secured seed from Japan in 1924.   It grows taller than the annual forms, produces coarse stems with increasing age, and sends up many stems per crown.   This crop develops rather slowly, but once established, stands have been maintained for over 20 years.

ACREAGE AND PRODUCTION

The acreage of lespedeza has increased rapidly since its introduction into the United States.   Indicative of this expansion is the increase in acreage and production of lespedeza hay, as shown in Table 77.   Over a period of

TABLE 77.   ACREAGE AND PRODUCTION OF LESPEDEZA HAY IN THE UNITED STATES

Year	Acreage harvested, thousands	Production, thousand tons
Average 1928–1932.........	504	516
1936....................	1,578	1,178
1937....................	2,036	2,107
1939....................	4,698	5,047
1942....................	6,525	7,426
1943....................	6,114	5,944

SOURCES: Agricultural Census 1939; U.S. Department of Agriculture: Agricultural Statistics 1944.

approximately 10 years, the increase of more than twelve times means that the merits of the crop are being widely recognized throughout the annual-legume region.   There has been a similar increase in the production of the crop for purposes other than hay.

CULTURAL PRACTICES

Soil Adaptation.   Adaptation of various varieties has been the subject of tests conducted at a number of the experiment stations.   Such studies are exemplified by a 3-year test carried on in Illinois and a 4-year one in Virginia from which the average yields per acre for the different varieties

TABLE 78. AVERAGE ACRE YIELDS OF HAY OF SEVERAL VARIETIES OF LESPEDEZA, POUNDS

Location	Korean	Tennessee 76	Kobe	Common
Virginia.................	2,832	2,090	3,150	1,490
Illinois..................	2,678	1,077	1,248	891

SOURCES: *Va. Agr. Expt. Sta. Bul.* 328 (1940); *Ill. Agr. Expt. Sta. Bul.* 416 (1935).

are given in Table 78.   Korean was the outstanding variety in the Illinois test, followed by Kobe.   In Virginia the Kobe variety proved superior to the others in productivity, with Korean being second.   Tennessee 76 and Common were very inferior.   Another study was made in Tennessee on two different soil types in which the performance of sericea and Tennessee 76 was compared with alfalfa and red clover.   On Memphis silt loam

TABLE 79. YIELDS OF HAY FOR SERICEA IN COMPARISON WITH OTHER LEGUMES IN TENNESSEE, TONS PER ACRE

Crop	Kind of soil	
	Memphis silt loam	Cumberland loam
Sericea..............	3.72	2.90
Alfalfa..............	5.55	1.98
No. 76..............	2.67	1.44
Red clover.........	....	2.00

SOURCES: *Tenn. Agr. Expt. Sta. Bul.* 154 (1935); *Tenn. Agr. Expt. Sta. Cir.* 42 (1932).

sericea outyielded Tennessee 76 but produced less hay than alfalfa.   However, the sericea proved to be superior to red clover and alfalfa on the Cumberland loam, and again, Tennessee 76 was the poorest producer. The alfalfa was grown on limed land in this study, whereas the lespedezas grew on unlimed soil.

Response to Fertilizer and Lime.   Although the lespedezas are credited with the ability to grow on poor and acid soils, they often respond to soil improvement.   Tests with fertilizer treatments with and without lime on four varieties of lespedeza were tried in Virginia[3] over a 6-year period. Nitrogen was added at the rate of 150 pounds per acre of nitrate of soda, phosphate as 400 pounds of 16 per cent superphosphate, and potash as 1,000 pounds of 50 per cent muriate of potash.   All the lespedezas responded to lime by a ¼ to ½ ton increase in hay yields.   They also responded with increased yields to all fertilizer amendments tried.

The effect of lime and fertilizer on Kobe and Korean lespedeza was studied in North Carolina and on sericea in Virginia, the data being given in Table 80. The fertilizers used in the North Carolina test were 200

TABLE 80. THE EFFECT OF LIME AND FERTILIZERS ON THE HAY YIELD OF KOREAN, KOBE, AND SERICEA LESPEDEZA

	Average hay yields (12% moisture), lb. per acre					
Treatment	Korean		Kobe		Sericea	
	With lime	Without lime	With lime	Without lime	With lime	Without lime
Check.............	941	813	2,337	1,934	3,122	3,048
P.................	974	1,062	2,200	1,807	3,256	3,121
K.................	1,074	985	2,305	1,500	3,726	3,131
NPK.............	1,080	1,112	2,167	1,701	3,921	3,913

SOURCES: *Jour. Amer. Soc. Agron.*, **31** (1939); *Va. Agr. Expt. Sta. Bul.* 328 (1940).

pounds of 16 per cent superphosphate per acre, potash as 100 pounds of 20 per cent manure salts, and complete fertilizer as 400 pounds of 2–10–4 mixture. Kobe showed a greater response to lime than Korean. Both varieties responded with increased yields to all fertility treatments. Applications of lime and fertilizer in the growing of sericea in Virginia showed only minor response. In this test fertilizer was added as 300 pounds per acre of 0–16–0, 300 pounds of 0–0–16, and 600 pounds of 4–8–8. In a series of three tests in Illinois,[9] Korean responded strongly by increased yields to lime treatments. These tests demonstrate the need to supply lime and fertilizer under many conditions where high yields of lespedeza hay are desired.

Seeding Practices. Seeding of the lespedezas is always made in the spring, the time ranging from the last half of February in the deep South to early April northward. Very late seedings may be injured by heat and drought. Tests have been carried out in many sections of the Southeastern area to determine the best seeding time for the adapted varieties. Such a test conducted in southern Illinois (see Table 81) showed that the

TABLE 81. EFFECT OF TIME OF SEEDING ON ACRE YIELDS OF LESPEDEZA HAY

Variety	Hay yields, lb. per acre		
	Mar. 15	Apr. 1	Apr. 25
Korean....................	3,776	4,086	3,043
Tennessee 76..............	3,485	2,349	2,678

SOURCE: *Ill. Agr. Expt. Sta. Bul.* 416 (1935).

Tennessee 76 variety produced better when planted about Mar. 15 and Korean was most productive when planted about Apr. 1. In Virginia a similar study[3] confirmed the above dates for the varieties given. Also, it was shown that in this locality the Kobe variety was favored by the Mar. 15 seeding date and Common by the later date of Apr. 1.

Seeding Rates. The rate of seeding lespedezas for hay production varies from 25 to 40 pounds per acre depending on the variety used. Generally the lower rate is the most satisfactory for Korean, while the higher rate is required for maximum production of Tennessee 76 and Kobe. A typical study on rate of seeding, as conducted in Illinois, compares the hay yields of two varieties at seeding rates of 10, 20, and 40 pounds per acre (see Table 82). The yield of the Korean variety was better at the 20-pound rate, whereas the 40-pound rate was superior for Tennessee 76.

TABLE 82. ACRE YIELDS OF LESPEDEZA HAY WITH DIFFERENT RATES OF SEEDING

Variety	Hay yields, lb. per acre		
	10-lb. seeding	20 lb. seeding	40-lb. seeding
Korean..............	3,725	4,086	3,430
Tennessee 76........	2,263	2,349	3,088

SOURCE: *Ill. Agr. Expt. Sta. Bul.* 416 (1935).

Seed Scarification. Scarifying the seed of sericea has proved beneficial in hay production. A study of this practice was made in Virginia over a period of 6 years in which the yields were compared from plantings made with scarified and unhulled seed on various seeding dates. Typical data taken from this study and shown in Table 83 show that, irrespective of planting time, scarifying the sericea seed resulted in yield increases.

TABLE 83. EFFECT OF TIME OF SEEDING AND SCARIFICATION ON THE AVERAGE YIELD OF DRY SERICEA HAY, POUNDS

Mar. 15		Apr. 1		Apr. 15	
Scarified	Unhulled	Scarified	Unhulled	Scarified	Unhulled
5,164	4,205	4,931	4,217	4,589	4,383

SOURCE: *Va. Agr. Expt. Sta. Bul.* 328 (1940).

Self-seeding. Self-seeding is common among the lespedezas. A study of different methods of seedbed preparation to aid self-seeding was made at Illinois, a portion of the data being given in Table 84. Disking and plowing

TABLE 84. ACRE YIELDS OF HAY RESULTING FROM DIFFERENT METHODS OF SEEDBED PREPARATION FOR SELF-SEEDED KOREAN LESPEDEZA, POUNDS

Seeding practice	No treatment	Disked	Plowed	Plowed and seeded to oats
Self-seeded.......	2,103	4,442	3,797	4,560
Reseeded........	3,014	4,569	3,334	5,057

SOURCE: *Ill. Agr. Expt. Sta. Bul.* 416 (1935).

aided in increasing hay yields, and such practices are best when carried out as early in the spring as soil conditions permit. The study indicates that little advantage was gained from reseeding where seedbed aids were given.

FIG. 19. A thick stand of Korean lespedeza volunteers each spring in a 1-year rotation with oats. (*Missouri Agricultural Experiment Station.*)

Use in Mixtures. While the lespedezas are usually seeded alone for hay, some mixtures are used. In Illinois the crop is sometimes grown with sweetclover and in the South with Bermuda, Dallis, or Johnson grass. Studies conducted in Arkansas with such grass mixtures are given in Table 85. The percentage of Korean lespedeza in the stand was reduced strongly with both Johnson and Bermuda grass, but with Dallis grass it reached an edaphic climax of a half-and-half proportion. Korean and Dallis grass would seem an excellent long-time mixture where such is

TABLE 85. KOREAN LESPEDEZA GROWN ALONE AND IN MIXTURE WITH THREE GRASSES, ARKANSAS

Crop	First year		Second year		Third year	
	Hay per acre, lb.	Stand of Korean, %	Hay per acre, lb.	Stand of Korean, %	Hay per acre, lb.	Stand of Korean, %
Korean alone...........	1,450	..	940	..	1,330	..
Korean and Johnson grass	2,048	30	1,431	16	2,080	6
Korean and Dallis grass..	1,654	51	1,568	46	939	52
Korean and Bermuda grass...............	1,535	82	700	60	674	4

SOURCE: *Jour. Amer. Soc. Agron.*, **34** (1942).

desired.   The mixture of Johnson grass and Korean was superior in productivity, but most of the yield was contributed by the grass.

Weed Infestations.   A common cause of difficulty in making hay or producing seed of the annual lespedezas is the presence of the plant parasite known as common dodder (*Cuscuta pentagona*).   Attempts to eradicate this weed have been unsuccessful, generally, and it is actually becoming more widespread each year.   The effect of the weed on hay yields in dodder-infested lespedeza plots was studied in North Carolina (Table 86).

TABLE 86. HAY YIELDS OF KOREAN LESPEDEZA AND DODDER ON A 12 PER CENT MOISTURE BASIS, POUNDS PER ACRE

Sample	Lespedeza grown with dodder			Lespedeza grown dodder-free
	Lespedeza	Dodder	Lespedeza and dodder	
1	2,750	653	3,403	3,395
2	3,061	1,307	4,368	3,868
3	2,389	1,051	3,440	3,516
4	2,898	819	3,717	3,416
5	2,285	1,147	3,432	3,887
6	2,474	1,226	3,700	3,941
Average....	2,643	1,034	3,677	3,670

SOURCE: *Jour. Amer. Soc. Agron.*, **32** (1940).

Dodder contributed one-third of the total yield from these plots but did not reduce the total yield per acre.   An analysis of lespedeza hay[13] and dodder indicates that the parasite does not affect the feeding value.   It is most significant in reducing seed yields and in contaminating lespedeza seed.

Hay Production. The annual lespedezas give one cutting of hay per year plus a seed crop, but the perennial form usually gives second hay crops. Work in Tennessee indicates that sericea is best cut twice a year there (see Table 87). Lower yields resulted from three and four cuttings a

TABLE 87. INFLUENCE OF NUMBER OF CUTTINGS ON YIELD OF SERICEA HAY

Cutting	Two cuttings		Three cuttings		Four cuttings	
	Date	Yield per acre, tons	Date	Yield per acre, tons	Date	Yield per acre, tons
First..........	May 15	0.84	May 15	0.83	May 15	0.75
Second........	Sept. 5	3.30	June 29	0.67	June 20	0.58
Third.........	....	....	Sept. 5	1.89	Aug. 17	1.39
Fourth........	....	....	....	....	Oct. 5	0.56
Total.......	....	4.14	....	3.39	....	3.28

SOURCE: *Tenn. Agr. Expt. Sta. Bul.* 154 (1935).

season. The first cutting should be made when the plants are about 20 inches high to escape coarseness and loss of quality. In order for the annual lespedezas to produce a seed crop, the hay must be cut in the early to full-bloom stage.

Feed Constituents. Something of the quality of lespedeza hay can be judged by considering the analysis of the feed constituents and the proportion of leaves and stems. The two cuttings of a season's crop of *Lespedeza sericea* hay grown in Tennessee were analyzed for their feed constituents, as shown in Table 88. Both the cuttings were remarkably uniform in protein content and other feeding factors. The lespedeza crop

TABLE 88. APPROXIMATE ANALYSES (AIR-DRY BASIS) OF LESPEDEZA SERICEA HAY, PER CENT

Sample	Date harvested	Moisture	Protein	Ether extract (fat)	N-free extract	Crude fiber	Ash
Leaves........	May 30	11.0	18.5	1.25	45.5	18.6	5.14
Stems.........	May 30	11.0	8.2	0.74	34.3	42.0	3.77
Whole plant....	May 30	11.0	14.5	1.05	41.1	27.7	4.61
Leaves........	Aug. 19	9.7	15.1	2.33	49.6	18.3	5.06
Stems.........	Aug. 19	9.2	7.9	0.51	36.4	42.6	3.44
Whole plant....	Aug. 19	9.5	12.2	1.61	44.4	27.9	4.42

SOURCE: *Tenn. Agr. Expt. Sta. Bul.* 154 (1935).

contains a high percentage of leaves, as indicated by Illinois studies.[9]   The three varieties Korean, Tennessee 76, and Kobe contained about 60 per cent leaves and 40 per cent stems when harvested at the full-bloom stage.

U.S. Department of Agriculture investigators[11] who were studying sericea hay found that there were changes in the percentage of leaves, stems, and various feed constituents with increasing age of the plants. The percentage of leaves decreased and that of stems increased as the age advanced.   At the time of the last cutting the proportion of leaves was only two-thirds as great as the first cutting.   The chemical analysis showed a consistent decrease in crude protein and ash as the plants grew older, while the fat, carbohydrate, and fiber contents increased.

Tannin Content.   The lespedezas are known to contain considerable quantities of tannin, although little is known about the quality of this material. Data on the tannin content of sericea are given in Table 89.   Most tannin is found in the leaves, although a small amount is present in the stems.   As the age of the plant advances, the tannin content of the leaves increases. Tannin probably is an undesirable constituent of the lespedezas.

TABLE 89.   PER CENT TANNIN CONTENT OF *Lespedeza sericea* HARVESTED FOR HAY AT VARIOUS GROWTH STAGES

Date harvested	Leaves	Stems	Whole plant
June 5	11.0	1.4	7.7
June 20	14.8	1.6	9.0
July 3	15.5	1.0	8.0
July 17	17.7	1.3	8.6
July 31	18.0	1.2	8.0

SOURCE: *Jour. Agr. Res.*, **58** (1939).

Feeding Trials.   Feeding trials for milk and beef production indicate the approximate value of lespedezas for hay.   Trials conducted in Virginia for milk production are summarized in Table 90.   The Korean and sericea were about 80 per cent as effective as alfalfa in producing milk.   A lespedeza hay feeding test[2] in North Carolina indicated similar results, the lespedeza proving 80 to 85 per cent as effective as alfalfa.

Sericea hay was compared with alfalfa in a feeding trial with beef steers in Tennessee.   The results indicate that sericea was less than 75 per cent as effective as alfalfa.   The investigators stated that 25 per cent of the sericea was crabgrass and that the cattle refused to eat about 7 per cent of it, while the alfalfa was pure and was entirely consumed.   This indicates that the quality of the sericea was inferior to the alfalfa and the test was hardly fair to lespedeza, but the data lend support to the belief that lespedeza is of somewhat less value than alfalfa as a hay.

TABLE 90.   POUNDS OF MILK PRODUCED BY GROUPS OF COWS ON MEDIUM- AND GOOD-QUALITY KOREAN LESPEDEZA, *Lespedeza sericea*, AND ALFALFA HAYS

Hay fed	Number of cow-days on test	Quality of hay	Quantity of hay fed, lb.	4% milk produced from hay, lb.	4% milk produced from 100 lb. hay	Amount of milk produced by lespedezas for every 100 lb. produced by alfalfa
Korean lespedeza....	236	Medium	4,279	3,190	77.1	78
	120	Good	1,865	1,348	73.6	82
Lespedeza sericea......	236	Medium	4,273	3,209	76.7	78
	120	Good	1,886	1,324	70.9	79
Alfalfa........	236	Medium	4,364	3,973	98.3	100
	120	Good	1,909	1,687	89.7	100

SOURCE: *Va. Agr. Expt. Sta. Bul.* 305 (1936).

References

1. Clarke, I. D., R. W. Frey, and H. L. Hyland: Seasonal variation in tannin content of Lespedeza sericea, *Jour. Agr. Res.*, **58**: 131–139 (1939).
2. Grinnells, C. D.: Lespedeza and alfalfa hay for dairy cows, *N.C. Agr. Expt. Sta. Bul.* 302 (1935).
3. Grizzard, A. L., and T. B. Hutcheson: Experiments with lespedeza, *Va. Agr. Expt. Sta. Bul.* 328 (1940).
4. Holdeway, C. W., W. B. Ellett, J. F. Eheart, and A. D. Pratt: Korean lespedeza and Lespedeza sericea hays for producing milk, *Va. Agr. Expt. Sta. Bul.* 305 (1936).
5. McKee, Roland: Lespedeza culture and utilization, *U.S. Dept. Agr. Farmers' Bul.* 1852 (1946).
6. May, D. W., Jr.: Changes in the proportion and yield of alfalfa and Korean lespedeza in mixtures with grasses, *Jour. Amer. Soc. Agron.*, **34**: 856–859 (1942).
7. Mooers, C. A.: Lespedeza sericea, *Tenn. Agr. Expt. Sta. Cir.* 42 (1932).
8. Mooers, C. A., and H. P. Ogden: Lespedeza sericea, *Tenn. Agr. Expt. Sta. Bul.* 154 (1935).
9. Pieper, J. J., O.H. Sears, and F. C. Bauer: Lespedeza in Illinois, *Ill. Agr. Expt. Sta. Bul.* 416 (1935).
10. Pieters, A. J.: Lespedeza sericea and other perennial lespedezas for forage and soil conservation, *U.S. Dept. Agr. Cir.* 524 (1939).
11. Pieters, A. J.: The annual lespedezas as forage and soil-conserving crops, *U.S. Dept. Agr. Cir.* 536 (1939).
12. Stitt, R. E.: The response of lespedeza to lime and fertilizer, *Jour. Amer. Soc. Agron.*, **31**: 520–527 (1939).
13. Stitt, R. E.: Yields of Korean lespedeza as affected by dodder, *Jour. Amer. Soc. Agron.*, **32**: 969–971 (1940).

CHAPTER 11

THE KUDZU VINE

The Kudzu vine (*Pueraria thunbergiana*) is a remarkable plant that is aiding to rebuild a depleted Southern agriculture. Introduced from the Orient and exhibited at the Philadelphia Centennial in 1876, it has spread vigorously to occupy more than 250,000 acres of cropland in 1941. First to recognize its virtues was C. E. Pleas from Chipley, Florida. In 1902 he set several plants around his house; later these were transferred to a trash area in his back yard. Here the Kudzu vine spread over an area of 40 by 60 feet in a few years. Cuttings were set out from these plants, and by about 1910 Pleas had 35 acres of Kudzu planted on his farms. Most of the Kudzu now grown in the South is said to trace back to the three plants started by Pleas in 1902.

Kudzu is the only perennial legume widely adapted throughout the Southeastern states. The crop has been grown with some success as far north as New Jersey and Illinois. Under irrigation it grows successfully in the Southwest. On the whole, Kudzu seems best adapted to the Eastern states south of Virginia and Kentucky and westward to the Mississippi River. It is particularly valuable in this area, where so much of the soil is worn out and eroded, because it will grow on such soils to conserve and improve them.

The characteristic which makes Kudzu an amazing plant is its ability to grow runners 50 to 100 feet long in a single season. Very few crops possess such vegetative vigor. Along with its perennial viny habit it develops a large taproot under favorable conditions. The plant is a legume with leaves that are large and abundant and stems that are soft and pliable, all of which characteristics make it valuable for hay, pasture, and soil conservation and improvement. In the northern area of its adaptation the vines often die back to the crowns, and new growth begins from these again in the spring. No varieties or strains of Kudzu have been developed in America as yet, although the crop is variable, and there is ample opportunity for selection and breeding of improved varieties.

PROPAGATION

Kudzu is propagated by seed and cuttings, cuttings being most widely used because of the difficulty in producing viable seed. The seeds are small, there being 30 to 45 thousand in a pound, and 50 to 60 pounds are required for a bushel. Seed is set sparingly in this country and then only from vines on trellises, trees, or fences. Some seed was collected for the soil-conservation program by members of the Civilian Conservation Corps.

Fig. 20. A vigorous stand of Kudzu in North Carolina. (*Soil Conservation Service, U.S. Department of Agriculture.*)

Hard Seed. Kudzu produces many hard seeds which do not germinate and some that are nonviable. This accounts for the low germination (40 to 50 per cent) often associated with the seed. Various scarifying methods have been tried, but usually either sulfuric acid or mechanical scarifiers are employed. The seeds have rather thick, brittle seed coats that crack easily, and this results in rapid loss of viability. The Soil Conservation Service recently recommended a disk type of scarifier which grinds the seed coats gently without cracking even the most fragile ones. An average germination after such scarification is said to be 50 per cent, with a few samples running as high as 70 per cent.

Planting Seeds. Kudzu seeds are usually planted in a nursery where the rows are relatively narrow, ranging up to 3 feet apart, and in which the spacing is close enough to allow 15 to 25 seeds per linear foot. The planting is shallow, usually ¼ to ½ inch, at a time when the soil is warm, normally late June or July. Well-drained soils with plenty of soil air give the best growth. The seedlings require about 4 months to develop to a plantable stage, that is, where they have four to six true leaves and one or more roots ⅓ inch in diameter and 6 inches long. They may be transplanted about the time of the first fall frost. In any case, there should be no cutting in the seedling year.

Cuttings. When seed or seedlings are not available, Kudzu crowns, which have been developed from cuttings, are used to establish farm and commercial plantings. The successful rooting of cuttings can be increased by using plant hormones or potassium permanganate. An experiment with commercial plant hormones, labeled A, B, and C in Table 91, showed

TABLE 91. STIMULATING ROOT FORMATION OF KUDZU CUTTINGS WITH PLANT HORMONES

Commercial product	Number set out	Number rooted	Number unrooted	Per cent of cuttings rooted
A Dilute............	75	51	24	68
A Standard.........	75	64	11	85
B Dilute............	75	46	29	61
B Standard.........	75	47	28	63
C Dilute............	75	48	24	67
C Standard.........	75	39	33	52
Untreated..........	75	38	37	51

SOURCE: *Science*, **88** (1938).

them to be valuable for increasing the percentage of rootings. A later test comparing the most effective hormone with a potassium permanganate solution showed that a dilute permanganate solution was superior to any of the rooting hormones (Table 92). Both the number and size of roots on the treated cuttings were greater than those on the untreated checks.

TABLE 92. EFFECT OF POTASSIUM PERMANGANATE SOLUTION IN STIMULATING KUDZU CUTTINGS TO ROOT

Treatment	Number planted	Number rooted	Number unrooted	Per cent rooted
No treatment........	302	128	174	42.4
Standard 1..........	300	160	140	53.3
Standard 2..........	150	90	60	60.0
Standard 3	299	127	172	42.5
Potassium permanganate..............	150	129	21	86.0

SOURCE: *Science,* **88** (1938).

Crowns. The success of Kudzu plantings from crowns is associated with the weight of the transplanted crown (see Table 93). In these tests the heavier the crown up to 82 grams, the higher the percentage of living

TABLE 93. PER CENT OF PLANTS LIVING AND THE RATE OF THE DEVELOPMENT OF PLANTS FROM TRANSPLANTED CROWNS OF VARIOUS SIZES

Test 1			Test 2		
Average weight of crowns, grams	Plants living, %	Plants making excellent growth, %	Average weight of crowns, grams	Plants living, %	Average length of vine growth, ft.
14.7	42.5	16.2	82	97	17.3
17.2	46.3	28.7	156	99	21.7
28.3	66.2	41.2	268	98	30.4

SOURCE: *Ala. Agr. Expt. Sta. Cir.* 83 (1939).

plants. The most rapid growth of vines also came from the heaviest crowns. For convenience of planting and general good performance, medium-sized well-rooted 2-year-old crowns are preferred to the large overgrown type.

The time of transplanting crowns to field plots varies with the latitude and soil-moisture conditions. In the far South the most favorable time is February or early March; northward the transplanting is usually accomplished while the plants are dormant, but it can be done after spring growth starts if extra care is exercised in lifting and setting the plants.

The number of crowns required to plant an acre will vary with the purpose of the planting. Where hay and grazing stands are desired for long-time use in rotations, wider plantings are most practical. Where the crop is used in fairly short rotations, close plantings are needed to give quick cover. Plants required per acre for different row widths and plant spacing are recorded in Table 94. Kudzu rows may be alternated with corn strips

TABLE 94. KUDZU PLANTS REQUIRED TO PLANT 1 ACRE IN ROWS OF SPECIFIED WIDTHS AND DISTANCES APART OF PLANTS IN ROW

Width of rows, ft.	Plants at different spacings in rows, ft.			
	4	6	8	10
10	1,089	726	545	436
15	726	484	363	290
20	545	363	272	218
25	436	290	218	147
30	363	242	182	145

SOURCE: *U.S. Dept. Agr. Farmers' Bul.* 1923 (1943).

in the planting year, thus giving a crop return.   On good cornland Kudzu vines will extend across a 40-foot strip of corn in a single season.

The most successful method for planting the crowns is to use a spade or shovel for making the opening.   Moist soil should be placed around the roots.   The crown buds should be set even with the ground surface and very lightly covered by soil.   Opening furrows with the moldboard plow followed by planting usually has been less satisfactory than the spading method.

CULTURE

Kudzu should never be mowed the first year and only once in the second season.   Cultivation to control weeds and to maintain a favorable soil-surface condition aid the "pegging down" and development of new plants at the nodes of the stolons.   Covering the nodal part of the stolon with soil stimulates rooting, which speeds up the rate of stand establishment. Inoculation of seed or cuttings is not necessary, since the plant normally nodulates throughout the region where it is now grown.

Yields.   Yields of Kudzu for hay have ranged from 1 to 4 tons per acre with 1 to 2 tons being fairly common (Table 95).   Variations occur, depending on soil conditions, climate, and management treatments.   Since Kudzu

TABLE 95.   ACRE YIELDS OF DRY MATTER FROM KUDZU IN SEVERAL OF THE SOUTHERN STATES, TONS

Alabama	Georgia	Mississippi*	South Carolina
1.83–3.40	1–4	3.80–5.68	2.0

* Green weight.

is often grown on rundown, depleted, and eroded soils, the addition of lime and fertilizer would seem to be very practical in securing good stands and high yields.   Actually the crop has been shown to respond vigorously after applications of phosphate and potash fertilizers.   Data from a lime and fertilizer test are given in Table 96.   Lime was applied at the rate of 1 ton per acre and muriate of potash at 100 pounds per acre.   The single application of phosphate fertilizer was equivalent to 400 pounds of 16 per cent superphosphate and the double application to 800 pounds.   In these tests the application of phosphate fertilizer gave highly significant yield increases.   Lime and potash applied together but without phosphate fertilizer also increased yields, but to a more limited extent.

The application of phosphate fertilizer in conjunction with cultivation was studied on a medium clay soil in Alabama.   The Kudzu was planted

TABLE 96. AVERAGE KUDZU YIELDS ACCORDING TO TREATMENTS, POUNDS PER ACRE GREEN WEIGHT

| Lime and potash | Yields from fertilizer treatments | | |
| | Phosphorus applications | | |
	None	Single	Double
None.................	6,114	10,212	12,175
Lime.................	6,033	11,292	12,156
Potash..............	6,191	11,686	12,371
Lime and potash.......	7,925	12,038	12,643

SOURCE: *Jour. Amer. Soc. Agron.*, **37** (1945).

in rows 12 feet wide. Partial cultivation consisted of plowing a strip 4 feet wide along each side of the Kudzu row, and complete cultivation meant plowing the entire area except a narrow strip along the rows. Partial and complete cultivation had some effect on the yield, but phosphate fertilizer again gave marked yield increases (see Table 97). Lime, phosphate, and potash fertilizers used together probably are most satisfactory for growing the crop.

TABLE 97. EFFECT OF VARIOUS RATES OF BASIC SLAG AND CULTURAL TREATMENTS ON THE GREEN-WEIGHT YIELD OF KUDZU, TONS PER ACRE

| Cultural treatment | Yield from basic slag applications | | | |
	None	400-lb. rate	800-lb. rate	1,600-lb. rate
No cultivation.............	0.87	1.33	5.04	7.20
Partial cultivation..........	1.37	1.84	5.99	8.32
Complete cultivation.......	0.87	1.57	5.67	7.34

SOURCE: *Jour. Amer. Soc. Agron.*, **37** (1945).

Mowing. Stands of Kudzu can be maintained easily if they are not cut or grazed too often. Cutting more than twice a season weakens the crop quickly, resulting in thin stands of weak plants. Where two cuttings are made, the first should be in June or early July and the other in the fall just before the first frost. An experiment conducted in Alabama over a period of 7 years showed the effect of time of cutting and of number of cuttings on yields and stand maintenance. The highest average yields were obtained from two cuttings a year made on June 1 and Aug. 1. The most favorable cutting schedule was the June 1 to Nov. 1 one where an excellent yield almost free of weeds was harvested even at the end of the seventh year.

TABLE 98. EFFECT OF TIME AND FREQUENCY OF CUTTING ON YIELDS
OF KUDZU HAY IN ALABAMA

Number of cuttings	Date of cutting	7-year ave. yield per acre, lb.	1938		1939	
			Yield per acre, lb.	Per cent weeds	Yield per acre, lb.	Per cent weeds
1	June 1	4,755	5,055	0	3,420	0
2	June 1, Aug. 1	6,615	5,865	33	5,970	20
3	June 1, Aug. 1, Nov. 1	6,560	5,700	55	0*	..
3	June 1, Aug. 1, Oct. 1	5,654	4,335	73	0*	..
2	June 1, Nov. 1	6,416	6,780	5	5,625	3

SOURCE: *Ala. Agr. Expt. Sta. Cir.* 83 (1939).
* The stand was so poor that the plot was not cut in 1939. The Kudzu was left to reestablish a stand.

One cutting per year resulted in excellent stand maintenance but lower
yields. Heavy and rapid loss of stand was the result of three cuttings
annually, whereas the one- and two-cutting systems maintained yields and
kept weed invasion at a minimum.

FIG. 21. Baling Kudzu hay in Georgia. (*Soil Conservation Service, U.S. Department
of Agriculture.*)

Mowing the crop is somewhat difficult because of its viny nature, which causes clogging of the cutter bar and difficulty in separating the swaths. The Alabama Station has developed a simple mower-bar attachment[11] that may be placed on the end of the cutter bar, and this successfully divides and frees the vines as the crop is mowed.

Curing Hay. The Kudzu vine has the reputation of maintaining high-quality forage over a considerable period of time, so it can be cut at the convenience of the grower and during favorable curing weather. The plant holds its leaves well and cures readily. As is common in the South in curing soybeans and cowpeas it is often put into haycocks for curing prior to moving to more permanent storage quarters. In some regions the hay is windrowed, cured, and then hauled directly to storage.

While the Kudzu vine is used primarily for soil conserving and improvement in the Southeast, it is being used widely for hay and pasture. This seems like a very desirable practice, if it goes along with good management, since cover and protection are given the soil while at the same time the crop gives some financial return to the operator. Kudzu is not a cure-all, but it is adding materially to the wealth of Southern agriculture. As livestock production becomes more intensive in the Southeast, there will be increasing interest in this crop for hay and pasture.

References

1. Bailey, R. Y.: Kudzu for erosion control in the Southeast, *U.S. Dept. Agr. Farmers' Bul.* 1840 (1939).
2. Bailey, R. Y., and E. L. Mayton: Kudzu in Alabama, *Ala. Agr. Expt. Sta. Cir.* 57 (1931).
3. Bowden, Roy A., and M. C. Myers: Stimulation of Kudzu cuttings, *Science*, **88**: 167 (1938).
4. Diseker, Ellis G.: A device to assist in mowing Kudzu, *Ala. Agr. Expt. Sta. Leaflet* 16 (1937).
5. McKee, Roland, and J. L. Stephens: Kudzu as a farm crop, *U.S. Dept. Agr. Farmers' Bul.* 1923 (1943).
6. Miles, I. E., and E. E. Gross: A compilation of information on Kudzu, *Miss. Agr. Expt. Sta. Bul.* 326 (1939).
7. Pieters, A. J.: Kudzu, a forage crop for the Southeast, *U.S. Dept. Agr. Leaflet* 91 (1932).
8. Richardson, E. C.: The effect of fertilizer on stand and yield of Kudzu on depleted soils, *Jour. Amer. Soc. Agron.*, **37**: 763–770 (1945).
9. South Carolina Department of Agricultural Education: Kudzu in South Carolina, *Clemson Agr. Col. Cir.* 164 (1938).
10. Sturkie, D. G., and J. C. Grimes: Kudzu: Its value and use in Alabama, *Ala. Agr. Expt. Sta. Cir.* 83 (1939).
11. Tabor, Paul: Kudzu, *Ga. Col. Agr. Bul.* 356 (1928).
12. Tabor, Paul: A disc scarifier for Kudzu seed, *Jour. Amer. Soc. Agron.*, **34**: 860–861 (1942).
13. Tabor, Paul: Observations of Kudzu seedlings, *Jour. Amer. Soc. Agron.*, **34**: 500–501 (1942).

CHAPTER 12

SOYBEANS AND COWPEAS

Soybeans are widely grown for hay over the humid eastern part of the United States as cowpeas are in the Southeastern states. These two annual legumes fill a role similar to that performed by the millets, Sudan grass, and the sorgos. They are rapid-growing summer annuals, capable of producing good yields either on an emergency basis or as a regular part of the farm rotation. Such legumes grown during late spring and summer will supply high-quality hay or silage.

SOYBEANS (*Glycine max*)

The soybean is a native of eastern Asia, being one of the earliest crops known to have been cultivated. First record of the plant is found in the ancient Chinese literature, in a publication called "Pen Ts'ao Kong Mu," written by Emperor Shen-nung in 2838 B.C.

The earliest record of the soybean in America is found in the writings of James Mease in 1804. He wrote that "the soybean is adapted to Pennsylvania and should be cultivated." For a long time the soybean remained an idle curiosity planted mostly in botanical gardens. Only since 1890 have the agricultural experiment stations and the Department of Agriculture made intensive efforts to improve the crop and determine its usefulness.

The introduction of many new varieties into the United States beginning about 1900 facilitated a rapid spread of this crop. The First World War gave strong impetus to growing soybeans for oil. The acreage climbed from almost nothing in 1900 to over 13½ million in 1940, and the crop elevated itself to one of major importance in America. While a large part of this area is planted for grain, about 3½ million acres are now grown each year for hay or silage.

VARIETIES

Varieties may be divided into three utilization groups: commercial, forage, and vegetable. Varieties for commercial seed production are preferably yellow-seeded and are used for processing for oil, oil meal, and flour, but these varieties may be used also for forage purposes if heavier rates of seeding are used. Forage varieties are, in general, black- and brown-seeded types usually with more foliage and finer stems than the commercial and vegetable types. Vegetable varieties are those which have been

110

found best for eating as green shelled or mature beans. They have a mild or nutty flavor and cook easily.

The great number of varieties with their range in characteristics have made it possible to grow the crop in any state or region. Variation is found in yield, maturity, quality, leaf retention, disease resistance, and many other factors. Range in maturity alone, for example, is from 75 to 200 days or more. Table 99 lists some varieties, classified as to length of

TABLE 99. VARIETIES OF SOYBEANS USEFUL FOR FORAGE CLASSIFIED AS TO LENGTH OF GROWING SEASON, DAYS

Very early, 100 or less	Early, 101–110	Medium early, 111–120	Medium, 121–130	Medium late, 131–140	Late, 141–160	Very late, 161 or more
Cayuga	Earlyana	Illini	Ebony	Laredo	Barchet	Avoyelles
Wisconsin	Hawkeye	Dunfield	Kingwa		Charlee	Biloxi
Black	Mukden	Lincoln	Norredo		Clemson	Creole
	Richland	Chief	Peking		Georgian	Gatan
	Seneca	Manchu	Virginia		Hayseed	Otootan
			Wilson		Missoy	
					Monetta	
					Palmetto	
					Tanner	
					Yelredo	

SOURCE: *U.S. Dept. Agr. Farmers' Bul.* 1520 (1939).

growing season, which are among those considered useful for forage. Many others are used interchangeably for grain and hay.

Productiveness is a characteristic that varies widely among the varieties, even though they may have similar maturity dates. The nitrogen content of varieties is another typical quality that would be of interest with such a crop. A study[1] of this factor was made on varieties grown in Mississippi. The nitrogen content was found to vary somewhat, although the differences were not highly significant. The Mamredo variety was high with 2.70 per cent nitrogen in the tops and Biloxi low with 2.23 per cent. Such variations might be caused by climate, soil, maturity, and other factors not related to the plant itself. It would be expected that the leafy varieties should show an even greater difference in protein than the more stemmy types.

CULTURE

Soybeans often have been credited with growing readily on infertile and acid soils. That this is not the case is borne out by many tests, data from one such in Illinois being reported in Table 100. Hay yields increased

TABLE 100. SHOWING YIELDS OF SOYBEAN HAY FROM DIFFERENT SOIL TREATMENTS ON DIFFERENT SOIL TYPES IN ILLINOIS, TONS PER ACRE

Soil type	Soil treatment			
	None	Manure	Manure-lime	Manure-lime phosphate
Yellow gray silt loam..........	0.69	0.86	1.37	1.58
Gray silt loam on tight clay....	0.70	0.86	1.28	1.34
Brown silt loam...............	1.43	1.61	1.70	1.81
Dune sand...................	0.00	1.05	1.41	1.35
Average.....................	0.71	1.10	1.44	1.52

SOURCE: *Jour. Amer. Soc. Agron.*, **16** (1924).

with the addition of lime, manure, and phosphate, or combinations of these. Thus, while the soybean will make fair yields on acid and poor soils, it produces considerably more when needed soil amendments are added. The crop grows well on nearly any type of soil but does best on fertile loams.

Planting Dates. The date of planting has been shown to be important in connection with the yield and quality of the hay as well as the rate at which soybeans mature. At the Ohio Agricultural Experiment Station a study[5] was made of the effect of planting time on the growth period of the Peking variety. Blooms were produced from the Apr. 15 planting in 112 days, whereas it required only 66 days, or slightly more than half the time, with the June 15 planting. Data on the interaction of time of seeding with time of harvesting as affecting yields are given in Table 101. Even

TABLE 101. ACRE YIELDS OF TOTAL TOPS FOR VARIOUS DATES OF SOWING AND HARVESTING, POUNDS

Date of harvest	Time of seeding			
	May 1	May 15	June 1	June 15
July 10–20...................	1,557	1,104	.....	.....
July 20–30...................	2,444	1,859	1,192	.....
Aug. 1–10...................	3,492	3,036	2,411	1,114
Aug. 10–20...................	4,365	4,165	3,201	1,681
Aug. 20–30...................	4,917	4,930	4,255	2,867
Sept. 1–10...................	5,331	5,326	5,085	3,755
Sept. 10–20...................	5,051	4,797	4,936	4,305
Sept. 20–30...................	.....	.....	5,062	4,611

SOURCE: *Ohio Agr. Expt. Sta. Bul.* 494 (1931).

though planting was delayed, the highest yields were secured at about the same time or only slightly later. This is in good agreement with the shorter blossoming period associated with late sowing. Another planting-date study made in Ohio in connection with rate of seeding showed that more and better hay is produced with plantings made from Apr. 15 to June 1 at that latitude. Earlier seedings result in poorer, more weedy stands, and later ones do not allow enough pod development.

Seeding Rates. An important consideration in the production of soybean hay is the thickness of the stand. Data from a 5-year study conducted in Ohio show how the seeding rate affects the yield of plantings made on different dates (Table 102). Thick plantings (plants 1 inch apart

TABLE 102.   FORAGE YIELDS OF MANCHU SOYBEANS SOWN AT DIFFERENT RATES
AND DATES, POUNDS

Dates sown	Rates sown			
	Thick	Medium	Thin	Average
Apr. 10	4,227	3,942	3,386	3,852
Apr. 15	4,813	4,448	3,902	4,288
May 1	5,179	4,416	4,027	4,541
May 15	5,121	4,252	3,706	4,360
June 1	4,772	4,115	3,865	4,251
June 15	4,259	3,532	2,843	3,545
Average of all dates	4,729	4,118	3,622	.....

SOURCE: *Ohio Agr. Expt. Sta. Bul.* 494 (1931).

in the row) gave higher yields than medium rates (plants 8 inches apart in the row). Similar conclusions were drawn from tests made in Kansas to determine the influence of row spacing and seeding rates (see Table 103) on the yield of hay. The heaviest planting rate made in 7-inch rows

TABLE 103.   YIELDS OF SOYBEAN HAY FROM DIFFERENT METHODS OF PLANTING AT
MANHATTAN, KANSAS

Method of planting	Width of rows	Rate of seeding per acre, lb.	Yield, tons per acre
Grain drill	7	86	1.58
Corn planter, double rows	19	38	1.25
Corn planter	38	26	1.13

SOURCE: *Kans. Agr. Expt. Sta. Bul.* 306 (1942).

resulted in the greatest yield, whereas wider spacing and lower seeding rates reduced the yields. Thin plantings tend to induce plant tillering and branching. This compensates the yield in thin plantings to a degree with increased yields per plant For instance, in Ohio[5] 1 pound of Manchu seed produced 43 pounds of cured hay at the thick planting rates, 137 pounds at the medium rate, and 247 pounds when planted thin. However, this does not compensate for the higher yield obtainable where the available space is more completely occupied in thicker sowings. In addition the quality of the hay is better at the highest planting rate, since the plants from thin stands have thicker stems and are less palatable and nutritious.

FIG. 22. A mixture of soybeans and Sudan grass.

Use in Mixtures. Mixtures of grasses and legumes are considered to be more valuable than either one grown alone. Soybeans planted with Sudan grass give a mixture valuable for hay or pasture. Sometimes Sudan grass or sorghum is planted with the soybeans for silage purposes. Mixing with corn is practiced to a limited extent, but in general, this does not seem too satisfactory. In the Kansas tests reported in Table 104, corn alone outyielded the mixtures irrespective of the proportions of one seed to the other. The suggestion usually given to growers when the mixture is desired for silage is to plant the soybeans and corn in separate fields and to mix them at the silage cutter.

TABLE 104. AVERAGE YIELDS OF SOYBEANS AND CORN GROWN TOGETHER AND SEPARATELY FOR SILAGE

| Stand of | | Method of planting | Silage produced | | Protein per acre, lb. |
Soybeans	Corn		Total weight of both crops, tons	Soybeans, %	
Full..........	Full	Grown in same row	13.23	19.5	378
Half..........	Half	Grown in same row	10.72	24.0	328
One-fourth.....	Full	Grown in same row	14.34	10.0	344
Half..........	Full	Grown in same row	13.68	15.5	367
Full..........	Full	Grown separately, ½ plot of each	11.59	26.0	365
	Full	Corn alone	17.14	....	343

SOURCE: *Kans. Agr. Expt. Sta. Bul.* 306 (1942).

HAY PRODUCTION

One of the problems in the production of soybean hay is that of curing it after mowing. From the comparative data given in Table 105, it is apparent that this process is slower for soybeans than for alfalfa and the finer stemmed forage crops. In this experiment, 48 hours after cutting, alfalfa hay contained 32 per cent moisture but the soybean crop still contained almost 60 per cent. This is because the beans in the pods, as well as the

TABLE 105. COMPARATIVE RATE OF DRYING OF ALFALFA AND SOYBEANS SWATH-CURED, SOYBEANS AT "BEANS ONE-THIRD GROWN" STAGE

| Hour | Hours of drying | Moisture in hay, % | |
		Alfalfa	Soybeans
1:00 P.M.............	..	.....	79.1
4:00 P.M.............	3	79.4*	74.4
7:00 A.M.............	18	73.3	79.6
10:00 A.M............	21	65.1	74.7
1:00 P.M.............	24	53.5	70.9
4:00 P.M.............	27	40.5	67.5
7:00 A.M.............	42	56.9	66.3
10:00 A.M............	45	44.6	61.7
1:00 P.M.............	48	32.0	59.2
4:00 P.M.............	51	†	49.9

SOURCE: *Ohio Agr. Expt. Sta. Bimo. Bul.* 20 (1935).

* Alfalfa cut at 3:00 P.M.   † Alfalfa hauled in.

thick heavy stems, cure slowly. The more and the larger the pods, the slower the rate of curing.

Curing Methods. Since soybeans cure slowly there is some question as to the best technique to use. Excess curing in the swath results in heavy loss of quality. In good curing weather the best procedure is to place the crop in windrows and turn these once or twice. Under unfavorable weather conditions, placing the hay in small stacks elevated a few inches off the soil by using straw or other material underneath has made excellent hay. A similar method, commonly used in the Southern states, employs ricks that hold the hay off the ground by means of a frame. This has proved very effective. In Michigan soybeans have been cut with a binder and placed in long narrow shocks two bundles wide and cured with considerable success. All these latter methods make a high-quality product but require extra labor.

Feeding Value

The feeding value of the crop is dependent on the time of harvest together with prevailing weather conditions. Soybeans maintain their protein content well into maturity, owing to formation of the beans which are high in this feed constituent. Fat content rises rapidly with advancing age for the same reason. There is little change in fiber and carbohydrate content, but the ash content decreases. Comparative yields at various stages of maturity indicate increases up to the seed-ripe stage with a decline thereafter.

Protein. Unlike the small-seeded hay crops such as clover, timothy, and alfalfa, the protein content of soybean hay is lowest at full bloom and increases as the pods form and develop. Actually this constituent of the leaves and stems decreases with advancing age, but since soybean seed contains 35 to 40 per cent protein the total percentage in the hay rises. The increase in protein is shown graphically in Fig. 78. Prior to pod formation all the protein is in the leaves and stems. At the advanced stages more than half of the protein is found in the pods and seeds.

Plant Organs. The proportion of stems to leaves varies with maturity, date of seeding and the variety employed. Data on time of harvesting from Ohio[5] show that pods and seeds become a factor only as the plants mature. The percentage of plant organs at various stages is shown in Table 106. The value for leaves decreases rapidly with advancing age. At the stage when most of the pods are brown only 13 per cent of the weight is leaves, for at this stage of maturity most of the leaves have turned brown and fallen off.

Soybeans versus Alfalfa. Soybean hay was compared with alfalfa hay for milk production in West Virginia, and some of the results are given in Table 107. Twenty cows fed on soybean hay along with a basal ration for

TABLE 106. ESTIMATED AVERAGE PERCENTAGES OF PLANT ORGANS AT VARIOUS STAGES OF MATURITY

Stage of growth	Leaves	Stems	Seeds and pods	Seed alone
Middle of bloom..............	66	34	..	..
Beans well formed............	60	29	11	1
First yellow leaves............	44	24	32	15
Leaves ½ dropped............	29	23	48	31
½ pods brown...............	19	26	55	39
Most pods brown.............	13	28	59	41

SOURCE: *Jour. Amer. Soc. Agron.*, **17** (1925).

TABLE 107. ALFALFA HAY AND SOYBEAN HAY COMPARED FOR MILK PRODUCTION

Periods	Milk, lb.	Butterfat, %	Butterfat, lb.
Soybean periods.....................	11,716.4	3.62	424.68
Alfalfa periods.....................	11,651.8	3.60	419.26
Difference in favor of soybean periods...	64.6	....	5.42

SOURCE: *W.Va. Agr. Expt. Sta. Bul.* 181 (1923).

21 days produced 64.6 pounds of milk and 5.42 pounds of butterfat more than the same 20 cows did when fed an equal period with alfalfa hay and the same basal ration. This indicates a feeding value at least equivalent to that of alfalfa hay. Tests conducted in Pennsylvania[3] have given similar results. Comparative analyses of alfalfa and soybeans show the soybean to be higher in protein and fat (Table 108).

TABLE 108. PER CENT COMPOSITION OF SOYBEAN AND ALFALFA HAY COMPARED

Hay	Ash	Crude protein	Fiber	Nitrogen-free extract	Fat
Soybean.....	4.78	16.51	20.72	35.55	5.43
Alfalfa......	6.92	13.20	20.26	41.29	1.41

SOURCE: *Pa. Agr. Expt. Sta. Bul.* 201 (1926).

Time of Cutting. Intermediate- and late-cut soybean hay were compared in feeding trials in Indiana. A portion of the data is given in Table 109. The same quantity and kind of concentrate feed was fed to the milk cows consuming the two kinds of hay. The late-cut hay produced 375 pounds, or 13 per cent, more milk than the medium mature hay and 18.5

TABLE 109. FEEDING VALUE OF INTERMEDIATE AND LATE-CUT SOYBEAN HAY FOR MILK PRODUCTION

Hay	Yield per acre, tons	Dry matter per acre, tons	Milk produced per acre, lb.	Butterfat produced per acre, lb.
Intermediate........	1.658*	1.488	2,874.9	99.67
Late...............	1.794*	1.604	3,249.7	118.15

SOURCE: *Ind. Agr. Expt. Sta. Bul.* 346 (1931).
* On air-dry basis.

pounds, or 18.5 per cent, more butterfat per acre of harvested hay.   This is what would be expected in the light of the finding that the protein and fat content of soybean hay increase with advancing age.

Feeding tests with steers also favor late-cut soybean hay to that cut just past bloom.   Data are given in Table 110.   In addition to the greater

TABLE 110. GAIN BY STEERS FED MEDIUM- AND LATE-CUT SOYBEAN HAY, POUNDS

Hay stage	Ave. weight of steers at end of expt.	Ave. daily gain
Just past full bloom......	544	1.35
Pods 3/4 mature..........	573	1.59

SOURCE: *Ky. Agr. Expt. Sta. Bul.* 435 (1942).

gains, the steers fed the late-cut hay had sleeker coats and appeared in better condition than the others.

Value as Silage.   The feeding value of soybeans preserved as silage appears to be similar to its value as hay.   In Ohio[10] a small increase in milk and butterfat from silage was considered insignificant, and it was pointed out that dairymen might well use either method as suited their convenience. In a Florida test 2.95 pounds of soybean silage was considered the equivalent of 1 pound of No. 1 quality alfalfa hay.

COWPEAS (*Vigna sinensis*)

Cowpeas are an old and revered crop, apparently native to central Africa.   They were cultivated as human food in the Mediterranean region by the Romans, Greeks, and Spaniards.   Following the discovery and development of the West Indies there was an early introduction of this crop.   They were reported in North Carolina in 1714, and their culture was described in Virginia in 1775. Since that time cowpeas have become widespread, especially in the South where they are often called "black-eyed peas" and used as human food.

The cowpea is adapted to a great variety of climatic and soil conditions, but it requires considerable heat and is extremely sensitive to cold. It withstands shade and drought. The general region of adaptation is the Southeast. Cowpeas grow best on good cornland, but any well-drained soils that are relatively fertile are suitable.

VARIETIES

There are many varieties of cowpeas, varying in productiveness, habit of growth, maturity, leaf retention, and other characters. The general adaptation of a few of the important varieties may be seen in Table 111.

TABLE 111. YIELDS OF HAY OBTAINED FROM IMPORTANT VARIETIES OF COWPEAS AT DIFFERENT AGRICULTURAL EXPERIMENT STATIONS

Variety	Average yields per acre, tons						
	Ala.	Ark.	Ga.	Miss.	N.C.	S.C.	Va.
Black..................	1.12	2.03	0.81	2.27	1.32	0.81	....
Brabham..............	....	....	1.12	1.80	1.29	1.12	1.89
Clay.................	1.42	2.88	0.60	2.27	0.97	....	....
Groit.................	1.23	....	....	2.04	1.47	....	1.90
Iron.................	1.55	....	1.03	1.98	1.35	1.08	1.88
Monetta..............	....	....	....	....	1.53	....	1.84
New Era..............	1.15	0.65	0.45	1.77	1.14	1.15	1.62
Red Ripper...........	1.86	1.73	0.93	2.21	1.07	1.86	....
Taylor...............	....	1.86	0.70	2.17	1.26	....	1.81
Unknown.............	1.57	2.46	0.66	2.33	1.88	1.56	....
Whippoorwill..........	1.36	0.91	0.86	1.92	1.41	0.86	1.83

SOURCE: *U.S. Dept. of Agr. Farmers' Bul.* 1153 (1920).

For hay, the most valuable ones appear to be Whippoorwill, Iron, New Era, Victor, Brabham, and Groit. Of lesser value are Unknown, Clay, Red Ripper, and Black.

CULTURE

As with soybeans, planting should be delayed until the soil is relatively warm. In the states of Virginia and North Carolina it has been shown that higher yields result from plantings made in late June or early July, whereas early June is favored in Kansas (see Table 112).

TABLE 112.　Yields per Acre of the Groit and New Era Varieties of Cowpeas in Time-of-sowing Tests, Tons

| Date sown | Groit variety | | Date sown | New Era variety |
	Virginia	North Carolina		Kansas
May 1...............	1.39	0.74	May 12..............	1.19
May 15..............	1.55	0.94	May 19..............	2.00
June 1...............	1.58	1.09	May 26..............	2.00
June 15..............	1.80	1.17	June 3...............	2.26
July 1...............	1.74	1.26	June 9...............	2.08
July 15..............	1.10	0.84	June 16..............	1.77
Aug. 1...............	0.41	....	June 28..............	1.10

Source: *U.S. Dept. Agr. Farmers' Bul.* 1148 (1920).

Seeding.　Methods of seeding have been investigated at several experiment stations.　Data from Arlington Farm, Virginia, are given in Table 113.　The broadcast plots were sown at the rate of 90 pounds per acre,

TABLE 113.　Average Yields per Acre in Method-of-culture Tests with Cowpeas at Arlington Farm, Virginia, Tons

Variety and method of culture	Hay	Variety and method of culture	Hay
Early Buff:		Brabham:	
Broadcast...............	1.32	Broadcast..............	1.83
18-in. rows..............	1.32	18-in. rows.............	1.90
40-in. rows..............	1.18	40-in. rows.............	1.66
Whippoorwill:		New Era:	
Broadcast...............	1.98	Broadcast..............	....
18-in. rows..............	1.90	18-in. rows.............	1.52
40-in. rows..............	1.84	40-in. rows.............	1.26

Source: *U.S. Dept. Agr. Farmers' Bul.* 1148 (1920).

the 18-inch rows at 45 pounds per acre, and the 40-inch rows at the rate of 30 pounds to the acre.　The best practice with cowpeas grown for hay seems to be broadcast sowing or close-drilled rows.　Less labor together with a higher quality hay is associated with this procedure.　Seeding rates in broadcast plots were studied in North Carolina with the Brabham variety.　The 90-pound planting rate gave superior production (see Table 114) and also kept weed encroachments at a minimum.　As a result of such tests the North Carolina station recommended broadcasting 90 to 100 pounds of seed per acre.

TABLE 114. RATE OF BROADCASTING BRABHAM COWPEAS IN NORTH CAROLINA

Seeding rate per acre	Hay yield, lb. per acre	
	Test 1	Test 2
30	6,836	2,434
60	6,006	2,200
90	8,973	2,633
120	7,100	2,773

SOURCE: *N.C. Agr. Expt. Sta. Bul.* 241 (1919).

Use in Mixtures. Mixtures of cowpeas with Sudan grass, sorghum, or sometimes Johnson grass are grown commonly in the South. Yield studies in Alabama show comparative data for cowpeas grown alone and in mixtures. Cowpeas help to increase yields in grass mixtures (Table 115), and similarly the grasses increase the productiveness of the legume.

TABLE 115. YIELDS OF COWPEAS ALONE AND WITH GRASS MIXTURES

Crop	Average yields per acre, lb.	Crop	Average yields per acre, lb.
Cowpeas...............	1,602	Sudan grass............	1,271
Cowpeas and Sudan grass..	1,919	Sorghum..............	1,565
Cowpeas and sorghum....	1,952		

SOURCE: *Ala. Agr. Expt. Sta. Cir.* 79 (1937).

HAYMAKING

The hay is difficult to cure, partly because of unfavorable curing weather in the Southern states and also because of its thick stems and heavy pods. Many methods of curing are utilized in the cowpea region. Curing in swath and windrow is common, so also is placing the hay in tall, narrow haycocks. Special devices such as triangular frames with crosspieces to keep them together are employed. Hay is piled up around these frames, which keep it from becoming too packed, thus permitting air circulation. Vines are also placed on top of long poles or frames where they are left to cure for several weeks. These methods employing frames require considerable labor and are, therefore, more expensive.

FEEDING VALUE

The feeding value of good cowpea hay is relatively high, and it compares favorably with alfalfa or soybeans, as may be noted in Table 116. It is an

TABLE 116. PER CENT ANALYSES OF COWPEA HAY AND OTHER IMPORTANT HAY CROPS

Kind of hay	Moisture	Protein	Fat	Nitrogen-free extract	Ash	Fiber
Cowpea..........	10.4	16.1	3.2	40.3	10.2	19.8
Soybean.........	8.4	15.9	3.9	38.8	8.9	24.1
Alfalfa...........	8.7	15.9	2.7	36.8	8.8	27.1

SOURCE: *U.S. Dept. Agr. Farmers' Bul.* 1153 (1920).

excellent source of protein and minerals and is low in fiber. A feeding trial in fattening steers was conducted in Missouri[8] which demonstrated the high value of cowpea hay for this purpose. The steers made nearly 50 per cent better gains when fed this hay than when fed timothy. Cowpea hay and red clover proved to be equally valuable.

Cowpea straw is a fair source of nutrients for wintering horses, mules, beef cattle, and idle dairy animals. It compares favorably with other

TABLE 117. DIGESTIBLE NUTRIENTS IN COWPEA STRAW COMPARED WITH THOSE IN THE STRAW OF OTHER CROPS

Kind of straw	Digestible nutrients in 100 pounds, lb.			
	Protein	Carbohy-drates	Fat	Total
Cowpea.............	3.4	39.1	0.7	43.2
Soybean.............	2.8	38.5	1.0	42.3
Oat................	1.0	42.6	0.9	44.5

SOURCE: *U.S. Dept. Agr. Farmers' Bul.* 1153 (1920).

straws in digestible nutrients. While no data from feeding tests are available, farmers and stockmen agree that it is valuable. Cowpeas will make a good silage when properly ensiled, and the silage produced when this crop is mixed with sorghum or corn is considered superior to that of corn silage.

References

1. Andrews, W. B., and Marion Gieger: Effect of variety and stand of soybeans on relative yield and percentage of total nitrogen in tops and roots, *Jour. Amer. Soc. Agron.*, **30:**434–437 (1938).
2. Anthony, Ernest L., and H. O. Henderson: Soybean vs. alfalfa hay for milk production, *W.Va. Agr. Expt. Sta. Bul.* 181 (1923).
3. Bechdel, S. I.: Soybean hay for milk production, *Pa. Agr. Expt. Sta. Bul.* 201 (1926).
4. Becker, R. B., W. M. Neal, C. R. Dawson, and P. T. D. Arnold: Soybeans for silage, *Fla. Agr. Expt. Sta. Bul.* 255 (1932).

5. Borst, H. L., and L. E. Thatcher: Life history and composition of the soybean plant, *Ohio Agr. Expt. Sta. Bul.* 494 (1931).
6. Dunton, H. L., and C. R. McGee: Curing soybean hay, *Mich. Quart. Bul.* 16:254–257 (1934).
7. Good, E. S.: Late-cut vs. early-cut soybean hay for stocker cattle, *Ky. Agr. Expt. Sta. Bul.* 435 (1942).
8. Grantham, A. E.: Cowpeas, *Mo. Agr. Expt. Sta. Bul.* 73 (1906).
9. Hackleman, J. C.: The future of the soybean as a forage crop, *Jour. Amer. Soc. Agron.*, **16**:228–236 (1924).
10. Hayden, C. C., and A. E. Perkins: Soybean hay and soybean silage, *Ohio Agr. Expt. Sta. Bimo. Bul.* 11:178–179 (1926).
11. Herman, V. R.: Soybeans and cowpeas for North Carolina, *N.C. Agr. Expt. Sta. Bul.* 241 (1919).
12. Hilton, J. H., J. W. Wilbur, and W. F. Epple: Early, intermediate and late cut soybean hay for milk and butterfat production, *Ind. Agr. Expt. Sta. Bul.* 346 (1931).
13. Metzger, J. E., M. G. Holmes, and Harlow Bierman: Soybeans, *Md. Agr. Expt. Sta. Bul.* 277 (1925).
14. Morse, W. J.: Cowpeas: Culture and varieties, *U.S. Dept. Agr. Farmers' Bul.* 1148 (1920).
15. Morse, W. J.: Cowpeas: Utilization, *U.S. Dept. Agr. Farmers' Bul.* 1153 (1920).
16. Morse, W. J.: Soybean hay and seed production, *U.S. Dept. Agr. Farmers' Bul.* 1605 (1939).
17. Morse, W. J., and J. L. Cartter: Soybeans: Culture and varieties, *U.S. Dept. Agr. Farmers' Bul.* 1520 (1939).
18. Newlander, J. A., H. B. Ellenberger, O. M. Camburn, and C. H. Jones: Digestibility of alfalfa, timothy, and soybeans as silages and as hays, *Vt. Agr. Expt. Sta. Bul.* 430 (1938).
19. Sturkie, D. G.: Experiments with hay crops in Alabama, *Ala. Agr. Expt. Sta. Cir.* 79 (1937).
20. Ten Eyck, A. M., and L. E. Call: Cowpeas, *Kans. Agr. Expt. Sta. Bul.* 160 (1909).
21. Willard, C. J.: The time of harvesting soybeans for hay and seed, *Jour. Amer. Soc. Agron.*, **17**:157–168 (1925).
22. Willard, C. J., L. E. Thatcher, and J. B. Park: Harvesting soybeans for hay, *Ohio Agr. Expt. Sta. Bimo. Bul.* 20:148–154 (1935).
23. Zahnley, J. W.: Soybean production in Kansas, *Kans. Agr. Expt. Sta. Bul.* 306 (1942).

CHAPTER 13

CRIMSON CLOVER, THE VETCHES, AND FIELD PEAS

Several fall- and spring-seeded annual legumes are useful for hay, pasture, silage, and soil protection and improvement. These legumes are of primary significance in the Southeast but are also valuable in the Northeast and the Northwest. Their rapid growth, high feed value, and comparatively good yields make them useful in situations where perennial and biennial legumes cannot be utilized readily.

CRIMSON CLOVER (*Trifolium incarnatum*)

This clover, said to be native to southwestern Asia Minor and southeastern Europe, is a valued forage in France and parts of central Europe.

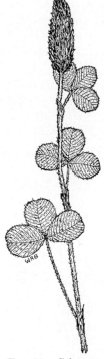

It was first reported growing in America in 1818 at Chestertown, Pennsylvania. In 1855 the U.S. Patent Office distributed seed widely; and by 1880 it had become generally recognized as an important agricultural clover. Crimson clover is considered a winter annual, usually being planted in the fall and harvested the succeeding season.

Adaptation. The crop is only moderately winter hardy and cannot be grown with any degree of success northward of central New Jersey. Crimson clover is most intensively seeded on the clay soils of the South Central states and on the light sandy areas of the Atlantic Coastal Plain where the soils are often lacking in fertility. In the northernmost area of its adaptation it is usually sown for soil improvement and protection, but in the Southern states it is often harvested for hay or pastured.

Some difficulty is experienced in securing good vigorous stands of crimson clover over much of the Coastal Plain and Piedmont regions. Several factors have been isolated and considered contributory to the general problem. Shallow drilling with light seed coverage is said to be more favorable than broadcasting. Liberal fertilizing together with inoculation and the addition of small quantities of boron are special considerations for success with this crop on the Coastal Plain.

FIG. 23. Crimson clover.

124

Yields. Early records of crimson clover hay production as reported by several experiment stations [12] show yields ranging from 2,154 to 5,121 pounds of cured hay per acre in Pennsylvania, 2,460 to 2,600 in New Jersey, 4,000 in Florida, and 4,057 in Alabama. These yields, ranging from about 1 to more than 2 tons per acre, are good considering that the crop is a winter annual. More recent tests in Georgia and Alabama (see Table 118) give

TABLE 118. THE YIELD OF WINTER FORAGE AND COVER CROPS IN GEORGIA
AND ALABAMA

Georgia		Alabama	
Crop	Air-cured hay average, lb. per acre	Crop	Average yields of hay, lb. per acre
Crimson clover........	4,200	Oats and crimson clover	2,796
Austrian winter pea....	4,100	Oats and hairy vetch...	2,378
Hairy vetch..........	3,875	Crimson clover.......	2,313
Tifton bur clover......	3,625	Hairy vetch..........	2,267
Yellow annual melilotus	2,400		
Hop clover (*T. dubium*).	1,200		

SOURCES: *Ga. State College Agr. Bul.* 321 (1926); *Ala. Agr. Expt. Sta. Cir.* 79 (1937).

crimson clover a high rating among other winter annual legumes tested. Crimson clover was superior to other legumes tested in Georgia, where Austrian field peas and hairy vetch were also very productive. Hop clover and yellow annual sweetclover were decidedly inferior. In Alabama crimson clover outyielded hairy vetch both when they were grown alone and when in mixture with winter oats.

Growth Rates. The time of planting crimson clover is known to affect the hay yields. Data from such an experiment in Alabama are given in Table 119. The early fall planting made on Oct. 1 resulted in over ¼ ton

TABLE 119. EFFECT OF PLANTING DATE ON YIELDS OF CRIMSON CLOVER AND HAIRY
VETCH, POUNDS PER ACRE

Crop	Oct. 1, 5-year ave.	Nov. 1, 5-year ave.	Difference
Hairy vetch..............	3,271	2,476	795
Crimson clover............	3,090	2,551	540

SOURCE: *Ala. Agr. Expt. Sta. Bul.* 232 (1930).

more cured hay per acre than Nov. 1 seeding. The crimson clover made more rapid growth from the later planting than hairy vetch. Actually many plantings are now made in July and August for fall and winter grazing.

Comparative spring-growth rates are of interest in making hay not only from a yield standpoint but also because earliness is undesirable because of poor curing weather. Where the crop is made into silage, the rate of crop maturity is less important. It is evident from the data in Table 120

TABLE 120. SPRING GROWTH OF WINTER ANNUALS, POUNDS OF CURED HAY PER ACRE

Name	Dates of harvesting			
	Mar. 1	Mar. 28	Apr. 6	May 6
Crimson clover................	1,600	2,800	2,900	4,200
Hairy vetch..................	700	1,750	2,250	3,900
Austrian winter pea...........	1,650	2,200	2,300	4,100
Tifton bur clover.............	1,350	2,250	2,420	3,900
Yellow annual melilotus.......	800	1,400	1,600	2,400

SOURCE: *Ga. State College Agr. Bul.* 321 (1926).

that crimson clover makes rapid early growth. Hairy vetch starts more slowly in the spring but catches up later. Austrian winter peas and bur clover are also vigorous early growers that produce good yields. The annual yellow sweetclover starts slowly and is a weak yielder. Highest yields were not reached until early in May by all the species tested. At the latitude of these Georgia tests crimson clover began blooming between Apr. 20 and 30 and continued for about 20 days. It blooms and matures somewhat earlier then hairy vetch and Austrian field peas but later than the bur clovers.

Protein Content. That the annual legumes maintain a high percentage of protein with advancing maturity is evident from the data given in Table 121. On Mar. 16 crimson clover contained 24.7 per cent protein in the

TABLE 121. PROTEIN ANALYSIS FOR SOME PRINCIPAL WINTER LEGUMES

Crop	Nitrogen on air-dry basis, %			
	Mar. 16	Apr. 6	Apr. 20	May 4
Crimson clover.........	24.7	24.7	16.8	14.7
Austrian peas..........	24.8	22.6	24.4	20.0
Hairy vetch...........	23.9	24.0	20.9	20.9

SOURCE: *Ga. Agr. Ext. Serv. Bul.* 374 (1929).

tops, on Apr. 20, 16.8 per cent, and on May 4, 14.7 per cent protein. Hairy vetch and Austrian peas were, however, superior in their retention of protein.

Crimson clover is said to make good hay, especially if cut at the early bloom stage. If it becomes too mature, the hairs on the stems and flower heads become stiff and unpalatable. In this mature stage masses of the hairs are said to form into indigestible balls in the stomachs of horses and mules, sometimes causing death. This difficulty is not encountered with cattle, sheep, or swine.

THE VETCHES (*Vicia* sp.)

There are 11 species of the genus *Vicia* that are considered of significance to American agriculture. The species together with their common names are given in Table 122. All are annuals except hairy, which is either annual

TABLE 122. VETCH SPECIES (*Vicia*) TOGETHER WITH THEIR COMMON NAMES

Species	Common name	Species	Common name
angustifolia.........	Narrowleaf	*monantha*.........	Monantha
atropurpurea.......	Purple	*pannonica*.........	Hungarian
calcarata..........	Bard	*sativa*.............	Common
dasycarpa..........	Woollypod	*villosa*............	Hairy
ervilia.............	Bittervetch	*villosa*............	Smooth
faba..............	Horsebean		

or biennial, depending on its utilization. They are all viny and weak-stemmed except horsebean, which is upright and possesses larger leaves than the other species. Bittervetch is not used commercially.

Adaptation. The vetches are adapted primarily to those regions possessing mild winter temperatures such as the Southern states, the Pacific coastal area, and the Coastal Plain area along the Atlantic seaboard. The only winter-hardy species is hairy vetch, which is commonly used for fall planting northward of the other species. The Hungarian, woollypod, and smooth vetches will withstand temperatures around 0°F. provided that the temperature does not fluctuate strongly or that there is a snow cover. Common vetch seldom can withstand less than 10°F., and bittervetch, purple, Monantha, and narrowleaf are even less hardy.

Uses. The most important uses of vetch are for cover, green manure, and soil-improvement purposes. All the vetches, however, make good hay, silage, pasture, and soiling crops. Seed of several of the commercial varieties is also produced in the United States, but much seed is imported from Europe. From a hay standpoint good yields are possible, and if the

product is carefully handled it is of high quality.   Data on yields as reported by several experiment stations[12] range from 2,540 to 6,560 pounds
per acre.   These show that $1\frac{1}{4}$ to more than 3 tons of hay per acre are
readily secured.

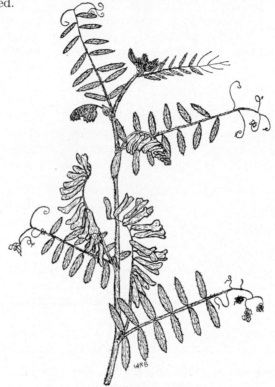

FIG. 24.   Hairy vetch.

Mixtures.   Although vetch may be sown alone for hay, the usual practice is to seed it with a small grain such as oats or wheat.   Yields from such
mixtures are somewhat higher, and the crop is much easier to harvest.
Since all the vetches except the horsebean are viny plants with soft stems,
the associated grain crop holds them erect, making mowing much easier.
Data from comparative yields of winter grains and vetch alone and in
combination as studied in Oregon and Alabama are given in Table 123.
Vetch alone outyielded the grains, and vetch in combination with any one
of the small grains was superior to vetch alone.

Seeding.   The time of planting varies, in general, with the latitude.   From
the Rocky Mountains eastward and north of latitude 40°, all the agricultural vetches are usually sown in early spring, excepting the hairy.   In this
region hairy is best seeded from late August through October.   On the
West Coast seeding from September to early October is practiced, depend-

TABLE 123. COMPARATIVE FORAGE YIELDS OF GRAINS, VETCHES, AND VETCH-AND-GRAIN COMBINATION SEEDINGS

Oregon		Alabama	
Crop	Average yield, tons per acre	Crop	Average yield, lb. per acre
White winter wheat......	3.42	Oats.................	1,043
Gray winter oats........	3.55	Hairy vetch...........	1,516
Vetch.................	3.57	Monantha vetch........	1,578
Vetch and white winter wheat...............	4.28	Oats and hairy vetch....	1,883
Vetch and gray winter oats	4.32	Oats and Monantha vetch	2,653

SOURCES: *Oreg. Agr. Expt. Sta. Bul.* 213 (1925); *Ala. Agr. Expt. Sta. Cir.* 79 (1937).

ing on the seasonal rains. Late seedings often winterkill or make very little growth. Seeding rates and dates of planting as studied in Alabama are reported in Table 124. In these tests the earlier the planting date, the higher the yield of green material produced per acre. It is also evident that Monantha vetch produced considerably higher yields than hairy vetch, indicating better adaptation. The most favorable seeding rate appears

TABLE 124. POUNDS OF GREEN MATERIAL PER ACRE AS INFLUENCED BY THE TIME AND RATE OF SEEDING HAIRY AND MONANTHA VETCH

Seeding rate, lb. per acre	Average yields per acre		
	Sept. 30	Oct. 26	Nov. 23
Hairy:			
10......................	1,027	791	354
20......................	1,577	1,682	676
30......................	2,228	1,893	918
Monantha:			
10......................	8,393	5,308	1,442
20......................	9,240	6,940	2,000
30......................	9,211	7,700	2,930

SOURCE: *Ala. Agr. Expt. Sta. Bul.* 232 (1930).

to be 30 pounds of seed per acre for both hairy and Monantha vetch, this rate being especially significant with the later planting. In milder climates, fall seedings of the vetches are preferred to spring plantings because of their greater productiveness. In Oregon[14] fall plantings of common vetch averaged 2.43 tons per acre, early spring seedings 1.81, and late spring seedings only 0.31 ton per acre.

TABLE 125. QUANTITY OF VETCH SEED TO USE PER ACRE WHEN SEEDED ALONE, POUNDS

Kind	Southern states	Northern and Western states	Kind	Southern states	Northern and Western states
Bard*	....	60–70	Narrowleaf	20–30	....
Common	40–50	60–80	Purple	....	60–70
Hairy	20–30	30–40	Smooth	20–30	30–40
Hungarian	40–50	60–80	Woollypod	25–35	40–50
Monantha	30–40	60–70			

SOURCE: *U.S. Dept. Agr. Farmers' Bul.* 1740 (1934).
* Bard vetch is adapted only to the Southwest.

The rate of seeding varies with the region and the species. Suggested rates for the respective regions of adaptation are indicated in Table 125. Rates are lower in the Southern states than in the Northern and Western regions because the winters are less severe.

Studies on methods of planting appear to favor drilling over broadcasting. In Alabama,[4] drilling resulted in increased yields irrespective of the time of planting for both hairy and Monantha vetch. Broadcasting compared with drilling at various seeding depths in Oregon[14] gave similar results. In Oregon there was no advantage in drilling deeper than 2 inches. Drilling required less seed per acre and gave a more uniform stand than broadcasting.

Maturity. Earliness is desired in vetch for soil-improvement and pasture purposes, but late maturity seems best for hay production. A comparison of blooming dates as related to maturity may be found in Table 126. Nar-

TABLE 126. RELATIVE EARLINESS OF WINTER LEGUMES BY INITIAL BLOOMING DATES, FROM PLANTINGS MADE NOV. 1

Kind of vetch	Average bloom dates	Days earlier than hairy vetch
Narrowleaf	Apr. 2	20
Bitter	Apr. 4	18
Monantha	Apr. 5	17
Crimson clover	Apr. 12	10
Woollypod	Apr. 14	8
Oregon vetch	Apr. 18	4
Hairy vetch	Apr. 22	
Austrian winter peas	Apr. 25	−3

SOURCE: *Ala. Agr. Expt. Sta. Bul.* 232 (1932).

rowleaf vetch averaged 20 days earlier in blooming than hairy. The Austrian winter peas were later than any of the vetches.

Some studies on time of cutting common vetch as related to yields were made in Oregon.[14] Cutting when the second set of flowers were in bloom gave 1.99 tons of dry matter per acre; when the lower pods were one-fourth filled, 2.77 tons; and when the lower pods were filled, 3.43 tons. Thus cutting when the lower pods were well filled increased dry-matter yields by 1.44 tons per acre over cutting when second set of flowers were in full bloom. From earlier data, vetch (see Table 121) is shown to maintain a high protein content over a considerable range of maturity.

Forage Quality. Vetch makes a high-quality hay that compares favorably with alfalfa, as shown in Table 127. It is as high in protein and ash content

TABLE 127. PER CENT ANALYSES OF HAY AND SILAGE GROWN IN WILLAMETTE VALLEY, OREGON

Product	Water	Ash	Crude protein	Ether extract	Crude fiber	Nitrogen-free extract
Alfalfa hay............	7.92	6.91	12.6	1.09	30.9	40.6
Vetch hay.............	8.36	6.10	13.3	0.97	25.8	45.5
Corn silage............	74.68	1.35	2.3	0.70	5.3	15.7
Vetch and oats silage....	73.58	1.92	2.2	0.60	8.9	12.9

SOURCE: *Oreg. Agr. Expt. Sta. Bul.* 213 (1925).

and somewhat lower in crude fiber. As silage it compares favorably with corn, although it is lower in energy content. The hay and silage are relished by cattle, horses, and sheep.

Vetch fits into many rotations. In the Southeast it may be grown as a winter crop and followed by summer hay, pasture, or other crops. Hairy vetch is similarly utilized in the North, but in the Northwest the vetches occupy the entire season and are often used in rotation with a small-grain or cultivated crop.

FIELD PEAS *(Pisum arvense)*

The field pea was brought to America by the early colonists, being reported first in Virginia in 1636. The cultivation of this crop developed slowly, becoming most popular in the northern humid states from New England to the eastern Dakotas and finally in the Northwestern states. Peas are a cool-season crop for early spring plantings or for regions where they can be fall-seeded because of the mild winters. The general regions of adaptation are shown in Fig. 25. Field peas are grown for hay, silage, green

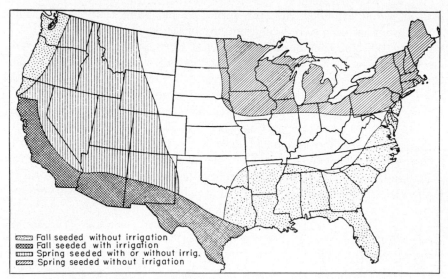

Fall seeded without irrigation
Fall seeded with irrigation
Spring seeded with or without irrig.
Spring seeded without irrigation

Fɪɢ. 25.　General regions of the United States in which the field pea is well adapted. (*Bureau of Plant Industry, Soils and Agricultural Engineering, U.S. Department of Agriculture.*)

manure, seed, canning purposes, and pasture.　When grown for canning or seed the vines are used for silage or straw.

Varieties.　In the Southern states and in the coastal region of the Pacific Northwest where fall seeding is practiced, the hardy Austrian winter pea is grown almost to the exclusion of other varieties.　The varieties of field peas commonly grown in America are given in Table 128.　Besides the

TABLE 128.　Vᴀʀɪᴇᴛɪᴇs ᴏꜰ Fɪᴇʟᴅ Pᴇᴀs Cᴏᴍᴍᴏɴʟʏ Gʀᴏᴡɴ ɪɴ ᴛʜᴇ Uɴɪᴛᴇᴅ States

Agnes	Canadian Beauty	French Gray
Austrian winter	Chancellor	Marrowfat
Alaska	Chang	Multiplier
Bluebell	Clamart	Scotch

Austrian, the Alaska and Bluebell varieties are grown in the Pacific Northwest.　Canadian Beauty and Agnes are suggested for hay and pasture in the Colorado area.　The Great Lakes states grow Marrowfat, Scotch, Chang, Chancellor, Canadian Beauty, and Multiplier.

Seeding.　In the Northern states, where spring planting is practiced, seeding as early as the seedbed can be prepared gives the best results. In Alabama, where fall seeding is used, Austrian winter peas planted Sept. 30 gave higher yields than later plantings in October and November (see Table 129).　At all planting dates the 60-pound seeding rate per acre was favored.　Similar studies on seeding rates for Austrian peas alone and

TABLE 129. POUNDS OF GREEN MATERIAL PER ACRE ON THE TIME AND RATE OF SEEDING EXPERIMENT OF AUSTRIAN WINTER PEAS

Seeding rate, lb. per acre	Sept. 30	Oct. 26	Nov. 23
30	7,412	4,747	2,313
45	8,138	5,668	3,322
60	8,653	6,931	3,669

SOURCE: *Ala. Agr. Expt. Sta. Bul.* 232 (1930).

with oats in Oregon[13] showed that the higher seeding rates increased the yields of hay but that there was no yield advantage gained by adding oats. These results are in agreement with those from Alabama given in Table 130. Austrian peas alone resulted in the highest yield, the oats-

TABLE 130. YIELDS PRODUCED BY AUSTRIAN WINTER PEAS, ALONE OR MIXED WITH OATS

Crop	Pounds of seed per acre	Method of seeding	Average yield of hay, lb. per acre
Oats......................	64	Broadcast	1,043
Oats......................	64 ⎱	Broadcast	2,613
Austrian winter peas........	60 ⎰		
Austrian winter peas........	60	Broadcast	3,499

SOURCE: *Ala. Agr. Expt. Sta. Cir.* 79 (1937).

peas mixed were intermediate and oats alone inferior. Somewhat different results were secured with field peas at the Ohio Station as shown in Table 131. Oats in combination with peas produced hay of higher protein

TABLE 131. EFFECT OF SEEDING RATES FOR OATS AND FIELD PEAS ON YIELD AND QUALITY OF HAY

Mixture of seed, bu. per acre	Average yield, tons	Average crude protein content, %
Peas 2, oats 1...............	2.66	10.1
Peas 1.5, oats 1.5...........	2.64	9.5
Peas 1, oats 2..............	2.78	9.0

SOURCE: *Ohio Agr. Expt. Sta. Bul.* 543 (1934).

content than oats alone, and the yields remained almost constant irrespective of the proportion of peas to oats in the mixture.

A comparison of methods of seeding Austrian peas indicates that drilling was superior to broadcasting irrespective of seeding date (see Table 132).

TABLE 132. POUNDS OF GREEN MATERIAL PER ACRE AS AFFECTED BY DATE AND METHOD OF SEEDING AUSTRIAN WINTER PEAS

Date of planting	Average acre yields, lb.	
	Broadcast	Drilled
Sept. 30............	5,186	6,906
Oct. 26............	3,455	5,061
Nov. 23............	1,928	3,216
Dec. 19............	651	1,283

SOURCE: *Ala. Agr. Expt. Sta. Bul.* 232 (1930).

That is probably because drilling gives better coverage and more uniform distribution of seed than broadcasting.

Maturity. The time to cut field peas for hay was studied at the Utah Station, the Golden vine variety being grown under irrigation. Data on the analyses and yields at different stages are given in Table 133. The

TABLE 133. FIELD PEA: ANALYSES AT DIFFERENT STAGES OF GROWTH

Date and stage of cutting	Yield dry matter to the acre, lb.	Leaves, %	Stalks, %	Flowers and pods, %	Protein, %
June 19—9 in. high......	936	79.0	21.0	0	22.3
June 26.................	1,628	76.6	23.4	0	26.1
July 3..................	2,583	72.8	27.2	0	23.2
July 10—early bloom.....	4,997	67.0	27.8	5.2	26.7
July 17.................	4,412	56.7	28.7	14.6	24.2
July 24—pods filled......	3,496	48.6	19.7	31.7	20.0
July 31—pods ripe.......	2,658	40.9	17.0	42.1	22.2

SOURCE: From Piper, "Forage Plants and Their Culture," rev. ed., copyright, 1924, by The Macmillan Company and used with their permission.

highest yield and protein content was secured at the early-bloom stage. The percentage of leaves decreased with advancing age from 70 to 41 per cent. The protein content remained high, being 20 per cent or more throughout the growth of the crop.

Variations in yield with advancing age for Austrian field peas are given in Table 134. The highest were secured on Apr. 17, from the Sept. 30 and

TABLE 134.   POUNDS OF GREEN MATERIAL PER ACRE ON THE RATE OF GROWTH TEST
OF AUSTRIAN WINTER PEAS

Date of planting	Date of harvesting			
	Mar. 22	Apr. 2	Apr. 17	May 2
Sept. 30........	5,909	6,996	9,436	7,515
Oct. 26........	4,265	5,948	8,724	7,116
Nov. 23........	1,645	2,372	4,548	4,745
Dec. 19........	426	761	1,756	2,446

SOURCE: *Ala. Agr. Expt. Sta. Bul.* 232 (1930).

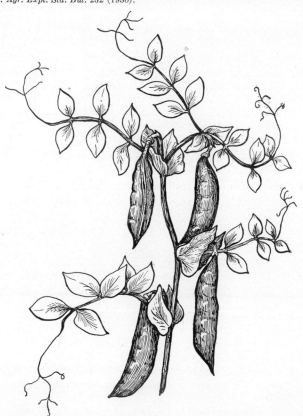

FIG. 26.   A branch of the field pea vine, showing the stems, leaves, and pods.

Oct. 26 plantings.   The November and December plantings produced their
highest yields on May 2.   Early planting favored the highest yields at all
dates of harvest.

If field peas are seeded with oats, as is often the case in the Northern states, the crop is usually harvested when the oats are in the milk stage of development.

Analyses. Field pea hay compares favorably with alfalfa, being somewhat higher in protein, but lower in carbohydrate, fiber, and energy content.[20] The feeding value is considered to be about equal to that of alfalfa.

Pea-cannery refuse, often called pea silage, is considered a valuable feed by most livestock men. Comparative analyses of pea silage, sun-cured pea hay, and dehydrated pea hay are given in Table 135. Pea silage from

TABLE 135. AVERAGE PER CENT COMPOSITION OF PEA SILAGE, SUN-CURED HAY, AND ARTIFICIALLY DRIED HAY (DRY-MATTER BASIS)

Material analyzed	Dry matter	Crude protein	Crude fiber	Ether extract	Nitrogen-free extract	Ash
Pea vine silage.........	24.9	12.5	32.5	3.5	42.7	7.0
Sun-cured.............	86.7	16.0	26.9	2.8	47.5	6.9
Artificially dried........	85.9	12.6	26.4	2.7	50.5	9.0

SOURCE: *Wash. Agr. Expt. Sta. Bul.* 364 (1938).

the cannery compares favorably with pea hay whether cured in the sun or artificially. Average digestibility of these forms of forage as shown in Washington tests[5] indicate somewhat lower digestibility for pea silage than the hay. As a by-product of the canning-pea industry the silage is very valuable for succulent livestock feed.

References

1. Alexander, E. D.: Winter legumes for Georgia, *Ga. Agr. Ext. Serv. Bul.* 374 (1929).
2. Alexander, E. D.: Austrian winter peas and the vetches, *Ga. Agr. Ext. Serv. Bul.* 453 (1939).
3. Anthony, J. L.: Production and utilization of hairy vetch, *Miss. Agr. Expt. Sta. Bul.* 408 (1944).
4. Bailey, R. Y., J. T. Williamson, and J. F. Duggar: Experiments with legumes in Alabama, *Ala. Agr. Expt. Sta. Bul.* 232 (1930).
5. Hodgson, R. E., and J. C. Knott: The composition and apparent digestibility of pea silage, sun cured pea vines and artificially dried pea vines, *Wash. Agr. Expt. Sta. Bul.* 364 (1938).
6. Hollowell, E. A.: Crimson clover, *U.S. Dept. Agr. Leaflet* 160 (1938).
7. Kephart, L. W.: Growing crimson clover, *U.S. Dept. Agr. Farmers' Bul.* 1142 (1922).
8. McKee, Roland, and Harry A. Schoth: Common vetch and its varieties, *U.S. Dept. Agr. Bul.* 1289 (1925).
9. McKee, Roland, and H. A. Schoth: Vetch culture and uses, *U.S. Dept. Agr. Farmers' Bul.* 1740 (1934).
10. McKee, Roland, and H. A. Schoth: Culture and pests of field peas, *U.S. Dept. Agr. Farmers' Bul.* 1803 (1938).

11. Naftel, James A.: Soil liming investigations: VI. Response of crimson clover to boron with and without lime on Coastal Plain soils, *Jour. Amer. Soc. Agron.*, **34**:975–985 (1942).

12. Piper, C. V.: Forage Plants and Their Culture, The Macmillan Company, New York, 1927.

13. Schoth, H. A.: Austrian winter field peas in Oregon, *Oreg. Agr. Expt. Sta. Bul.* 286 (1931).

14. Schoth, H. A., and G. R. Hyslop: Common vetch, *Oreg. Agr. Expt. Sta. Bul.* 213 (1925).

15. Simmons, Charles F.: Hairy vetch, *Ark. Agr. Expt. Sta. Cir.* 201 (1941).

16. Stephens, J. L., and E. A. Hollowell: Crimson clover in the Coastal Plain of the Southeast, *Jour. Amer. Soc. Agron.*, **34**:1057–1059 (1942).

17. Sturkie, D. G.: Experiments with hay crops in Alabama, *Ala. Agr. Expt. Sta. Cir.* 79 (1937).

18. Tabor, Paul: Winter forage and cover crops, *Ga. State Col. Agr. Bul.* 321 (1926).

19. Thatcher, L. E.: Cereal hays for Ohio, *Ohio Agr. Expt. Sta. Bul.* 543 (1934).

20. Vinall, H. N.: The field pea as a forage crop, *U.S. Dept. Agr. Farmers' Bul.* 690 (1915).

CHAPTER 14

TIMOTHY CULTURE

Timothy is the most widely grown hay grass in the Northern part of the United States east of the Mississippi River. It requires a relatively cool and moist climate for best performance and is unadapted to dry, hot situations. It is also grown in the valleys of the intermountain states and the coastal region of Washington and Oregon. Heavy-textured soils, such as clay loams, possessing good moisture capacity, are most suited to its culture. Timothy is extremely cold-resistant, seldom winterkilling even under extreme conditions.

A Popular Hay Crop. The acreage devoted to timothy production has been declining since the beginning of the twentieth century. Data on acreage in clover and timothy, of which timothy is usually half or more, are given in Table 136. The reduction from 34 million acres in 1909 to 18½

TABLE 136. ACREAGE OF TIMOTHY AND CLOVER GROWN IN THE UNITED STATES, 1909–1939

Year...............	1909	1919	1929	1939
Acreage, thousands..	34,228	30,290	25,547	18,543

million in 1939 is due to a decreasing horse population and to an influx of such crops as alfalfa, bromegrass, annual hays, and others. Horses are heavy consumers of timothy hay, and as their numbers decreased so did the demand for this product. Most of the timothy hay now grown is fed on the farms where it is produced.

Good Qualities. Timothy is still the favorite grass in the Northeast for a number of reasons, the most significant being as follows: (1) it is highly palatable when mowed early; (2) the relative cost of seeding and harvesting is low; (3) new seedings usually produce a stand; (4) a fairly permanent stand results under favorable conditions; (5) timothy ranks high among the grasses in productivity; (6) it makes a compatible grass partner for many of the biennial and perennial hay legumes. While timothy is grown on more acres than any other hay grass in the United States, there is a need to develop superior varieties for both hay and pasture. Seed of the unimproved type is still generally used for plantings.

Varieties and Strains. Breeding work has been most intensive in Ohio, where the State Experiment Station and the U.S. Department of Agriculture are engaged in a cooperative project. Selection of strains classified as very early, early, medium, late, and very late has been under way. Several of these selections have been adequately tested and given names. Thus Marietta is an early-maturing variety adapted to the southern latitudes of the timothy belt. Lorain is 2 to 3 weeks later than Marietta and appears to be most valuable northward. A late variety called Huron was once popular in the Pacific Northwest and an early one, Shelby, in southern Indiana. Another variety, Cornell 4059, is somewhat later than common timothy, but it has not attained any particular popularity. In fact, none of these varieties has become widely adopted as yet.

Comparative yields of the early, medium, and late selections have been measured at several localities. A few of these are given in Table 137. There thus appears to be considerable difference among varieties in their performance at different latitudes. The early-maturing strains usually

FIG. 27. A typical timothy plant. (*Bureau of Plant Industry, Soils and Agricultural Engineering, U.S. Department of Agriculture.*)

TABLE 137. COMPARATIVE YIELDS OF TIMOTHY STRAINS AT SEVERAL STATIONS

Strain	Hay yields, lb. per acre			
	Kentucky	Columbus, Ohio	Southern Ohio	Northern Ohio
Early..................	2,350	4,360	. . . . .	. . . . .
Medium...............	1,700	4,015	3,890	3,300
Late..................	1,300	. . . . .	3,060	3,725

SOURCE: *Ohio Agr. Expt. Sta. Bimo. Bul.* 31 (1946).

give higher yields in the southern latitudes, whereas late-maturing strains produce more hay in the northern latitudes.

Comparative Yields. In the region where timothy is adapted, its production compares favorably with yields of other grasses. In an Ohio test (see Table 138) timothy produced over ½ ton more hay per acre than redtop

TABLE 138. COMPARATIVE ACRE YIELDS OF TIMOTHY WITH OTHER GRASSES

Grass	Ave. yield, lb.	Relative yield, %	Grass	Ave. yield, lb.	Relative yield, %
Timothy.........	5,309	100	Meadow fescue...	3,539	67
Redtop..........	4,129	78	Ryegrass........	3,021	57
Orchard grass.....	3,938	74	Meadow foxtail..	2,464	46

SOURCE: *Ohio Agr. Expt. Sta. Bul.* 603 (1939).

and almost a ton more than meadow fescue. Its closest competitor in the Northeast is bromegrass.

Timothy is best suited, however, to growing in association with legumes. Some data on yield increases from growing with red clover are given in Table 139. In all cases reported timothy yields have been benefited by

TABLE 139. AVERAGE YIELDS OF TIMOTHY GROWN ALONE AND WITH RED CLOVER, TONS PER ACRE

Crop	Ohio 3-year	New Jersey 3-year	New Hampshire long-time	Tennessee 3-yr	New York 2-yr
Timothy........	1.52	2.13	1.00	1.47	1.18
Timothy and clover........	3.57	3.24	1.50	3.32	1.90

the addition of a legume partner. The legume has also tended to increase the quality of the hay produced. The common practice throughout the timothy area is to seed clover or alfalfa with it. As the legumes disappear from the stand the timothy endures, thus permitting a lengthened rotation where it may be desired.

Seeding Rates. The proportion of timothy seed to clover to sow is a subject of considerable importance. It is desirable to use the quantity of each seed that will result in the highest yield and quality of product. Some data from North Ridgeville, Ohio, indicate that relatively low rates of timothy seed and higher rates of clover are most satisfactory (see Table 140). Total yields were greatest when 2½ to 5 pounds of timothy was seeded with 10 pounds of red clover. These rates also produced the highest

TABLE 140. AVERAGE YIELDS OF CLOVER AND TIMOTHY OBTAINED BY VARYING THE SEEDING RATE FOR TIMOTHY

Seed per acre		Hay per acre, lb.	% of constituents in first cutting		
Kind	Pounds		Timothy	Clover	Weeds
Timothy................ Red clover..............	2½ } 10	5,831	53	44	3
Timothy............... Red clover.............	5 } 10	5,955	65	34	1
Timothy................ Red clover.............	10 } 10	5,633	67	31	2
Timothy................ Red clover..............	20 } 10	5,363	68	31	1
Timothy................ Red clover..............	40 } 10	5,157	69	28	3

SOURCE: *Ohio Agr. Expt. Sta. Bul.* 603 (1939).

proportion of clover and maximum protein. As timothy seeding rates increased above 5 pounds, the hay yields and the quality, as measured by the proportion of clover in the hay, decreased. Common seeding rates in the Northeast are 3 to 4 pounds of timothy seed per acre for fall planting and 6 to 8 pounds for spring seeding, provided that a legume is added.

YIELD AND QUALITY

Whenever possible timothy should be grown with a legume partner and the crop handled according to those practices which favor the legume. Timothy, however, is sometimes seeded alone, or it may persist after the legumes have disappeared. The main problems in growing timothy alone for hay are to obtain adequate yields and a high-quality product.

Effect of Nitrogen Fertilizers. Yields can usually be increased by adding sufficient fertilizer, especially those containing a high proportion of nitrogen. Results of a 10-year fertilizer study at North Ridgeville, Ohio, and a 3-year study in New Hampshire are given in Table 141. The fertilizers were applied on an annual basis. In Ohio nitrogen alone increased the yields somewhat, but the complete fertilizer treatment gave the largest gain. In New Hampshire nitrogen alone almost doubled production, but again yields were highest with the complete fertilizer. Relatively good yields of timothy thus are shown to be attainable by top-dressing with a suitable fertilizer mixture. Even so, these yields are usually inferior to those obtained when timothy is grown with adapted clovers or alfalfa.

Season to Apply. The season of the year at which nitrogen treatments are applied for timothy is known to influence the total yield of hay and the quantity of protein produced. An example of such a study from New

TABLE 141.   YIELDS OBTAINED FROM TOP-DRESSING TIMOTHY WITH DIFFERENT KINDS
AND QUANTITIES OF FERTILIZER

| Fertilizer | Hay, lb. per acre | | | |
| | Ohio | | New Hampshire | |
	10-year ave.	Increase	3-year ave.	Increase
Check..................	2,393	.....	1,868	.....
N.....................	3,186	793	3,330	1,462
NP...................	3,483	1,090	.....	.....
NK...................	.....	.....	2,596	728
NPK.................	3,699	1,306	4,027	2,159

SOURCES: *Ohio Agr. Expt. Sta. Bul.* 603 (1939); *N.H. Agr. Expt. Sta. Bul.* 306 (1938).

TABLE 142.   COMPARISON OF SPRING AND FALL APPLICATIONS OF NITRATE OF SODA
ON TIMOTHY, 3-YEAR AVERAGE

| Treatment | Dry matter | | Protein | |
	Hay, lb. per acre	Diff. from check, lb.	Lb. per acre	Diff. from check, lb.
Check (no treatment)....	1,939	.....	171	...
Nitrate of soda in fall....	3,022	1,083	264	93
Nitrate of soda in spring...	3,014	1,075	275	104

SOURCE: *N.H. Agr. Expt. Sta. Bul.* 306 (1938).

Hampshire is given in Table 142.   Spring applications gave some increase
over fall application in harvested protein, but the difference was not large.
Application of soluble nitrogen fertilizers 10 to 20 days prior to harvesting
timothy are reported (see Table 143) to increase protein content considerably.   Nitrogen was added at the rate of 20.5 pounds per acre 20 days
before harvest, and this resulted in an increase in crude protein from 144 to

TABLE 143.   INFLUENCE OF SOLUBLE NITROGEN TREATMENT APPLIED 20 DAYS BEFORE
HARVEST ON TIMOTHY YIELDS AND PROTEIN CONTENT

Treatment	Cured hay per acre, lb.	Crude protein in dry matter, %	Crude protein per acre, lb.
Nitrogen...........	2,778	6.74	187
Control............	2,692	5.35	144

SOURCE: *N.J. Agr. Expt. Sta. Bul.* 644 (1938).

187 pounds per acre, or about 2 pounds for each pound of nitrogen added. Total hay yield was affected very little. Nitrogen is apparently assimilated and converted into crude protein at a rapid pace by the timothy plants in late spring.

Amount Needed. The quantity of nitrogen supplied per acre influences not only the yield but also the percentage of protein in the hay. In Ohio,[4] the percentage of protein increased from 5.80 per cent when 50 pounds of nitrate of soda was added per acre up to 8.04 per cent with 800 pounds. The addition of 200 to 400 pounds of nitrate of soda appeared to be the most economical per unit of material added. The best time for application of soluble nitrogen was also studied by applying 200 pounds of nitrate of soda at various dates. April and early May applications were a little more valuable than those made in October. When made as late as May 15 and June 1 the yield of hay per acre decreased, but the protein harvested per acre was increased. It would appear, however, that either late fall or early spring applications were satisfactory.

Effect of Stage of Maturity. As the timothy plant matures it gradually loses its green color. Color is the primary factor in grading the hay grasses. Some data on color loss with advancing age are given in Table 144. The

TABLE 144. AVERAGE NUMBER OF LEAVES WITH BLADES ENTIRELY OR PARTIALLY GREEN ON 14 ELONGATED FERTILE TIMOTHY SHOOTS AT DIFFERENT DATES

Date observed	Average number of green leaf blades per shoot	Date observed	Average number of green leaf blades per shoot
May 8...............	6.7	June 26..............	3.9
May 15..............	6.0	July 5...............	3.2
May 23..............	6.0	July 10..............	2.6
June 5...............	6.2	July 17..............	1.7
June 12..............	5.5	July 23..............	1.0
June 19..............	4.9	July 31..............	0.0

SOURCE: *U.S. Dept. Agr. Bul.* 1450 (1927).

greatest number of green leaves was found on May 8, and this average number decreased rather consistently until on July 31 there were no green leaves at all. From the standpoint of green leaves this would indicate that the earlier the timothy was cut, the more green leaves would be harvested.

Plant Organs. The timothy plant was graded for color by Hosterman and Hall and the proportion of organs determined at various stages of maturity (see Table 145). A hue reading of 7.4 is considered equivalent to 100 per cent green color. The timothy was shade-cured and, therefore, kept its color better than if it had been cured in the sun. The highest percentage of leaves and leaf sheaths were found at the nearly headed stage,

TABLE 145. TOTAL WEIGHT AND COLOR OF TIMOTHY HAY CUT AT DIFFERENT STAGES OF MATURITY AND THE WEIGHT AND PERCENTAGE OF TOTAL FOR LEAF BLADES, LEAF SHEATHS, STEMS, AND HEADS

Stage harvested	Total weight, grams	Color		Leaf blades		Leaf sheaths		Stems		Heads	
		Hue	% green	Grams	%	Grams	%	Grams	%	Grams	%
Nearly full-headed....	500	10.5	100	191	38	116	23	133	27	60	12
Early bloom..........	528	10.0	100	155	29	105	20	174	33	94	18
Just past full bloom...	658	9.1	100	135	21	103	16	310	47	110	17
10% heads straw-colored............	706	7.6	100	81	12	91	13	323	46	211	30
Heads matured.......	1,090	4.5	45	108	10	122	11	422	39	437	40

SOURCE: *Jour. Amer. Soc. Agron.*, **30** (1938).

FIG. 28. Mowing timothy for hay. (*New Idea, Inc.*)

and these decreased rapidly thereafter. Heads and stems increased with increasing age.

Time of Cutting. Dry-matter production advances with increasing age of timothy plants until the seeds are fully ripe. Thereafter, there is a slight decrease in dry matter. The influence of time of cutting on total yields is very marked. Early cutting and very late cutting both mean a loss in yields. Cutting slightly past full bloom gave the highest total yield in

Ohio tests (see Table 146) irrespective of fertilizer treatment. The time of making the first cutting also influenced the yields from the second. Early cutting resulted in more aftermath production than late cutting, but these yields were low irrespective of treatment and would not warrant the expense involved in harvesting.

TABLE 146. EFFECT OF TIME OF CUTTING ON THE YIELD OF TIMOTHY HAY

| Stage of growth at time of first cutting | Hay yield, lb. per acre | | | |
| | First cutting | | Second cutting | |
	No treatment	Nitrate of soda	No treatment	Nitrate of soda
Beginning to head............	1,367	3,167	522	510
Fully headed................	1,880	3,799	457	475
Early bloom.................	2,296	4,215	396	385
Just past full bloom...........	2,396	4,300	245	278
Earliest heads straw-colored....	2,546	4,463	137	201
Seeds mature................	2,501	4,365	91	166
Average....................	2,164	4,051	308	372

SOURCE: *Ohio Agr. Expt. Sta. Bul.* 603 (1939).

It has been established that the percentage of protein is highest in early-cut timothy hay and that it decreases with advancing age. Greatest total amount of protein per acre is usually secured at the full-headed to early-bloom stages (see Table 147). Protein content seems to be a fair measure of quality and must be considered in determining the most favorable stages at which to cut timothy for hay. Since timothy hay is classified for

TABLE 147. PERCENTAGE OF PROTEIN AND COLOR IN HAY CUT AT DIFFERENT STAGES OF GROWTH TOGETHER WITH GRADE RATING

Stage of growth at cutting	Per cent protein*	Pounds of protein in hay	Per cent color	U.S. Grade
Beginning to head............	8.75	108	87	1 EG
Fully headed................	7.16	128	82	1 EG
Early bloom.................	6.53	136	82	1 EG
Just past full bloom...........	5.52	119	69	1
Earliest heads straw-colored....	5.28	116	46	2
Seeds mature................	5.06	110	33	3

SOURCE: *Ohio Agr. Expt. Sta. Bul.* 603 (1939).
* To reduce the percentages of protein to a moisture-free basis, divide by 0.875.

grade primarily on the basis of its green color, provided that it is free from other crops, the stage of harvest is also significant from this standpoint. Highest quality, as shown in the table, is regularly made from early-cut timothy and the quality decreases with advancing age of the plants.

Seeding in Alfalfa. Timothy is a relatively practical crop to use in re-seeding of thinning alfalfa fields. Alfalfa and other legumes usually do not develop from such plantings, but timothy seedings have given fairly good results (see Table 148). Either by spring toothing or a light disking

TABLE 148. COMPARISON OF METHODS OF SEEDING TIMOTHY IN A THIN ALFALFA FIELD

Treatment	Yield per acre			
	No timothy		Timothy sown	
	Total, lb.	Timothy in first cutting, %	Total, lb.	Timothy in first cutting, %
No preparation of soil. Timothy drilled........	7,750	0	7,960	49
Stand spring-toothed before seeding..........	6,880	0	7,720	60
Stand disked before seeding.................	8,000	0	8,860	71
Average...............	7,540	0	8,180	60

SOURCE: *Ohio Agr. Expt. Sta. Bimo. Bul.* 21 (1936).

a seedbed can be prepared and a fair stand of timothy established, depending on favorable climatic conditions. Drilling timothy has also been successful, as indicated in Table 148, but broadcasting on unprepared land usually results in failure. The timothy is best sown following the last cutting of alfalfa in the fall, but early spring seedings are also often successful.

VALUE AS FEED

Changes in feed analysis follow a fairly consistent pattern. Protein and ash content decrease with advancing age and fiber content increases, indicating a reduction in true feeding value. A rather complete analysis of the timothy plant made by Hosterman and Hall[5] shows that the leaves and heads are the most valuable constituents for feeding. The development of timothy heads partially compensates for the loss in feed value in the leaf blades with advancing age of the plant. Fiber content increased with advancing age in all constituents except the timothy heads.

Early-cut nitrogen-fertilized timothy apparently makes hay of equal feeding value to alfalfa. This type of timothy hay was used in feeding trials with milking cows at Cornell. The cows fed the timothy averaged just as high in milk and fat production as those fed the alfalfa hay. Both lots of animals consumed the same quantity of grain, hay, and silage, and other conditions were equal. This attests to the high feeding value of early-cut nitrogen-fertilized timothy. Timothy cut early also makes a good-quality silage high in carotene content, as tests in New Jersey[1] have shown. Holstein and Guernsey dairy heifers fed timothy silage alone made 0.67 pound gain a day, and when fed timothy silage and hay they gained 0.80 pound daily. These gains are considered satisfactory for growing heifers about 18 months of age.

While timothy stands tend to persist for many years, there is some evidence now to indicate that early cutting long continued soon results in partial loss of the timothy stand. Infestation by weeds increases rather rapidly, and this is followed by declining yields and loss of quality. There is much to be learned yet regarding the growing and managing of the timothy crop, but the basic work is completed. Early cutting is known to be essential for high quality. Yields and quality can both be increased by fertilizer applications, especially nitrogen, and feeding trials indicate the high value of good-quality timothy hay.

References

1. Bender, C. B., and H. H. Tucker: Timothy silage as a dairy feed, *N.J. Agr. Expt. Sta. Cir.* 374 (1937).
2. Evans, Morgan W.: The life history of timothy, *U.S. Dept. Agr. Bul.* 1450 (1927).
3. Evans, Morgan W.: Varieties of timothy suited to Ohio, *Ohio Agr. Expt. Sta. Bimo. Bul.* 31:136–141 (1946).
4. Evans, Morgan W., F. A. Welton, and Robert M. Salter: Timothy culture, *Ohio Agr. Expt. Sta. Bul.* 603 (1939).
5. Hosterman, W. H., and W. L. Hall: Time of cutting timothy: Effect on the proportion of leaf blades, leaf sheaths, stems, and heads, and on their crude protein, ether extract, and crude fiber content, *Jour. Amer. Soc. Agron.*, **30**:564–568 (1938).
6. Prince, F. S., T. G. Phillips, P. T. Blood, and G. P. Percival: Experiments with grass hay, *N.H. Agr. Expt. Sta. Bul.* 306 (1938).
7. Salisbury, G. W., and F. B. Morrison: Early cut, nitrogen-fertilized timothy hay as compared with alfalfa hay for feeding dairy cows, *Cornell Agr. Expt. Sta. Bul.* 604 (1938).
8. Sprague, Howard B., and Arthur Hawkins: Increasing the protein content of timothy, without sacrificing yield, by delayed applications of nitrogenous fertilizers, *N.J. Agr. Expt. Sta. Bul.* 644 (1938).
9. Trowbridge, P. F., L. D. Haigh, and C. R. Moulton: Studies of the timothy plant, *Mo. Agr. Expt. Sta. Res. Bul.* 20 (1915).
10. Willard, C. J.: Sowing timothy in thin alfalfa stands, *Ohio Agr. Expt. Sta. Bimo. Bul.* 21:93–95 (1936).

CHAPTER 15

MORE BROMEGRASS

Smooth bromegrass (*Bromus inermis*) was first cultivated in Hungary and introduced from there into California about 1884. After widespread trials by experiment stations in the North Central and Prairie regions, it was found to be a very satisfactory species regarding adaptation and production. The crop spread slowly but steadily in the dry-land areas of the northern prairie states from the time of its introduction there and it has since become one of the important forage species throughout the northern prairie and Intermountain states.

Although bromegrass was tried in the North Central states at an early date, it is only in recent years that it has gained prominence there. The tendency of the Midwestern farmer has been to plow up the prairie land for grain crops rather than to establish grass sod crops. The appearance of grain surpluses and soil deterioration caused by the grain system of farming is causing some interest throughout this area in the possibilities of grasslands. Brome seems well suited to this region, and gradually it is extending its frontiers of growth into the Northeast.

TYPES AND VARIETIES

There are two general types of bromegrass in America. These are known for convenience as Northern and Southern, but it would be better if varietal names were used. In the southern latitudes of the region where brome is adapted, the Southern type has proved superior to the Northern. There are at least four recognized varieties of this type: Fisher, Achenbach, Lincoln, and Elsberry. The productiveness of different strains of bromegrass may be compared from the records taken in Iowa and Nebraska, as shown in Table 149. The Southern varieties were similar in performance in these tests and were about 20 per cent more productive than the Northern type in Iowa. In Nebraska they were even more productive, possessed greater seedling vigor, matured earlier, and were more tolerant of heat and drought.

There are only two named Northern varieties, the Parkland and Superior, both having been developed in Canada. Parkland is a noncreeping type that tends to form bunches instead of a dense heavy sod such as is readily formed by the Southern varieties. The Northern varieties have not attained any wide degree of popularity in the Central and Southern regions.

148

Fig. 29. The Southern type bromegrass (*right*) is more vigorous than the Northern type (*left*) in New Jersey trials. (*New Jersey Agricultural Experiment Station.*)

TABLE 149. SUMMARY OF FORAGE YIELDS OF BROMEGRASS STRAINS IN IOWA AND NEBRASKA, PER CENT

Strain	Iowa	Strain	Nebraska
Southern:..................		Southern.................	100
Lincoln..................	101		
Fisher.................	100		
Achenbach.............	99		
Average.............	100		
Northern:...............		Northern.................	61
Western Iowa*..........	84		
Canadian*.............	81		
Northern commercial*....	72		
Average.................	79		

SOURCES: *Iowa Agr. Expt. Sta. Bul.* P75 (1945); *Jour. Amer. Soc. Agron.*, **35** (1943).
* Source of seed; not varieties.

They do possess superior seed qualities, being more plump and less chaffy than seed of the Southern type.

CHARACTERISTICS

Because of its palatability and high productive capacity, bromegrass seems certain to become of increasing significance among the forage crops of America. The crop is extremely winter hardy and moderately tolerant of drought. It is best adapted to well-drained fertile soils. Although it will grow remarkably under dry-land conditions, its productivity is much reduced.

Moisture Relationships. Early comparative tests of bromegrass with other grasses indicated its promise in the northern Great Plains region. Some data from this work are shown in Table 150. In North and South Dakota the bromegrass was superior to the other grasses tested, especially the timothy which is better adapted eastward. However, its superiority over the wheatgrasses varies with moisture relationships. In the Wyoming study where moisture was a limiting factor, the bromegrass proved to be the least productive.

TABLE 150. COMPARATIVE YIELDS OF BROME AND OTHER GRASSES IN THE NORTHERN PRAIRIE STATES

Grass	North Dakota yield, tons		South Dakota yield, lb.	Wyoming yield, lb.	
	Test 1	Test 2		Test 1	Test 2
Bromegrass............	2.09	3.31	2,279	530	844
Slender wheatgrass......	2.07	....	1,630	692	1,050
Timothy..............	1.39	2.30	.....	...	....
Crested wheatgrass......	....	....	2,140	825	978

SOURCES: *N.Dak. Agr. Expt. Sta. Cir.* 24 (1919); *U.S. Dept. Agr. Tech. Bul.* 307 (1932).

Although brome will survive and grow under dry-land conditions, its productiveness is closely correlated with rainfall. Since moisture conditions are critical in the prairie states, it is of interest to examine into the yields of bromegrass with advancing age, when conceivably its moisture needs would become greater. The data given in Table 151, in general,

TABLE 151. AVERAGE YIELDS OF AIR-DRY HAY OF BROMEGRASS 1 TO 4 YEARS AFTER SEEDING AT PLACES NAMED, POUNDS PER ACRE

Station	Method of seeding	1st year	2d year	3d year	4th year
Moccasin, Montana.........	Close drills	2,538	3,059	1,399	1,528
Havre, Montana............	Rows	1,118	2,123	2,410	982
	Close drills	1,208	1,708	1,770	875
Sheridan, Wyoming.........	Rows	2,560	2,540	2,557	2,053
	Close drills	1,760	1,440	980	460
Average.................	....	1,837	1,974	1,645	1,180

SOURCE: *U.S. Dept. Agr. Tech. Bul.* 307 (1932).

indicate the highest yields in the first and second year of the stand. By the fourth year in the prairie states bromegrass yields often deteriorate because of excessive root accumulations and also an increasing moisture deficiency. As shown in Illinois studies,[2] growth of the crop fluctuates considerably, depending on moisture supplies. During dry seasons there is a shortage of subsoil moisture, and this becomes severe as the crop stand improves and the crop requirements for moisture expand. Thus in the prairie states row plantings appear better able to produce vigorously and maintain production than do solid seedings.

Longevity. The long life of bromegrass is evident from the data in Table 152. In this Illinois study with a mixed pasture seeding, bromegrass

TABLE 152. PERSISTENCE OF BROMEGRASS IN A MIXED PASTURE SEEDING, PER CENT OF EACH PLANT SURVIVING

Sampling date	Bromegrass (40% in seeding)	Kentucky bluegrass (27% in seeding)	Redtop (20% in seeding)	White clover (13% in seeding)
July 8, 1936................	89.8	8.7	1.36	0
Apr. 19, 1938..............	60.2	38.5	1.00	0
Apr. 19, 1939..............	65.3	32.9	1.80	0
Aug. 21, 1939..............	57.1	42.9	Trace	0
Oct. 16, 1940..............	50.0	49.0	Trace	0
Nov. 3, 1941...............	52.8	46.0	Trace	0

SOURCE: *Ill. Agr. Expt. Sta. Bul.* 496 (1943).

thinned out somewhat, and bluegrass filled in. Nevertheless, brome constituted more than 50 per cent of the stand at the end of this 5-year test, and it actually seemed to be arriving at a condition of equilibrium. Redtop and white clover were not aggressive enough to compete with the brome and bluegrass. In the prairie states some fields of bromegrass have been in existence for 25 to 30 years or more. The longevity of any particular stand is partly due to grazing and cutting management. Frequent mowing or continued close grazing reduces bromegrass stands and encourages encroachment by bluegrass.

CULTURAL PRACTICES

One of the criticisms of this crop is said to be its slowness in developing a sod, 2 years being often required. Important factors in obtaining rapid come-up and development are seeding methods and soil fertility. Records at some stations indicate rapid establishment where fall-sown plantings developed so quickly that they were ready to graze early the following spring.

Seeding Methods. As with any crop, much of the success of bromegrass as a desirable forage crop depends on the management practices employed to produce a high-quality product.   A problem not completely solved as yet is the best method of seeding brome.   The seed is large and does not flow freely through normal seeding equipment.   Methods used therefore include seeding by hand, mixing with seed of a small grain and running through the grain hopper of a drill, or mixing with fertilizer at the rate of 100 to 200 pounds of fertilizer per acre and applying through the fertilizer attachment on grain drills.   Shallow planting and a firm seedbed are essential for good stands and also ensure more rapid establishment.

FIG. 30.   Bromegrass panicles.

Use in Mixtures. In the Midwest and East, bromegrass is usually grown with legume partners, the most important one being alfalfa.   The use of alfalfa contributes to the yield and quality of the hay produced.   Alfalfa and bromegrass together, as shown in Table 153, proved superior to either one alone and also to the alfalfa-timothy mixture in all three tests.   The mixture of alfalfa and bromegrass yielded two to three times more hay than bromegrass alone.   For productive long-lasting stands, wilt-resistant varieties of alfalfa must be sown.   Earlier it was thought that brome tended

TABLE 153. COMPARATIVE YIELDS PER ACRE OF ALFALFA, BROMEGRASS, AND ALFALFA MIXTURES, TONS

Crop	Wisconsin, 4-year ave.	Iowa, 3–4-year ave.	Illinois, 2-year ave.	New Jersey, 3-year ave.
Alfalfa and brome.......	3.75	3.77	2.72	3.59
Alfalfa and timothy......	2.89	3.30	....	3.43
Alfalfa.................	2.56	3.40	....	3.40
Bromegrass.............	1.96	1.33	0.95	1.48

to drive out alfalfa, but this was shown later to be caused by alfalfa wilt. Even in case the alfalfa thins out, a satisfying feature of this mixture is that the bromegrass tends to fill in, thus maintaining a thick stand of vegetation which keeps the weeds out.

The management of brome-alfalfa mixtures presents other problems. Frequent cuttings are now known to reduce alfalfa and thus to make conditions favorable for rapid increase in brome. Data are given in Table 154.

TABLE 154. PERCENTAGE OF HARVESTED BROMEGRASS, BY WEIGHT, FROM A BROMEGRASS–ALFALFA SEEDING AS AFFECTED BY TIME OF CUTTING

Stage at harvest	Bromegrass in first crop year	Bromegrass in third crop year
Full bloom (2 or 3 cuttings)...........	26	36
Prebud (4 cuttings).................	22	54

SOURCE: *Iowa Agr. Expt. Sta. Bul.* P75 (1945).

In this study it was shown that two or three cuttings a year permitted brome to increase by 10 per cent, but cutting four times seasonally resulted in a 32 per cent increase. Thus the more frequent or severe the cutting treatment, the more rapidly brome will increase in stand at the expense of the alfalfa. If carried too far, the brome may also thin out, resulting in bluegrass and weed infestation.

Response to Nitrogen. The effect of nitrogen fertilizer is as marked with bromegrass as with timothy. In the case of brome it is also considered to be a method of combating a sod-bound condition. Old stands of brome from which the legume has largely disappeared may be revitalized through renovation. This process consists of breaking up the old sod by disking or harrowing and reseeding the legume at the most opportune time.

Data on increased productivity following the addition of 250 pounds of ammonium sulfate per acre are given in Table 155. The application of

TABLE 155. EFFECT OF NITROGEN TREATMENTS ON BROMEGRASS YIELDS IN NEBRASKA, TONS

Treatment	Southern type	Northern type	Average
None.....................	1.15	0.81	0.98
Nitrogen added.............	1.41	1.08	1.25

SOURCE: *Jour. Amer. Soc. Agron.*, **35** (1943).

TABLE 156. YIELD IN POUNDS DRY WEIGHT PER ACRE CALCULATED FROM SQUARE-FOOT HARVESTS MADE IN 1938

Treatment	Hay	Stubble	Roots	Rhizomes	Total
June 25 harvest, 1937 seeding					
Check..................	1,300	1,550	1,370	80	4,300
N-fertilized*............	5,890	2,590	1,540	50	10,070
Shaded................	1,180	440	350	5	1,975
Mixture:					
Bromegrass............	1,100	750	760	20	2,630
Alfalfa................	4,080	710	1,100	. . .	5,890
Total................	5,180	1,460	1,860	20	8,520
July 5 harvest, 1936 seeding					
Check..................	2,170	3,280	3,400	340	9,190
N-fertilized*.............	4,930	2,950	2,940	240	11,060
Shaded................	2,580	1,290	1,580	70	5,520
Shaded N-fertilized*......	2,970	1,850	1,410	70	6,300
Aug. 2 harvest, 1937 seeding					
Check..................	1,730	1,030	2,570	90	5,420
N-fertilized*............	6,930	2,110	2,370	60	11,470
Shaded................	1,460	360	280	15	2,115
Mixture:					
Bromegrass..........	1,710	550	920	30	3,210
Alfalfa................	2,820	390	1,050	. . .	4,260
Total................	4,530	940	1,970	30	7,470

SOURCE: *Jour. Amer. Soc. Agron.*, **32** (1940).

* Ammonium sulfate at the rate of 150 pounds per acre was applied on Mar. 24 and July 2, 1938. The 1937 seeding was fertilized at the same rate on Sept. 20, 1937.

a nitrogen fertilizer thus resulted in an average increase of 0.27 ton of cured hay per acre.

An extensive test studying the effect of shade, nitrogen fertilizer, and a legume partner was conducted in Ohio. Data are given in Table 156. The yield of hay was several times as great on the nitrogen-treated plots as in the untreated ones. Shading decreased total yields compared with the checks. The yield of alfalfa and bromegrass together approached that from the nitrogen-treated plots. Highest yields of rhizomes were secured from the untreated plots, whereas nitrogen fertilizer retarded rhizome production. Shade and the alfalfa mixture also reduced the production of rhizomes. This information casts some light on methods of reducing the sod-bound characteristics of bromegrass stands.

Time of Cutting. The most favorable time of cutting brome for hay has been investigated in Washington. Data are given in Table 157.

TABLE 157. MOISTURE CONTENT AND CHEMICAL COMPOSITION OF SMOOTH BROMEGRASS CLIPPINGS AS RELATED TO HEIGHT OF PLANTS AND STAGE OF MATURITY

Date	Height of plants, in.	Stage of maturity	Chemical composition on dry-weight basis, %					
			Moisture content	Protein	Crude fiber	N-free extract	Ether extract	Ash
May 3.....	4.5	....	72.4	13.6	19.8	53.4	3.7	9.5
May 17....	10.0	Vegetative	73.5	13.8	21.8	52.4	3.4	9.1
June 15....	24.0	Heads well formed	71.7	8.2	30.2	51.1	2.4	8.1
June 30....	36.0	10% anthers	61.9	7.2	29.7	53.0	1.9	8.3
July 15....	36.0	Water stage of seed	52.8	6.9	28.9	55.3	1.4	7.6
July 30....	36.0	Seeds hard	43.9	5.1	29.8	54.4	1.8	8.9
Aug. 15....	36.0	Seeds fully mature	41.0	4.0	35.9	52.0	1.6	6.5

SOURCE: *Jour. Agr. Res.*, **63** (1941).

Moisture content, protein, fat, and ash decrease with advancing age. There is an increase in crude fiber, while the carbohydrate content remains relatively stable. This would indicate that bromegrass should be cut for hay sometime after the heading stage but before seed formation.

Digestible nutrients in bromegrass are highest when the plant is young in the pasture stage, and they decrease with advancing age.[6] The apparent digestibility of feed constituents is lowest in the hay-stage material. The rate of decrease in digestibility increases with advancing age.

Development of "Sod-bound" Condition. Another difficulty encountered frequently when bromegrass is seeded alone is a condition known as "sod-bound," in which the growth becomes stunted and yellowish after 3 or 4 years. Two explanations have been offered, namely, nitrogen starvation and root interactions. When the crop is grown with a legume, this condition does not develop. Since bromegrass is long-lived, it would seem best to use this crop for long rotations, such as are sought in the grassland system of farming, where planting with a legume partner would be very desirable.

Residual Effect on Soil. In an attempt to determine if bromegrass left toxic residues in the soil, a number of grasses were grown in flats in the greenhouse on Kansas soil which had previously grown bromegrass or wheat. All the grasses when grown on the bromegrass soil were pale green and lacking in vigor. The marked response from nitrogen fertilizers led

TABLE 158.　THE EFFECT OF BROMEGRASS SOD WITH AND WITHOUT NITROGEN FERTILIZER ON THE YIELD OF GRASSES

Previous crop	Average oven-dry yield for 6 grasses, grams	
	No treatment	Ammonium sulfate, 200 lb. per acre
Bromegrass, 4 years......	28.2	38.2
Bromegrass, 2 years......	25.0	39.8
Wheat (no bromegrass)....	35.1	53.7

SOURCE: *Jour. Amer. Soc. Agron.*, **34** (1942).

these investigators to conclude that the application of nitrogen fertilizer helped to overcome any negative influence exerted by the bromegrass sods. The large amount of carbonaceous material left by the bromegrass residues caused a temporary deficiency of nitrogen in the soil unless some were added as fertilizer.

Eradication. Bromegrass does not seem to be difficult to eradicate in the more humid sections of America where corn often follows a sod crop. In the prairie states, however, where wheat may follow, this appears to be a significant problem. Enough bromegrass grows back after plowing to reduce the yield of wheat. Studies on this problem indicate the best solution to be early plowing followed by successive harrowings of the seedbed to keep all green growth down. Early plowing in the summer previous to spring planting of wheat is most effective in destroying the bromegrass. Plowing late in the fall or early the next spring just before planting results in considerable yield reduction. The superior procedure is to cut bromegrass hay promptly after flowering and then to plow immediately in preparing the soil for wheat.

TABLE 159. TIME OF PLOWING IN RELATION TO CONTROL OF BROMEGRASS AND YIELD OF SPRING-PLANTED WHEAT

Time of plowing	Volunteer brome plants per sq. yd.	Average yield per acre, bu.
July 16, 1926.............	1.7	36.2
Aug. 16, 1926.............	3.0	36.2
Sept. 20, 1926............	4.7	37.5
Oct. 15, 1926.............	9.7	30.8
Apr. 25, 1927.............	17.3	29.4

SOURCE: *Sci. Agr.*, **10** (1930).

FEEDING VALUE

Feeding trials indicate that bromegrass mixed with alfalfa makes a valuable silage equal to that made from corn. Comparative analyses of the feeds used for such a trial in Indiana (see Table 160) show that the

TABLE 160. AVERAGE PER CENT COMPOSITION OF SILAGE USED IN FEEDING TRIALS

Components	Alfalfa-bromegrass silage	Corn silage
Moisture................	66.4	68.4
Crude protein...............	4.9	2.3
Ether extract............	2.3	1.4
Crude fiber..............	10.4	7.2
Nitrogen-free extract.......	16.0	20.7

SOURCE: *Jour. Dairy Sci.*, **26** (1943).

alfalfa-brome silage was twice as high in protein as the corn silage, but it contained less carbohydrates per 100 pounds. These silages were fed to milking cows, and the average daily milk production was similar for both silages. The corn silage maintained a somewhat better body weight of the animals.

ADVANTAGES

The use of bromegrass will undoubtedly increase in America, especially as it is grown with alfalfa. There are a number of advantages possessed by this grass.

1. It is highly productive, especially when grown with alfalfa on good soils.

2. It produces a fair growth of aftermath for hay or pasture.

3. It can be used for hay, pasture, silage, or seed production.

4. It is palatable after being fully headed and remains green at the mature stage longer than most other grasses.

References

1. Ahlgren, H. L., and F. V. Burcalow: Brome grass and alfalfa, *Wis. Agr. Ext. Cir.* 344 (1944).

2. Fulleman, R. F., W. L. Burlison, and W. G. Kamulade: Brome grass and brome grass mixtures, *Ill. Agr. Expt. Sta. Bul.* 496 (1943).

3. Myers, H. E., and Kling L. Anderson: Brome grass toxicity vs. nitrogen starvation, *Jour. Amer. Soc. Agron.*, **34**:770–773 (1942).

4. Newell, L. C., and F. D. Keim: Field performance of brome grass strains from different regional seed sources, *Jour. Amer. Soc. Agron.*, **35**:420–434 (1943).

5. Newton, R., and J. G. Mallock: Time of plowing brome grass sod in relation to the yield and quality of the succeeding wheat crop, *Sci. Agr.*, **10**:607–611 (1929–1930).

6. Sotola, Jerry: The chemical composition and apparent digestibility of nutrients in smooth brome grass harvested in three stages of maturity, *Jour. Agr. Res.*, **63**: 427–432 (1941).

7. Waldron, L. R.: Brome grass, slender wheatgrass and timothy, *N.Dak. Agr. Expt. Sta. Cir.* 24 (1919).

8. Waldron, L. R.: Some physical and chemical studies of certain clones and sibs of brome grass, *N.Dak. Agr. Expt. Sta. Bul.* 152 (1921).

9. Watkins, James M.: The growth habits and chemical composition of brome grass, *Bromus inermis* Leyss, as affected by different environmental conditions, *Jour. Amer. Soc. Agron.*, **32**:527–538 (1940).

10. Waugh, R. K., S. M.Hauge, J. W. Wilbur, and J. H. Hilton: A comparison of alfalfa–brome grass silage and corn silage for dairy cows, *Jour. Dairy Sci.*, **26**:921–928 (1943).

11. Westover, H. L., J. T. Sarvis, Leroy Moomew, George W. Morgan, John C. Thysell, and M. A. Bell: Crested wheatgrass as compared with brome grass, slender wheatgrass, and other hay and pasture crops for the Northern Great Plains, *U.S. Dept. Agr. Tech. Bul.* 307 (1932).

12. Wilbur, J. W., R. K. Waugh, S. M. Hauge, and J. H. Hilton: Alfalfa–brome grass silage for dairy cows, *Ind. Agr. Expt. Sta. Cir.* 285 (1943).

13. Wilsie, C. P., M. L. Peterson, and H. D. Hughes: Brome grass in Iowa, *Iowa Agr. Expt. Sta. Bul.* P75 (1945).

CHAPTER 16

LOWLAND GRASSES: REDTOP, REED CANARY GRASS, AND MEADOW FOXTAIL

There is a large acreage of low, moist, and wet soil in the United States which is adapted to hay or pasture crops. Some of it is already performing this function, but much progress remains to be made. As previously indicated, alsike and ladino clover are well adapted to such soils. Grasses having lowland potentials suitable for growing with these legumes include redtop, reed canary grass, and meadow foxtail.

REDTOP (*Agrostis alba*)

Redtop was recognized as an important agricultural grass in New Jersey as early as 1804. It is the only grass of promise for hay purposes in the genus *Agrostis*. It is a perennial grass, making a coarse, loose turf and maturing somewhat later than timothy. Redtop will survive for a great many years. Fields lasting for 5 to 20 years have been reported, depending on soil and climatic conditions. It is versatile and can be used for hay, pasture, or grass silage. Much of the hay area in the New England states is composed at least in part of this species. Actually, redtop is more useful for lawns and turf purposes than it is for forage.

Adaptation. No grass will grow more successfully than redtop under a greater variety of conditions. It will grow on strongly acid soils where other grasses will fail and on a wide variety of soils ranging from wet to dry, fertile to infertile. It is the most important grass in that part of southern Illinois where the soils are "sour," poorly drained, and possess impervious hardpan subsoils. Redtop thrives with an abundance of moisture and will grow on land too wet for most other tame grasses. The region of adaptation as shown in Fig. 31 extends from the Northern Atlantic states westward to Kansas and thence northward to Minnesota. Scattered local areas of redtop are found in the Western states in areas where an adequate moisture supply exists. No improved varieties have been produced as yet.

Yields. Yields of redtop grown in pure stands have been reported from several experiment stations, a few of which are given in Table 161. These yields are fairly good for straight grass hays, but much better results are obtained from redtop when it is sown with a legume partner (see Table 162). Thus in Tennessee, West Virginia, and New York the yields of hay were

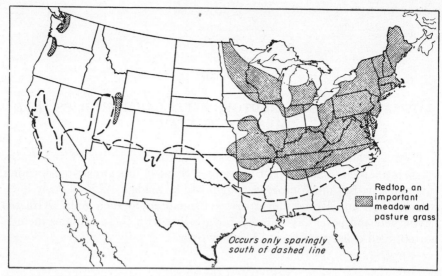

Fig. 31. Distribution of redtop in the United States. (*Illinois Agricultural Experiment Station.*)

TABLE 161. Yields of Redtop Hay at Various Locations in America, Pounds per Acre

Ohio	Kansas	Illinois	Michigan	North Carolina
5,634	3,399	3,600	3,493	2,940

Source: From Piper, "Forage Plants and Their Culture," rev. ed., copyright, 1924, by The Macmillan Company and used with their permission.

TABLE 162. Yields of Redtop Alone and with Legume Partners

Crop	Tennessee, 3-year ave., tons	West Virginia, 3-year ave., tons	New York, 2-year ave., lb.
Redtop......................	1.67	1.29	2,243
Alsike and redtop................	2.83	2.45*	3,264†
Red clover and redtop............	3.25	....	.....

* Also timothy.
† Also timothy and red clover.

increased 1½ to 2 times by growing redtop with alsike or red clover. The quality of hay produced was undoubtedly higher.

Although redtop grows on poor, wet, and acid soils, it will respond favorably to soil-improvement practices. Results of a residual fertilizer study are given in Table 163. The addition of lime, phosphate, and potash all

TABLE 163. EFFECT OF SOIL TREATMENT ON YIELDS PER ACRE OF REDTOP HAY*

Odin field		Newton field	
Treatment	Data for 1 year, lb.	Treatment	Data for 3-year average, lb.
Check.............	940	L...............	1,280
L................	1,890	LP†.............	1,420
LP...............	2,240	LP‡.............	1,660
LPK.............	3,230		

SOURCE: *Ill. Agr. Expt. Sta. Bul.* 404 (1934).
* Residual fertility.
† 200 lb. of rock phosphate per acre each year.
‡ 400 lb. of rock phosphate per acre each year.

resulted in an increase in hay yields in these Illinois tests. Very likely the use of a complete fertilizer mixture would have increased the yields even further.

Seeding. Fall seedings of redtop are usually considered superior to spring seedings. Data as given in Table 164 show an increase in hay and

TABLE 164. INFLUENCE OF TIME OF SEEDING ON YIELDS OF REDTOP SEED AND HAY, POUNDS

Season harvested	Seeded in October, 1926		Seeded in February, 1927	
	Seed	Hay	Seed	Hay
1927	42	380	30	300
1928	69	2,220	49	2,220

SOURCE: *Ill. Agr. Expt. Sta. Bul.* 404 (1934).

seed yields for the fall seeding over the spring seeding in the first year of harvest. By the second year, the difference in hay yield had disappeared, but seed production was still in favor of the fall planting.

Feed Value. The comparative feed analysis of redtop and timothy is given in Table 165. Redtop compares favorably with timothy, being a little higher in protein and carbohydrates but lower in fat content. The hay is said to be tough and not so popular as timothy in the hay markets.

TABLE 165. PER CENT COMPOSITION AND DIGESTIBLE NUTRIENTS OF REDTOP AND TIMOTHY HAYS

Hay	Water	Ash	Crude protein	Crude fiber	Nitrogen-free extract	Fats
Redtop.......	8.9	5.2	7.9	28.6	47.5	1.9
Timothy......	12.5	5.4	6.8	28.3	44.3	2.7

SOURCE: *Ill. Agr. Expt. Sta. Bul.* 404 (1934).

REED CANARY GRASS (*Phalaris arundinaceae*)

This grass apparently is native to the temperate regions of Europe, Asia, and North America. It was reported first cultivated in England in 1824 and later in Germany about 1850. Cultivation in America probably began sometime after the European culture and somewhere along the North

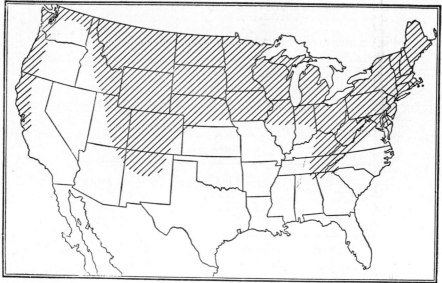

FIG. 32. Region of the United States to which reed canary grass is adapted. (*Bureau of Plant Industry, Soils and Agricultural Engineering, U.S. Department of Agriculture.*)

Atlantic coast. Since that time, however, Oregon, Washington, and northern California have taken the lead and now grow the largest acreages of reed canary. It is found widely scattered along stream banks and lake shores throughout the region where it thrives. The first known planting is credited to Edward Schmidt of Mankato, Minnesota, who purchased 2 pounds of seed from the John A. Salzer Seed Company, LaCrosse, Wisconsin, and sowed it in the spring of 1899. Only two varieties, one a synthetic hybrid, Ioreed, and the other a selection named Superior adapted to uplands, have been produced in America by plant breeding.

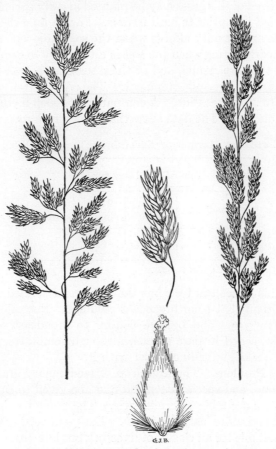

FIG. 33. Panicles and seed of reed canary grass.

The acreage appears to be expanding in the Eastern and Midwestern states, where many successful stands are being obtained and the forage yields are usually high. The general region of adaptation is given in Fig. 32. Moisture conditions must be favorable for maximum growth, or water must be supplied by irrigation.

Adaptation. Fertile, moist, and even swampy soils are ideally suited habitats, but saline areas and alkali soils are unsuited. Although naturally adapted to low, wet soils, reed canary also makes good growth on upland, well-drained soils provided that they possess adequate lime and sufficient moisture for spring and early-summer growth. Reed canary is favored by cool, moist weather but withstands periods of drought, high temperature, and extreme cold very successfully. Cold winter weather actually seems to benefit the grass.

Planting. Seed of this grass may be planted in early spring, late summer or in the late fall just prior to hard freezes. In wet land the seedbed must be prepared as opportunity affords when the soil is dry enough. Planting in late fall or early spring when the soil is alternately freezing and thawing seems to give the best results, and at these seasons the soil is usually firm enough to hold machines and equipment. The crop is often sown broadcast or in rows 16 to 24 inches wide. A comparison of such methods of seeding is given in Table 166. The data show that the 48-inch rows gave the high-

TABLE 166. EFFECT OF METHOD OF SEEDING ON YIELD OF REED CANARY GRASS

Tons of cured hay per acre

Broadcast	16-in. rows	24-in. rows	48-in. rows
3.3	3.9	3.9	4.6

SOURCE: *Wisc. Agr. Expt. Sta. Cir.* 264 (1933).

est yields in this Wisconsin test, but the hay was described as coarser and less desirable than that from broadcast seedings. Row plots fill in completely in a few years and become similar to broadcast seedings. The crop is usually seeded in pure stands, although some attempts are being made to grow alsike and ladino clover with it.

The Quality Problem. The first crop of reed canary grass tends to be coarse and heavy, and special attention must be given to early harvesting to reduce this undesirable characteristic. The second crop maintains a finer stemmed and more leafy condition. Early-cut reed canary grass has been found palatable for all classes of livestock but late-cut, coarse material low in protein seems best suited for horses or idle stock. Cattle seem to need a short period to acclimate themselves to the grass before they will consume it readily. Many growers harvest seed from the first crop before cutting it for hay, but this is undesirable from the standpoint of making good hay.

Time of Cutting. Studies on producing highest possible quality hay from this grass have been conducted at several stations. Data from a Minnesota study are given in Table 167. Considering quality as measured by chemical analysis, the best time to cut reed canary is between the time the first panicles appear and the majority of them are out. This gives a

Fig. 34. Under favorable conditions reed canary grass is a tall, vigorous species.

TABLE 167. AVERAGE YIELDS OF REED CANARY HAY (15 PER CENT MOISTURE) PER ACRE

Stage of maturity when cut	Height, in.	Dry matter at cutting, %	Hay per acre, tons	Crude protein, %	Crude protein per acre, lb.
First cutting:					
Few panicles showing...	20	22.4	1.10	14.0	313
Many panicles showing.	45	25.4	1.66	12.4	407
Few seeds ripe.........	50	27.8	2.58	11.1	573
All seeds ripe.........	50	29.6	2.48	11.0	526
All seed shattered......	50	28.4	2.41	10.9	524
Second cutting..........	36	27.8	1.92	12.1	469

SOURCE: *Minn. Agr. Expt. Sta. Bul.* 263 (1939).

medium yield of hay of good protein content that is said to possess palatability equivalent to second-cut material. Early harvesting also permits the second crop to develop more quickly, resulting in a high yield of aftermath. Similar studies conducted at Madison and Coddington, Wisconsin, are shown graphically in Fig. 35. Protein content was very high in these studies, ranging from 21.6 per cent when the grass was 13 inches tall to 11.3 per cent at the seed-ripe stage. The yields ranged from 2 to 3½ tons per acre.

Value of Leaves. The leaves are by far the best source of feed nutrients. These vary in protein content and other constituents from top to bottom

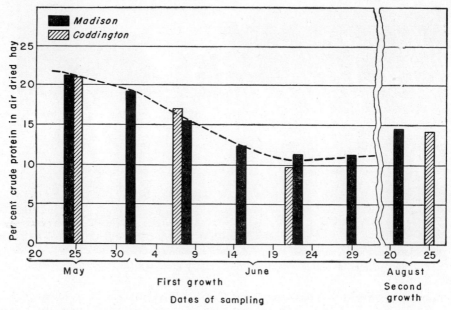

Fig. 35. The decrease in crude protein content of reed canary grass hay with advancing maturity. (*Wisconsin Agricultural Experiment Station.*)

on the plants. The greenest leaves are found on the tops, and the color becomes less intense on those leaves nearer the base of the stem, some of these being brownish and lacking in green. A comparison of protein in the various hay constituents (see Table 168) shows that leaves nearest the inflorescence contain two to three times as much protein as those near the base of the stem, presumably due to their greener color. The culms increased in protein content slightly with advancing age, and the leaves and

TABLE 168. PERCENTAGE OF PROTEIN ON A MOISTURE-FREE BASIS IN THE CULMS, INFLORESCENCES, AND LEAF BLADES OF REED CANARY GRASS ON DIFFERENT DATES

Plant part	June 16	June 23	June 29	July 7	July 14	July 20
Culms.....................	....	2.8	2.6	3.1	3.6	3.6
Inflorescences...........	....	10.7	6.8	5.5	5.4	4.9
Leaf blade:						
1.....................	14.8	14.5	13.0	13.9	12.4	9.1
2.....................	16.8	17.6	13.4	14.4	14.6	13.4
3.....................	17.2	15.1	14.8	14.4	13.4	11.5
4.....................	14.8	15.1	12.5	12.2	10.7	8.7
5.....................	12.8	12.5	9.1	9.2	7.6	6.1
6.....................	8.8	9.9	5.5	6.1	7.3	4.7
7.....................	4.9	4.0	4.0	3.7	5.9	4.3

SOURCE: *Jour. Amer. Soc. Agron.*, **33** (1941).

inflorescences decreased. Another rather complete analysis[1] of the plant for protein and dry-matter values showed the protein content decreased with advancing age in all plant constituents in the first cutting. In studies made on the second and third cuttings this feed constituent has averaged over 15 per cent, which is very high for a grass hay.

Nitrogen Treatment. The protein content of reed canary grass can be increased considerably by adding nitrogen fertilizer. In the test reported in Table 169 the average increase in protein content was 1.8 per cent over

TABLE 169. COMPARISON OF PROTEIN CONTENT IN REED CANARY GRASS WITH AND WITHOUT NITROGEN FERTILIZER, PER CENT

Date of sampling	Without nitrogen fertilizer	With nitrogen fertilizer	Difference
June 1.............	10.8	15.1	4.3
June 8.............	10.7	13.1	2.4
June 23............	10.0	14.4	4.4
June 30............	10.7	12.6	1.9
July 7.............	10.9	10.6	−0.3
July 15............	9.8	9.6	−0.2
July 21............	9.8	9.8	0.0
Average............	10.4	12.2	1.8

SOURCE: *Jour. Agr. Res.*, **40** (1940).

the untreated reed canary. The reed canary grown without nitrogen fertilizer yielded 0.5 ton of hay per acre and 66 pounds of protein; with nitrogen the yield was 1.5 tons of hay and 248 pounds of protein. Since reed canary competes primarily with timothy in areas where it is used, the two were compared in another test. Reed canary grass produced 78 pounds more protein per acre than timothy under the nitrogen treatment, while the hay yields were the same.

Feeding Value. Comparisons of the feeding value of reed canary indicate a favorable rating for the grass. In Table 170 the data indicate that reed

TABLE 170. COMPARATIVE ANALYSES OF REED CANARY GRASS AND OTHER FORAGE CROPS, PER CENT

Forage	Dry matter	Ash	Crude protein	Crude fiber	Fat	Other carbohy-drates
Reed canary hay....	92.9	4.79	4.85	27.2	1.06	55.0
Timothy hay........	88.4	4.90	6.20	29.8	2.50	45.0
Reed canary silage...	30.5	1.97	1.48	11.2	0.58	15.3
Corn silage.........	26.3	1.70	2.10	6.3	0.80	15.4

SOURCE: *U.S. Dept. Agr. Farmers' Bul.* 1602 (1929).

canary is equivalent to or better than timothy as hay.   However, the silage seems to be somewhat inferior to that from corn, being lower in protein and higher in fiber content.   Yields of silage may range from 15 to 20 tons per acre, and the silage is relished by both dairy and beef cattle.

FIG. 36.   Meadow foxtail.   (*Bureau of Plant Industry, Soils, and Agricultural Engineering, U.S. Department of Agriculture.*)

MEADOW FOXTAIL   (*Alopecurus pratensis*)

Very few studies have been made of the culture and adaptation of this grass.   It appears to be best adapted for wet soils and cool moist conditions as found in the extreme Northeast and Pacific Northwest.   The grass is exceptionally early in spring growth, and its heavy leaf production at the base of the stems makes it more valuable for pasture; yet it is used to a limited extent for hay.   It is not drought-resistant but appears to be extremely winter hardy.

Yields.   Yields of hay have been reported from a few stations, indicating that where it is adapted the yields approach those from timothy.   In Oregon tests, meadow foxtail produced 4.88 tons of green material per acre, compared with 3.63 tons for timothy.

Mixed Plantings.   Meadow foxtail produces an open type of growth, and it is, therefore, suggested for use in mixed plantings.   In Washington the mixtures given in Table 172 are recommended, depending on moisture conditions.   The legumes best suited for companions appear to be ladino and alsike clover and birdsfoot trefoil.   The seed is light, adhesive, and difficult to plant by usual methods.   This is a major limiting factor in its utilization as a forage crop.

TABLE 171.   YIELDS OF HAY PER ACRE FROM MEADOW FOXTAIL AT VARIOUS STATIONS

Utah, lb.	New Jersey, lb.	Michigan, lb.	Ontario, lb.	Oregon, tons
1,500	1,965	2,906	3,100	4.88*

SOURCE: From Piper, "Forage Plants and Their Culture," rev. ed., copyright, 1924, by The Macmillan Company and used with their permission.

* Green forage.   *Oreg. Agr. Expt. Sta. Bul.* 427 (1945).

Feeding Value.   A study of meadow foxtail conducted in Canada casts some light on the nutritive value of the grass.   The data given in Table 173 show that the protein content is higher than that normally found in timothy and the fiber content lower.   The grass thus appears to be an excel-

Table 172. Meadow Foxtail Mixtures Suggested for Western Washington

Low, wet areas	Low, well-drained areas	Irrigated lands
Meadow foxtail Redtop Birdsfoot trefoil	Meadow foxtail Perennial ryegrass Orchard grass Alsike clover Ladino clover	Meadow foxtail Perennial ryegrass Alta fescue Kentucky bluegrass Ladino clover

Source: *Wash. Agr. Ext. Cir.* 82 (1944).

Table 173. Yields per Acre of Dry Matter and Feed Constituents in Grass, Chiefly Meadow Foxtail

Cutting treatment	Dry matter, lb.	Total crude protein, lb.	Crude protein, %	Crude fiber, %
Every week............	2,918	439	21.2	19.4
Every 2 weeks..........	3,344	466	18.6	20.5
Every 3 weeks..........	4,304	571	17.2	22.1
Once a year............	5,311	520	10.2	28.7

Source: *Jour. Agr. Sci.*, **20** (1930).

lent source of protein, and since it is relatively low in fiber content its feed value is enhanced.

Meadow foxtail will probably be used only in a limited way until better strains are made available and until the seeding problem can be solved.

References

1. Alway, Frederick J., and G. H. Nesom: Protein content of reed canary grass on peat soils, *Jour. Agr. Res.*, **40:**297–320 (1930).
2. Arny, A. C., R. E. Hodgson, and G. H. Nesom: Reed canary grass for hay and pastures, *Minn. Agr. Expt. Sta. Buls.* 252 and 263 (1929 and 1930).
3. Burlison, W. L., C. L. Stewart, R. C. Ross, and O. L. Whalen: Production and marketing of redtop, *Ill. Agr. Expt. Sta. Bul.* 404 (1934).
4. Evans, Morgan W., and J. Elbert Ely: Growth habits of reed canary grass, *Jour. Amer. Soc. Agron.*, **33:**1017–1027 (1941).
5. Holden, E. D., and A. R. Albert: Reed canary grass for Wisconsin lowlands, *Wis. Agr. Ext. Cir.* 264 (1933).
6. Law, Alvin G., and I. M. Ingham: Grasses for greater production in western Washington, *Wash. Agr. Ext. Cir.* 82 (1944).
7. Mooers, C. A.: Clovers and grasses for hay and pasture, *Tenn. Agr. Expt. Sta. Bul.* 165 (1938).
8. Rampton, H. H.: Alta fescue production in Oregon, *Oreg. Agr. Expt. Sta. Bul.* 427 (1945).
9. Schoth, H. A.: Reed canary grass, *U.S. Dept. Agr. Farmers' Bul.* 1602 (1929).
10. Shutt, Frank T., S. N. Hamilton, and H. H. Selwyn: The protein content of grass, chiefly meadow foxtail as influenced by frequency of cutting, *Jour. of Agr. Sci.* **20:**126–134 (1930).

CHAPTER 17

ORCHARD GRASS, TALL OAT, AND TALL FESCUE

Although the grasses discussed in this chapter are grown on fewer acres than timothy and bromegrass, they nevertheless are important in economic forage production. Orchard grass and tall oatgrass are adapted latitudinally to a large area south of the timothy-clover region and overlapping northward into that area. The tall fescue has gained in popularity particularly in Oregon and Washington, where it is proving highly productive.

ORCHARD GRASS (*Dactylis glomerata*)

No records are available to indicate the time or place that orchard grass was introduced into America. It was cultivated in Virginia prior to 1760, and in that year seed was sent back to England. The crop has become widely cultivated in Europe, where it is now generally known as cocksfoot.

Characteristics. Orchard grass begins growth earlier in the spring than timothy and continues more strongly into the summer period, being less sensitive to heat and drought. It is less resistant to winterkilling than timothy but more cold-tolerant than Bermuda grass. In comparative tests in Missouri, orchard grass made fair growth at a soil and air temperature of 40°F., whereas Bermuda grass made no growth and was actually injured by the 40° temperature. The optimum temperature for growth of orchard grass proved to be 70°F., although good growth was made between 50 and 80°F. Root growth increased from 40 to 60°F. and was maintained at 70°. The ability of this grass to grow well at midsummer temperatures is demonstrated by the large quantity of aftermath it produces during that period. It succeeds better in shade than any other cultivated grass used for hay.

Orchard grass matures slightly earlier than alfalfa and red or alsike clover. It is 2 to 3 weeks earlier than timothy in this respect. The hay is somewhat coarse, and aside from producing a larger second growth than timothy, it is doubtful that it could compete successfully with this latter crop under most conditions. Another disadvantage in making hay from orchard grass is its early maturity, making haying too early for favorable curing weather.

In the southern part of the region where orchard grass is adapted it may be safely seeded in the fall. In the northern area, however, because of its tendency to winterkill it must be seeded in late summer or early spring. The seed is somewhat chaffy and unless well cleaned is difficult to sow with regular seeding equipment.

Loam soils of moderate to good fertility are most satisfactory, but orchard grass will also grow well on light, dry soils and even on poor soils. It responds readily to lime and fertilizer applications.

Fig. 37.   Panicles of orchard grass.   (*New Jersey Agricultural Experiment Station.*)

Yields.   Comparative data from yield trials of orchard grass and timothy at several stations are reported in Table 174.   These data indicate that orchard grass is capable of making good yields where conditions favor its growth.   In the Tennessee tests it outyielded timothy by 0.44 ton of hay per acre.   The aftermath cutting was not considered in these tests.   This might well have improved the status of orchard grass compared with

TABLE 174.   COMPARISON OF TIMOTHY AND ORCHARD GRASS YIELDS, TONS OF CURED HAY PER ACRE

Hay	West Virginia, 7-year ave.	Oregon, 5-year ave.	Tennessee, 2-year ave.
Orchard grass........	1.44	1.62	1.78
Timothy............	2.35	1.99	1.34

timothy. Practical farmers and forage-crop investigators generally agree, however, that orchard grass is better suited for pasture than for hay and that yields are much higher when used for grazing than when used for hay. It makes good-quality silage when properly preserved.

Orchard grass performs best when grown with a legume partner, of which a number are well suited. Results of several tests with alfalfa and red clover are given in Table 175. Mixing with either of these legumes resulted

TABLE 175. ACRE YIELDS OF ORCHARD GRASS ALONE AND WHEN GROWN WITH A LEGUME PARTNER, TONS

Crop	West Virginia, 3-year ave.	Tennessee, 3-year ave.
Orchard grass.....................	1.48	0.73
Orchard grass with red clover........	1.74	3.12
Orchard grass with alfalfa...........	1.85	....

SOURCES: *W.Va. Agr. Expt. Sta. Bul.* 250 (1932); *Tenn. Agr. Expt. Sta. Bul.* 165 (1938).

in increased hay yields. Ladino clover is often planted with orchard grass in the Northeast as a multiple-purpose mixture especially valuable for pasturing.

Yields of dry matter and protein in orchard grass hay may be greatly increased by the timely application of a suitable soluble nitrogen fertilizer, according to tests conducted in Virginia (see Table 176). These data show

TABLE 176. EFFECT OF NITROGEN ON THE YIELD OF HAY AND PROTEIN CONTENT OF ORCHARD GRASS

Nitrogen application per acre, lb.	Yield of hay, lb. per acre	Protein	
		%	Lb. per acre
0	1,099	9.83	99
25	1,985	9.45	169
50	2,957	9.98	268
75	3,842	10.53	371
100	5,099	11.37	528

SOURCE: *Va. Agr. Expt. Sta. Bul.* 404 (1947).

that yields were increased several fold by the addition of various quantities of nitrogen fertilizer. Equally important, the protein harvested per acre was increased from 99 pounds with no added nitrogen to 528 pounds on those plots given 100 pounds of nitrogen equivalent.

Comparison with Timothy. Factors of particular interest in considering orchard grass are related to the growth habits of this grass. When compared with timothy they appear to be as follows:

1. It is bunchy and thus less suited than timothy to growing in pure cultures.
2. It is better adapted southward because of better summer growth.
3. More difficulties are encountered in seeding, especially when mixing with legume seeds.
4. It produces several times more aftermath than timothy.
5. Early maturity makes it less desirable for hay, since weather is often unfavorable to curing.

A number of plant breeders are attempting to produce varieties of this grass that possess greater winter hardiness, disease resistance, and higher productivity than is presently available in any strains. Late-maturing types are also being sought as well as strains especially adapted for pasture purposes.

Feed Value. Orchard grass hay compares favorably with timothy from a feed-analysis standpoint, a comparison of the two being given in Table 177. Orchard grass was higher than timothy in crude protein and carbo-

TABLE 177. COMPARISON OF ORCHARD GRASS AND TIMOTHY HAY FOR FEED NUTRIENTS

Hay	Total dry matter in 100 lb.	Digestible nutrients in 100 lb.			
		Crude protein	Carbohydrates	Fat	Total
Orchard grass.......	88.4	4.7	41.1	1.6	49.4
Timothy............	85.1	2.4	39.0	1.4	44.6

hydrates and thus in total feeding value. Since feed analysis varies greatly depending on the vegetative stage at harvest and other factors, more complete information is needed for critical comparisons. Because orchard grass is more stemmy than timothy, it is probably less palatable.

TALL OATGRASS (*Arrhenatherum elatius*)

This is perhaps one of the most interesting of the hay grasses. It is a tall vigorous perennial resembling the regular oat plant in general appearance, whence its name. The plants often reach a height of 3 to 5 feet, and it grows in bunches with a rather open habit, making it a good grass partner for shorter species.

Tall oat is primarily a hay grass, but it is also useful for pasture. It is well adapted for cutting two or three times a year. It grows back more rapidly and produces more aftermath where it is acclimated than any other cultivated hay grass of perennial habit, being almost equal to alfalfa in this respect. It is seldom seeded with other grasses, but it is sown with the clovers, lespedezas, and alfalfa. The most common use is in the West in mixture with sweetclover for short-rotation pastures. Since it matures 10 days to 3 weeks earlier than medium red clover, there are certain disadvantages in using it for hay in such mixtures.

Fig. 38. Tall oatgrass. (*Bureau of Plant Industry, Soils and Agricultural Engineering, U.S. Department of Agriculture.*)

Adaptation. The grass was cultivated in Europe during the eighteenth century, and records of its use are found in Massachusetts in 1807 and South Carolina in 1821. Since that time tall oatgrass has spread and become climatically adapted to the same geographic region as orchard grass. Some is also grown in the Pacific Northwest, but the region lying between and overlapping into the clover-timothy and annual legume regions seems to be its natural home in this country. It is also promising at high elevations in the intermountain region of the Western states.

From the standpoint of soil adaptation it will grow on poor, sandy, and even gravelly soils, and probably better under such conditions than any other hay grass. It thrives best on fertile, well-drained soils and responds readily to lime and fertilizer applications. It is drought- and heat-tolerant, but unadapted to shady conditions or wet soils.

Yields. Acre yields of tall oatgrass have been reported by a number of the experiment stations, a few of these being given in Table 178. These yields are relatively good, indicating the high potential value of the grass.

Because of its bunching habit and the high cost of seed, tall oatgrass is usually suggested for growing in mixtures rather than straight stands. This practice appears to increase yields. The results of two tests in which tall oatgrass was grown alone and with red clover are given in Table 179.

TABLE 178. YIELD PER ACRE OF CURED HAY FROM TALL OATGRASS, TONS

N. Carolina	Louisiana	Kansas	Virginia	Tennessee
1.50	1.70	1.23	1.86	2.30

TABLE 179. DRY MATTER YIELDS PER ACRE FROM TALL OATGRASS GROWN ALONE AND WITH RED CLOVER, TONS

Crop	Tennessee, 3-year ave.	West Virginia, 3-year ave.
Tall oat................	1.81	2.61
Tall oat and red clover......	2.86	2.63

SOURCES: *Tenn. Agr. Expt. Sta. Bul.* 165 (1938); *W.Va. Agr. Expt. Sta. Bul.* 250 (1932).

A strong increase in yield resulted from adding red clover in the Tennessee test, and a slight increase was found in the West Virginia trial.   A more complete analysis of the value of tall oatgrass in various mixtures is reported from further West Virginia trials.[3]   In five mixtures containing tall oatgrass but not timothy the average yield was 2.58 tons of dried hay per acre.   The mixtures containing timothy but no tall oat averaged 2.27 tons, indicating a yield advantage in using tall oat.   The two mixtures containing tall oat and timothy but no orchard grass averaged 2.84 tons; the mixtures containing tall oat and orchard grass but no timothy, 2.41 tons; and those containing timothy and orchard grass but no tall oat, 2.1 tons per acre.   Tall oatgrass was thus shown to be superior to both orchard grass and timothy in yield capacity.   In the legume-grass mixtures the highest average yields were obtained when tall oatgrass was used as one of the components.

It is suggested that tall oatgrass be cut for hay after heading and just prior to blooming or at least in early bloom, because the stems become woody and unpalatable shortly after the plants bloom.   No chemical analysis nor total dry-matter yields have been presented to substantiate this suggestion, but in this respect it is probably similar to other grasses. The hay cures readily because of the hollow, rather light, narrow stems.

Seed Problems.   Reasons for slow acceptance of this grass even in the regions where it is adapted appear to be closely related to undesirable characteristics of the seed.   The seed is expensive because it is not produced in volume.   It is difficult to seed because the attached appendages, including the lemma and palea plus the long pliable awn, prevent free flow through normal seeding equipment.   Hand seeding, which is slow, tedious, and expensive, has been resorted to for the most part.

Recent attempts to solve the seeding problem have met with encouraging results. Dehulling the seed by mechanical methods has been tried. This leaves a caryopsis the size of timothy. The effects of dehulling as given in Table 180 show considerable reduction in germination, on the order of 15 to 20 per cent. The method, however, appears to hold real promise as a seeding aid until superior techniques are developed.

TABLE 180. THE RETENTION OF VIABILITY IN PROCESSED SEED OF TALL OATGRASS AS INFLUENCED BY DEGREE OF MILLING

Date of test	Months after processing	Duration of germination, days	Germination, %			
			Unmilled check	Milled once	Milled twice	Seed 100% dehulled
January, 1939	..	13	88.0	....	90.0	....
March 25, 1940	14	7	96.0	90.5	92.0	79.5
March 26, 1941	26	13	94.5	85.0	87.0	75.0
January 23, 1943	48	25	92.5	89.0	74.5	74.0
December 13, 1943	59	16	88.5	85.5	74.5	67.0

SOURCE: *Jour. Amer. Soc. Agron.*, **36** (1944).

TALL FESCUE (*Festuca elatior arundinacea*)

During recent years tall fescue has found its greatest support in Oregon, Washington, Tennessee, and Kentucky, where it is being recommended especially for pasture but also for meadow purposes. No record of its introduction into America has been found, but it is said to have come here at an early date. Meadow fescue (*Festuca elatior*), a relative of tall fescue, has been grown sporadically over the timothy-clover region, where it has come in rather naturally, seldom being seeded. It is found especially on low, moist, fertile areas throughout this region. It has been regularly cultivated since 1877 in Kansas, where a considerable seed-production enterprise developed but later declined and now is of no significance.

Varieties. There are only two known varieties of tall fescue. The Alta variety was developed in Oregon and has become popular in Oregon and Washington, where it is widely planted in mixtures. A selection found growing wild in Kentucky has been named Kentucky 31.

The grass produces a rather open type of growth and possesses an abundance of bottom leafiness. It develops an open sod, is tolerant of moderately alkaline and acid soils, and fairly tolerant of drought. It can be grown successfully on poorly drained soils with impervious, tight subsoils.

Yields. Records of hay production of meadow fescue are available from a number of stations, some being reported in Table 181. Yields in these trials are inferior to more common grasses and, in general, have been

TABLE 181. ACRE HAY YIELDS FROM MEADOW FESCUE AT VARIOUS STATIONS, TONS

Ohio	Kansas	Virginia	West Virginia	Tennessee
1.05	1.08	1.54	0.70	0.73

FIG. 39. Tall fescue. (*Bureau of Plant Industry, Soils and Agricultural Engineering, U.S. Department of Agriculture.*)

TABLE 182. AVERAGE HAY YIELDS OF GRASSES IN EASTERN OREGON

Species	Yield per acre, tons	Species	Yield per acre, tons
Alta fescue................	4.11	Smooth bromegrass.........	1.82
Reed canary grass..........	2.71	Crested wheatgrass.........	1.68
Slender wheatgrass.........	2.01	Orchard grass..............	1.62
Timothy..................	1.99	Meadow fescue.............	1.42
Tall oatgrass..............	1.84		

SOURCE: *Oreg. Agr. Expt. Sta. Bul.* 427 (1945).

inferior to timothy in the Northeast. The Oregon Station reports rather extensive tests with Alta fescue (see Table 182), where it proved several times more productive than most of the other grasses tried and was almost three times as productive as meadow fescue.

Tall fescue is usually grown in mixtures, and two of these as suggested for Oregon are given below:

Mixture 1. For poorly drained lands in Willamette Valley.
Alta fescue 12 pounds, perennial ryegrass 6, and white clover and alsike clover 2 pounds per acre.
Mixture 2. For Eastern Oregon meadows wet in spring.
Alta fescue 4 pounds, meadow foxtail 1, redtop 1, and alsike clover 1 pound per acre.

In Tennessee it is suggested for hay or pasture in combination with alfalfa, ladino clover, or lespedeza.

No data have been reported regarding the effect of cutting time on protein and total dry-matter yields, nor are data available on yield as influenced by mixtures. The fescues probably should be cut at blooming time for highest quality hay.

References

1. Brown, E. Marion: Orchard grass in Missouri, *Mo. Agr. Ext. Cir.* 431 (1941).
2. Brown, E. Marion: Some effects of soil and air temperatures on the growth of certain grass species, *Sci. Monthly,* **57:**283–285 (1943).
3. Garber, R. J., and T. E. Odland: Varietal experiments with red clover and alfalfa, and field tests with meadow mixtures, *W.Va. Agr. Expt. Sta. Bul.* 250 (1932).
4. Jones, G. D., T. J. Smith, and M. H. McVickar: Nitrogen on orchard grass pays, *Va. Agr. Expt. Sta. Bul.* 404 (1947).
5. Kenney, Ralph, and E. N. Fergus: Fescue project for 4-H clubs, *Ky. Ext. Cir.* 442 (1947).
6. Mooers, C. A.: Clovers and grasses for hay and pasture, *Tenn. Agr. Expt. Sta. Bul.* 165 (1938).
7. Piper, C. V.: Forage Plants and Their Culture, The Macmillan Company, New York, 1927.
8. Rampton, H. H.: Alta fescue production in Oregon, *Oreg. Agr. Expt. Sta. Bul.* 427 (1945).
9. Schwendiman, John L., and Lowell A. Mullen: Effects of processing on germinative capacity of seed of tall oat grass, *Jour. Amer. Soc. Agron.,* **36:** 783–785 (1944).
10. Wellhausen, H. W.: Alta and Kentucky 31 fescue production in Tennessee, *Tenn. Ext. Leaflet* 95 (1947).

CHAPTER 18

PRAIRIE HAY

The Plains region extends approximately from the 98th meridian westward to the eastern slope of the Rocky Mountains and from Canada to central Texas, including the Panhandle. It comprises an area that is roughly one-sixth of the total land in the United States. The semiarid climate resulting in natural grass cover makes the region well-suited to its important livestock industry.

On the Great Plains of America the vegetation is dominantly grasses. However, in the drier portion sedges, rushes, sagebrush, greasewood, ferns, and other plants are common. A complex botanical condition exists in this area due to the large number of species, each possessing characteristics related to its adaptation. The region is a transition zone divided into areas of tall, mixed, and short grasses, the grass species becoming shorter as one proceeds westward. It is from the tall and mixed grasses that much of the wild and prairie hay is produced, whereas the short grasses are used primarily for grazing.

THE NATIVE GRASSES

Nearly all the significant grasses, excepting bromegrass and crested wheat, are of native origin. Some of the native species have been brought under cultivation for seed production, but natural reseeding together with good management practices are also relied on to maintain satisfactory stands. During the First and Second World Wars considerable exploitation of the prairie lands occurred because of plowing up and planting to wheat. Wind erosion and conservation problems resulted, and now attempts should be made to get such marginal croplands back to adapted sod cover.

Livestock ranching consists of raising beef cattle or sheep. These enterprises are considered essential for profitable farming in this region, although much wheat and some corn are produced on the eastern part of the Great Plains. Consistent production of cereal crops is uncertain, but some range and hay can nearly always be secured in spite of weather hazards. Prairie hay is fed as a maintenance or even part of a fattening ration for range cattle and sheep.

Variability. Some idea of the variability found among the grasses and plants that comprise the mixed prairie hay in North Dakota can be gained

179

by examining Table 183. In this study six tall, five medium, and six short species were found. These varied in height from 4 to 60 inches and in maturity from May to October. There are many places on the prairie where the species mixtures are not nearly so complex, and in some areas even relatively pure stands of single species may be found.

TABLE 183. HEIGHT AND MATURITY OF THE GRASSES AND PLANTS OFTEN FOUND IN NORTH DAKOTA PRAIRIE HAY

Species	Common name	Height	Height, in.	Maturity
Agropyron caninum	Bearded wheatgrass	Tall	12–36	July–Aug.
Agropyron smithii	Western wheatgrass	Tall	18–36	July–Aug.
Andropogon furcatus	Big bluestem	Tall	30–48	Aug.–Sept.
Andropogon scoparius	Little bluestem	Medium	12–24	Aug.–Oct.
Aristida longiseta	Wiregrass	Short	6–12	July–Aug.
Bouteloua gracilis	Blue grama	Short	1–4	July–Sept.
Bouteloua curtipendula	Tall grama	Medium	12–20	July–Sept.
Koeleria cristata	Prairie junegrass	Medium	6–15	June–July
Stipa comata	Western needlegrass	Medium	12–24	July
Stipa spartea	Porcupine grass	Tall	12–48	July–Aug.
Stipa viridula	Feather bunchgrass	Tall	18–36	July–Aug.
Calomovilfa longifolia	Big sandgrass	Tall	30–60	July–Sept.
Artemisia dracunculoides	Green sage	Medium	12–24	Sept.–Oct.
Artemisia frigida	Pasture sage	Short	10–20	Aug.–Sept.
Artemisia gnaphalodes	White sage	Short	10–20	Sept.–Oct.
Carex filifolia	Nigger wool (sedge)	Short	4–8	May
Carex heliophylla	Western prairie sedge	Short	4–10	May–June

SOURCE: *N.Dak. Agr. Expt. Sta. Tech. Bul.* 260 (1932).

In the northern part of the prairie the main tall grass types consist of prairie beardgrass, blue and side-oat grama, blue goose turkey-foot, western wheatgrass, prairie dropseed, and bluegrass. In the short- and mixed-grass areas the dominant species are western wheatgrass, blue grama, needle-and-thread, green needlegrass, buffalo grass, sandberg bluegrass, and threadleaf sedge. Also found in restricted parts of this northern area are prairie sandgrass, sand dropseed, sandhill muhly, Indian ricegrass, and many other lesser species. In addition sagebrush, greasewood, and salt-bush are widely distributed.

In the southern prairie region such grasses as blue and side-oats grama, little bluestem, buffalo grass, sand lovegrass, switchgrass, and Indian grass are common. Also found are Texas bluegrass, Canada wild-rye, and western wheatgrass. No perennial legumes have been found that are of much value for growing with these prairie grasses.

Warm- and Cool-season Species. The grasses of the prairie region are classified as warm- or cool season species. The cool-season grasses make most of their growth in early spring or late fall if moisture conditions are favorable. They grow very little during the hot summer. Unlike these, the hot weather of summer favors the warm-season species. These begin growth late in the spring and cease with the first frosts of early autumn.

A classification of the important prairie grasses found in South Dakota on the basis of temperature adaptations may be found in Table 184. The cool-weather grasses include such important species as the wheatgrasses,

TABLE 184

Cool-season grasses	*Warm-season grasses*
A. Long-lived perennials: 　1. Bunch type: 　　Crested wheatgrass (*Agropyron cristatum*) 　　Russian wild-rye (*Elymus junceus*) 　　Feather bunchgrass (*Stipa viridula*) 　　Needle-and-thread (*Stipa comata*) 　2. Rhizomatous type: 　　Western wheatgrass (*Agropyron smithii*) 　　Smooth brome (*Bromus inermis*) 　　Kentucky bluegrass (*Poa pratensis*) 　　Intermediate wheatgrass (*Agropyron intermedium*) *B.* Short-lived perennials: 　1. Bunch type: 　　Slender wheatgrass (*Agropyron trachycaulum*) 　　Canada wild-rye (*Elymus canadensis*) 　　Sandberg bluegrass (*Poa secunda*) 　　Indian ricegrass (*Oryzopsis hymenoides*)	*A.* Long-lived perennials: 　1. Bunch type: 　　Blue grama grass (*Bouteloua gracilis*) 　　Little bluestem (*Andropogon scoparius*) 　　Prairie dropseed (*Sporobolus heterolepis*) 　2. Rhizomatous type: 　　Big bluestem (*Andropogon furcatus*) 　　Switchgrass (*Panicum virgatum*) 　　Side-oats grama (*Bouteloua curtipendula*) 　　Indian grass (*Sorghastrum nutans*) 　3. Stoloniferous type: 　　Buffalo grass (*Buchloe dactyloides*) *B.* Short-lived perennials: 　1. Bunch type: 　　Sand dropseed (*Sporobolus cryptandrus*)

SOURCE: *S.Dak. Agr. Expt. Sta. Bul.* 361 (1942).

bromegrass, wild-rye, needle-and-thread, and Indian ricegrass. Warm-weather grasses are the gramas, bluestems, buffalo grass, the dropseeds, switchgrass, and Indian grass. The number of grasses is about equally divided between the two groups. It is also noteworthy that short- and long-lived perennials are found in both groups as are species having the bunching growth habit and those which are sod-forming because of rootstocks. Buffalo grass is the only important prairie species which spreads by means of stolons.

INTRODUCED GRASSES

Of the introduced species adapted to the prairies only two at present are widely used. These are bromegrass (see Chap. 15) and crested wheatgrass. Of some importance in the northern Great Plains are Russian wild-rye and

Intermediate wheatgrass. Other introductions of minor significance include Caucasian and Turkestan bluestem and weeping, Lehmann, and Boer lovegrasses, all in the southern Great Plains.

Crested wheatgrass (*Agropyron cristatum*) is a native of the cold dry plains of Siberia, introduced into America by the U.S. Department of Agriculture in 1898. It did not become recognized as a valuable species for the northern Great Plains until after 1915, at which time extensive tests were undertaken. By 1930 its adaptation and productiveness had been determined, and it has since become the leading hay and pasture grass in the northern prairie region. It is very drought- and cold-resistant, possessing a bunch habit of growth and producing seed readily. It is related to such species as slender (*A. trachycaulum*) and western wheatgrass (*A. smithii*).

Growing Prairie Hay

The native hay crop is grown without the need to lime and fertilize as is the normal practice in the humid areas. Moisture is the most limiting factor except in restricted areas where irrigation is practiced. Reseeding, however, is necessary where the native species have been destroyed by plowing, poor management, or exposure to extreme droughts.

Seeding Practices. Cropland or run-down and depleted grasslands may be reseeded by a number of methods. Where no danger of wind erosion exists, it is practical to prepare a weed-free seedbed by regular methods. The soil moisture is conserved often by summer fallowing for a season previous to seeding. This also serves to destroy many weeds and reduces this hazard when reseeding. In less favorable areas the seed is often drilled directly into grain or sorghum stubble fields. Spreading hay with mature seed on it has been practiced in a limited way. Deferred grazing or mowing of depleted range lands is helpful since this permits the natural formation and spread of seeds. Such a procedure is slower but quite certain.

Seeding of the prairie grasses may be made in (1) early fall, (2) late fall, (3) early spring, or (4) late spring, depending on the species or seed mixture being planted. The cool-season grasses are most successfully planted in early fall provided adequate soil moisture is available. They are also sown in late fall after any possibility of immediate germination is past. Such seeds lie dormant over winter and germinate early the following spring. The warm-season grasses are best seeded in mid- or late spring after the soil becomes warm.

Comparative seeding trials conducted at Havre, Montana, concerning time of making spring seedings give some valuable data on this problem (see Table 185). On the average, planting on May 10 was most successful at this latitude for the three grasses studied. Earlier or later plantings resulted in reduced stands.

Fig. 40. Special seeding techniques are often employed in dry-land areas. (*Soil Conservation Service, U.S. Department of Agriculture.*)

TABLE 185. COMPARISON OF TIME OF SEEDING THREE WESTERN GRASSES, HAVRE, MONTANA

Kind of grass	Method of seeding	Per cent stand from sowings made approximately on				
		Apr. 15	May 10	June 1	June 20	Ave.
Crested wheatgrass.....	Rows	59	66	52	57	59
	Close drilled	70	79	63	60	68
Slender wheatgrass.....	Rows	57	61	70	59	62
	Close drilled	62	83	77	59	70
Bromegrass..........	Rows	39	50	52	50	48
	Close drilled	57	84	69	56	67
Average..............	....	54	71	64	57	..

SOURCE: *U.S. Dept. Agr. Tech. Bul.* 307 (1932).

Drilling seed is considered superior to broadcasting in this area. Uniform seeding at the proper depth is best accomplished with a drill, the spacings varying from 6 to 12 inches or more, depending on available moisture. The results of a series of tests on seeding at several Great Plains stations

TABLE 186. AVERAGE HAY YIELDS PER ACRE OF THREE GRASSES IN SEEDING TESTS IN THE NORTHERN GREAT PLAINS, POUNDS

Species	Planting method	Mandan, N.D., 7-year ave.	Dickinson, N.D., 4-year ave.	Havre, Mont., 10-year ave.	Sheridan, Wyo., 6-year ave.
Crested wheatgrass...	Rows	1,941	2,199	1,800	2,063
	Close drilled	....	1,903	1,398	2,073
Slender wheatgrass...	Rows	1,610	1,603	....	....
	Close drilled	1,267	1,474	....	1,280
Bromegrass..........	Rows	1,260	2,312	1,476	1,900
	Close drilled	1,049	1,349	1,005	1,430

SOURCE: *U.S. Dept. Agr. Tech. Bul.* 307 (1932).

are given in Table 186. In nearly all trials the row plantings resulted in higher hay yields of the three grasses than did close drilling. This is undoubtedly a direct response to available moisture supplies. Nevertheless when these crops are used for hay or pasture, they are commonly seeded in close-drilled rows.

The prairie grasses are usually seeded alone without a companion crop because of the severe competition for moisture. New stands of grasses are seldom grazed or mowed the first year, since they need ample opportunity to establish themselves.

MAKING HAY

The cool-season grasses usually contain more crude protein than the warm-season species.[9] They are, therefore, probably more valuable as hay, but this depends on total yields and local adaptations. Crested wheatgrass is now the most important hay grass in the central and northern prairie states, and bromegrass is next in significance. The large bulk of the prairie hay is probably composed, however, of the native species.

Protein. It has been established that the protein content of prairie grasses decreases as the grasses mature. A Nebraska study,[1] for example, showed that prairie hay cut in July contained 7.18 per cent crude protein; in August, 5.68; and in September, 4.09. Analyses of prairie hay cut at various seasons of the year at Mandan, North Dakota, are given in Table 187. It is evident that the October and April cuttings yielded similar hay from a feed-analysis standpoint. This may be explained on the basis of the small amount of rainfall in this prairie region. Hay standing in the field in October would be exposed to a minimum of leaching and would be essentially the same as that permitted to stand over winter and harvested in April. It is also apparent that the protein content of hay cut in July

F$_{IG}$. 41. A hay-baling operation using a stationary baler. (*Soil Conservation Service, U.S. Department of Agriculture.*)

T$_{ABLE}$ 187. C$_{OMPOSITION}$ $_{OF}$ P$_{RAIRIE}$ H$_{AY}$ H$_{ARVESTED}$ $_{AT}$ D$_{IFFERENT}$ S$_{EASONS}$, $_{PER}$ C$_{ENT}$

Season of mowing	Ash	Crude protein	Ether extract	Crude fiber	Nitrogen-free extract
July.....................	6.71	8.14	3.08	24.0	43.1
August (annual).........	6.99	6.24	3.28	28.1	40.4
October...............	7.40	3.54	3.80	30.5	39.8
April...................	6.32	3.38	2.76	30.8	41.7
August (biennial)........	6.25	6.09	3.94	27.8	40.9

S$_{OURCE}$: *N.Dak. Agr. Expt. Sta. Bul.* 236 (1930).

was higher than that in August and this in turn better than the October harvest. Hay cut on a biennial basis in August appeared to be of equivalent quality to that harvested on an annual basis.

Quality and Yields. In this region, as elsewhere, it is necessary to consider the quality of the hay produced and also the quantity in relation to cutting treatment. The results of an Oklahoma study on these factors are given graphically in Fig. 42. The June cutting resulted in the largest concentration of T.D.N. per pound of hay harvested but at a sacrifice of total yield. Harvesting in July gave the most feed per acre of prairie hay, considering both total yields and total digestible nutrients. August and September harvests were inferior both for yield and quality. Actually

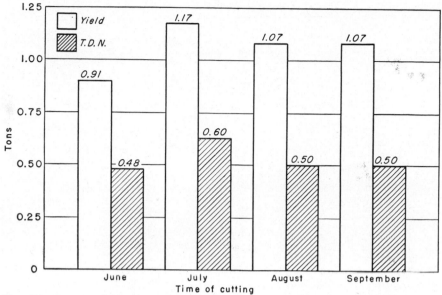

Fig. 42. Average yield and total digestible nutrients per acre of prairie hay cut in June, July, August, and September. (*Oklahoma Agricultural Experiment Station.*)

the feed value of the prairie grasses deteriorates less from weathering than the crops in the humid area. After mowing the prairie hays some livestock men use the fields for later pasturing.

Some average analyses of individual prairie grasses indicate their relatively high feeding value (see Table 188). They, in general, are somewhat inferior to bromegrass, but it is evident that they are all relatively low in fiber content and high in ash compared with those species produced under humid conditions.

TABLE 188. AVERAGE COMPOSITION OF VARIOUS PRAIRIE GRASSES ON A 15 PER CENT MOISTURE BASIS, PER CENT

Crop	Ash	Crude protein	Ether extract	Crude fiber	Nitrogen-free extract
Bearded wheatgrass......	9.72	10.18	4.23	27.9	32.9
Crested wheatgrass.......	5.88	7.76	1.83	30.9	38.6
Western wheatgrass......	7.00	8.20	2.46	29.2	38.2
Slender wheatgrass.......	6.02	6.74	1.90	29.7	40.6
Big bluestem............	5.66	5.94	2.71	28.7	42.0
Tall grama.............	8.18	5.39	1.65	27.9	41.9
Switchgrass.............	5.32	5.48	1.91	28.5	43.8
Bromegrass.............	7.43	10.52	3.21	25.7	38.1

SOURCE: *N.Dak. Agr. Expt. Sta. Bul.* 236 (1930).

The effect of annual and biennial mowing on total yields of prairie hays has been studied in North Dakota.[12]   Results from these long-time studies show that annual mowing has averaged 310 pounds of hay per acre, whereas the biennial treatment yielded 736 pounds, or 2.37 times as much.   The hay is said to be about equivalent in feed constituents.

New seedings are known to deteriorate in yield with advancing age even though they are carefully managed.   Studies with crested wheatgrass, slender wheatgrass, and bromegrass[11] show that yields increased in the second year, were good in the third, and began to decrease in the fourth year.   For crested wheatgrass and bromegrass the yields were fair in the fifth year, but the slender wheatgrass had disappeared.   These results are probably a direct response of the grasses to available moisture supplies.

OTHER CROPS

Alfalfa and sweetclover are the two most important legumes grown in the prairie states.   In favorable areas they are usually seeded alone, or they may be included with grass mixtures.   These legumes not only improve the quality of the hay produced, but they supply much needed nitrogen for the associated grasses.

Still other crops include corn for fodder, rye and wheat hay, sorghum, the foxtail millets, and Proso and Sudan grass.   These crops are considered supplemental as hay and are often used also for pasture.   Corn is used to a limited extent for silage, but the forage varieties of sorghum are more popular and valuable for this purpose.

IMPORTANT VARIETIES

There are very few improved varieties of the prairie grasses.   Until 1934, seed of the native grasses could not be obtained.   Since then new harvesting methods together with an increasing demand for such seed has stimulated its production.   Recently a few improved strains have been developed.

Of the bromegrasses, the Lincoln and Achenbach strains are well adapted for the eastern part of the prairie region beginning with Nebraska and extending southward.   Two distinct strains of crested wheatgrass are recognized: Standard and Fairway.   The Fairway strain is smaller but more leafy than the Standard.   It is grown primarily in Canada, whereas the standard strain, which possesses a more vigorous growth habit, is preferred and better adapted in the United States.

Agropyron intermedium, a species introduced from Russia in 1932, is a true perennial with rootstocks capable of producing a heavy sod.   This introduction is more heat- and cold-resistant than bromegrass in the central and northern Great Plains.   It is being increased under the name of "Ree" wheatgrass in South Dakota.[6]   Other improved strains adapted to the northern Great Plains are Mandan wild-rye, a selection from Canadian wild-rye, and green stipagrass, an improved feather bunchgrass.

The apparent neglect of the native grasses is due partly to their exploitation and sacrifice for the sake of grain farming. Overgrazing, drought, rodents, and insect pests have further contributed to the deterioration of the grasslands in parts of the prairie states. The importance of the prairie grasses is evident when one considers the large and significant livestock industry which they have helped to develop. There is need for greater emphasis on soil and water conservation, including reseeding of the prairie grasses together with improved management practices, if this area is to remain productive and continue to engage in profitable agriculture.

References

1. Baker, Marvel L., *et al.:* Effects of time of cutting on yield and feeding value of prairie hay, *Nebr. Agr. Expt. Sta. Bul.* 385 (1947).
2. Briggs, H. M., W. D. Gallup, and A. E. Darlow: The yield and feeding value of prairie hay as related to time of cutting, *Okla. Agr. Expt. Sta. Bul.* B–320 (1948).
3. Christensen, F. W., and T. H. Hopper: Effect of weathering and stage of maturity on the palatability and nutritive value of prairie hay, *N.D. Agr. Expt. Sta. Tech. Bul.* 260 (1932).
4. Dillman, A. C.: The beginning of crested wheatgrass in North America, *Jour. Amer. Soc. Agron.*, **38:**237–250 (1946).
5. Franzke, C. J., and A. N. Hume: Regrassing areas in South Dakota, *S.D. Agr. Expt Sta. Bul.* 361 (1942).
6. Franzke, C. J.: Ree wheatgrass, *S.D. Agr. Expt. Sta. Cir.* 58 (1945).
7. Hopper, T. H., and L. L. Nesbitt: The chemical composition of some North Dakota pasture and hay grasses, *N.D. Agr. Expt. Sta. Bul.* 236 (1930).
8. Jackman, E. R., D. E. Stephens, and D. E. Richards: Crested wheatgrass in Eastern Oregon, *Oreg. Agr. Ext. Bul.* 494 (1936).
9. Newell, L. C., and F. D. Keim: Effects of mowing frequency on the yield and protein content of several grasses grown in pure stands, *Nebr. Agr. Expt. Sta. Res. Bul.* 150 (1947).
10. Oakley, R. A., and H. L. Westover: Forage crops in relation to the agriculture of the semi-arid portion of the northern Great Plains, *U.S. Dept. Agr. Dept. Bul.* 1244 (1924).
11. Reitz, L. P., M. A. Bell, and H. E. Tower: Crested wheatgrass in Montana, *Mont. Agr. Expt. Sta. Bul.* 323 (1936).
12. Sarvis, J. T.: Grazing investigations on the Northern Great Plains, *N.D. Agr. Expt. Sta. Bul.* 308 (1941).
13. U.S. Department of Agriculture Yearbook, 1948, pp. 203–232.
14. Westover, H. L., *et al.:* Crested wheatgrass as compared with bromegrass, slender wheatgrass, and other hay and pasture crops for the northern Great Plains, *U.S. Dept. Agr. Tech. Bul.* 307 (1932).
15. Whitman, Warren, T. E. Stoa, and Herbert C. Hanam: Grasses and legumes for pasture and hay, *N.Dak. Agr. Expt. Sta. Cir.* 64 (1939).

CHAPTER 19

JOHNSON AND BERMUDA GRASS

The production of livestock and the raising of forage crops are enterprises especially well suited to the Southeastern states. However, in spite of favorable climatic and soil conditions, this section has not developed into a strong livestock region. Part of this lack of livestock enterprise can be attributed to low soil fertility, the type of farming practiced, and the forage species available. The South has good perennial grasses for summer use, but the region needs better species or varieties for winter use as pasture. There is also a need for superior perennial legumes for summer production. Learning to use the available species better should contribute to an increasing livestock industry.

JOHNSON GRASS (*Sorghum halepense*)

The most important perennial hay grass in the Southeast is Johnson grass (*Sorghum halepense*). It has been and still is regarded as a serious weed pest in many areas, but stockmen are beginning to recognize it as a crop of real potential hay and pasture value. In many respects this grass resembles Sudan grass in appearance. It differs, however, by producing large and tenacious rootstocks which are extremely difficult to eradicate. It is this characteristic which makes it a perennial and gives it such a persistent habit.

Johnson grass was introduced into the United States from Turkey in 1830 by Governor Means of South Carolina. A large plantation owner, Colonel William Johnson, living near Selma, in the Black Belt section of Alabama, carried seed there from South Carolina in 1840. On the rich bottom lands of the Alabama River, where the seeds were planted, it thrived wonderfully and became known as Johnson grass, after the Colonel.

The exceptional vigor associated with this crop resulted in its rapid spread from the Atlantic Coast to central Texas south of the 35th parallel. Throughout this area it acts as a true perennial. To the northward it loses this character and succumbs to winterkilling. It has been reported as a weed in southern Illinois, Iowa, and Indiana. From western Texas to the Pacific Coast it is found in the irrigated districts and is considered a serious weed along irrigation canals.

As a crop it is adapted primarily to the rich alluvial river bottoms and black soils of the Gulf states. Under fertile conditions it comes into cotton and other cultivated fields, greatly increasing the cost of producing such crops. It will grow well on any soil that will produce good yields of cotton. Abundant moisture, supplied by rainfall, stream overflow, or irrigation, is helpful for full production but not essential. It is a sun-loving grass that grows well at high temperatures.

Method of Spreading

Very few of the stands of Johnson grass hay- or pasture fields have been seeded intentionally. Recurring floods in the river valleys have scattered the seed far and wide. Oats contaminated with Johnson grass seed and purchased Johnson grass hay crops moving from one section of the South to another have also contributed to its spread. Thus a grower seldom needed to sow the crop since it was already on his land; he had only to encourage its growth by fertilizing and good management to secure ample production. Where it is planted, regular seeding techniques are employed.

Cultural Practices

Two distinct problems have developed in utilizing this crop in the South. One of these is maintaining continuous high productivity, and the other is eradicating Johnson grass so that other crops can be utilized in the rotation.

Maintaining Productivity. Even on the richest soils Johnson grass fails to maintain high yields without some assistance, and on inferior soils improvement practices are even more imperative. Applications of fertilizer together with varied crop treatments were tried with Johnson grass on a sandy soil in Alabama (see data in Table 189). Largest yields were made where a winter hay crop was followed by Johnson grass. The plowing

TABLE 189. THE EFFECT OF FERTILIZER AND CROP TREATMENTS ON THE YIELD OF JOHNSON GRASS

	Yield of hay per acre, lb.			
Treatment	First test			Second test
	Winter crop	Johnson grass	Total	Johnson grass
Check......................	.....	2,015	2,015	600
N..........................	.....	5,220	5,220	550
LN.........................	.....	6,000	6,000	800
LNPK......................	.....	6,380	6,380	1,850
NPK oats..................	3,780	6,645	10,425	1,350
NPK oats and vetch.........	3,720	7,235	10,955	1,600
PK Austrian peas plowed in....	.....	4,245	4,245	2,000

SOURCE: *Ala. Agr. Expt. Sta. Cir.* 79 (1937).

under of a winter annual legume did not stimulate higher production of the grass and indicated that better use of the legume would have resulted from harvesting it for hay. Responses to lime and fertilizer are apparent. Yields from the first test represent normal cuttings, whereas those of the second are from one cutting only.

Some Johnson grass hay producers make a practice of plowing their meadows each fall and seeding winter annual hay crops. This gives an early spring crop and, in addition, two to three cuttings of Johnson grass later in the season. The plowing serves to stimulate the Johnson grass as well as to provide a seedbed for the fall planting. Summer annuals also can be planted on Johnson grass meadows to increase the quality of the hay. This necessitates early spring preparation of the seedbed before Johnson grass has made much growth. Cowpeas or soybeans are then drilled in at regular planting rates. The first cutting of hay will be of the mixture, and later cuttings will consist mostly of pure Johnson grass. Mixtures of alfalfa and Johnson grass are found in some sections of the South. These mixtures occur where alfalfa is planted for hay and the Johnson grass comes in naturally.

As the meadows thin out, another common practice is to cultivate to encourage new vigorous growth. Cultivation is accomplished by disking or harrowing, or even by plowing and harrowing. This practice would destroy most grasses but only serves to stimulate Johnson grass.

Eradication. In trying to determine the best means of eradication, the time of rootstock formation from a new seeding was studied. No rootstocks appeared until the plants were in the heading stage (Table 190).

TABLE 190. TIME OF FORMATION OF ROOTSTOCKS BY JOHNSON GRASS PLANTS GROWN FROM SEED IN GREENHOUSE POTS

Age harvested, weeks	Stage of growth	Dry weight, grams	
		Tops	Rootstocks
1	2¾ in. high	0.3	0.0
2	4 in. high	0.8	0.0
3	10 in. high	2.1	0.0
4	16 in. high	6.8	0.0
5	31 in. high (booting)	11.5	0.0
6	Heading	23.3	1.0
7	Blooming	31.2	3.6
8	Seed in milk stage	38.8	6.2
9	Seed in dough stage	55.8	8.8
10	Some seed mature	50.7	11.1
11	Most of seed mature	41.6	14.3
12	Seed well matured	42.2	23.0

SOURCE: *Jour. Amer. Soc. Agron.*, **22** (1930).

After this they began to accumulate rapidly and were most abundant at the stage of fullest maturity.

The reason for deterioration in vigor is closely related to the development of the rootstocks. This can be partly regulated in the field by cutting or grazing treatments, as shown in Table 191. Any cutting treatment is

TABLE 191. EFFECT OF STAGE OF CUTTING ON THE YIELD OF HAY AND ROOTSTOCKS OF JOHNSON GRASS

| Stage cut | Dry weight, lb. per acre | | | | | |
| | First year | | | Second year | | |
	No. of cuttings	Hay	Root-stocks	No. of cuttings	Hay	Root-stocks
1 ft. high..............	5	4,450	619	8	2,051	48
2 ft. high..............	4	7,159	1,247	5	3,580	242
Booting...............	3	7,492	1,528	4	6,045	662
Blooming.............	3	9,605	1,942	3	8,606	876
Seed in late milk........	2	10,552	2,803	3	11,709	2,356
Seed mature............	2	11,071	3,684	2	9,087	3,518
At end of growing season.................	1	5,812	5,616	1	7,987	6,098

SOURCE: *Ala. Agr. Expt. Sta. Cir.* 79 (1937).

shown to reduce the production of rootstocks, and the more frequent the cuttings, the greater the reduction. Cutting earlier than the late milk stage lowered the hay and rootstock yields and reduced the vigor and quality of yields the second year. This and similar studies point the way toward controlling the grass under field conditions by frequent cutting or grazing. In a livestock system of farming this practice could be widely employed.

Time of Cutting. The effect of the number of cuttings per season on subsequent yields was studied also in Alabama. The hay was cut at the blooming, booting, and late milk stages for each cutting treatment, and average yields are reported (Table 192). Yields were highest when the crop was cut continuously as it reached the respective hay stages. When cut only up until the middle of the summer, there was an average loss of about ½ ton of hay, and when harvested only every other year, this loss was increased to over 1½ tons annually. It is interesting to note, however, that in the last year of the study the yields were lowest with full-season cutting. Most investigators agree that Johnson grass should be given a chance to build rootstock reserves until about midsummer for superior yields and good maintenance of stand.

Cutting for hay in the booting stage produces the most protein and ash

TABLE 192. EFFECT OF FREQUENCY OF CUTTING ON THE YIELD OF JOHNSON GRASS HAY

Frequency of cutting	Yield per acre, lb.	
	1933	5-year ave., 1929–1933
Continuously.............	3,463	4,618
Until middle of summer....	3,691	3,672
Every other year*........	6,343	5,275

SOURCE: *Ala. Agr. Expt. Sta. Cir.* 79 (1937).
* For average annual yields divide by two.

TABLE 193. EFFECT OF STAGE OF CUTTING ON AVERAGE YIELD AND PER CENT COMPOSITION OF JOHNSON GRASS HAY

Stage cut	Yield per acre, lb.	Moisture	Ash	Protein	Fat	Fiber	Carbohydrates
Booting..........	3,854	8.6	4.6	8.1	1.9	31.0	45.8
Blooming........	5,314	8.3	3.9	8.0	1.7	32.0	46.1
Late milk........	4,526	8.2	3.7	7.8	1.9	32.2	46.2

SOURCE: *Ala. Agr. Expt. Sta. Cir.* 79 (1937).

and the least fiber, but the differences are not enough to be very significant (see Table 193). Highest yields have been obtained in the blooming to late milk stage, and this seems to be the preferred time for cutting.

Quality of Hay. The production of quality hay is another big problem with this crop. Much of the Johnson grass hay placed on Southern markets is of inferior value and sometimes has been unable to compete with hay shipped in from the West and North. Its low value results from delayed cutting, inadequate curing, and contamination with weedy materials. Analyses of samples of hay from various sources are given in Table 194. The green color of Johnson grass ranged from 31 to 68 per cent. The proportion of foreign material in the hay ranged from 2 to 21 per cent. Much of the inferior-quality hay is the result of meadow mismanagement and neglect. Hay produced on cultivated and fertilized meadows contains a minimum of weeds and other foreign materials.

While early cutting is recognized as an important factor in quality production, it is not always possible of attainment. Uneven growth in many meadows results in irregular heading of the grass. Thus many plants may have matured seed while others are still in the head-forming stage of development. Early cutting to escape seed formation is desirable, especially if the hay is to be sold off the farm.

TABLE 194. SEPARATION AND COLOR ANALYSIS OF JOHNSON GRASS AND JOHNSON GRASS MIXED HAYS PRODUCED IN DIFFERENT STATES, PER CENT

State of origin	Green color	Johnson grass	Alfalfa	Other grass	Foreign material
Texas..................	31.0	79.0	0	13.0	8.0
Texas..................	61.0	78.0	0	1.0	21.0
Texas..................	68.0	84.0	0	Trace	16.0
Alabama...............	45.0	86.0	5	6.0	3.0
Alabama...............	61.0	43.0	37	2.0	17.0
Mississippi.............	38.0	97.0	0	1.0	2.0
Mississippi.............	64.0	80.0	0	8.0	12.0

SOURCE: *Tex. Agr. Expt. Sta. Cir.* 43 (1927).

TABLE 195. AVERAGE COMPOSITION OF FEED CONSTITUENTS IN THE DRY MATTER OF JOHNSON AND SOME OTHER HAYS, PER CENT

Kind of hay	Ash	Crude protein	Crude fiber	Nitrogen-free extract	Ether extract
Johnson grass...........	7.7	9.0	32.6	47.7	3.0
Sudan grass.............	8.6	10.2	29.5	49.9	1.8
Timothy................	6.2	7.8	32.3	50.6	3.1

SOURCE: *U.S. Dept. Agr. Farmers' Bul.* 1476 (1926).

Johnson grass hay as feed seems to compare favorably with other grass hays. A feed analysis is given in Table 195. These analyses show it to be similar to Sudan grass and of about equivalent feeding value to timothy. Cattlemen throughout the cotton belt agree that it may be used advantageously in place of timothy.

Legal Restrictions. Certain of the Southern states have laws forbidding the sale of Johnson grass seed or the shipment of this type of hay having seed in it. Others require cutting the grass before mature seeds have developed, in order to prevent its spread. These are probably good precautions, especially if the hay is to be sold off the farm, and in addition, they aid in getting growers to cut the crop at an early stage of development.

BERMUDA GRASS (*Cynodon dactylon*)

Bermuda grass was introduced into America from India sometime prior to 1807. It is adapted throughout the cotton belt, being to the South what Kentucky bluegrass is to the North. The general region where it is grown is shown in Fig. 43. Cold impairs its growth, and severe frosts will destroy it. It is widely adapted to many soil types, and while used primarily for pasture, it makes satisfactory hay crops on the low, rich soils of the South.

Like Johnson grass, this grass is seldom seeded but comes in naturally. It spreads by seed and by both rootstocks and stolons, which give it a most persistent habit of growth and make it difficult to eradicate. It is resistant both to saline conditions along the seashore and to the alkaline soils of the Southwest.

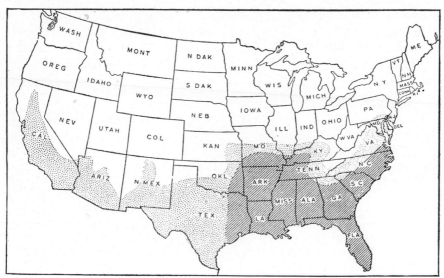

FIG. 43. Distribution of Bermuda grass in the United States. Heavily shaded area is where the grass is most valuable. (*Bureau of Plant Industry, Soils and Agricultural Engineering, U.S. Department of Agriculture.*)

Types and Varieties. Many forms of this grass are to be found. Two Bermuda varieties known as Coastal and Suwannee have been developed through plant breeding. Coastal Bermuda is a tall-growing form, and in comparative tests with Tift (a selection) it appears particularly suited for hay. From four cuttings, Coastal Bermuda produced 75 per cent more hay than Tift did (see Table 196). A yield of 3¾ tons per acre is a most im-

TABLE 196. THE 1942 YIELDS OF AIR-DRY HAY OBTAINED FROM DUPLICATE TENTH-ACRE PLOTS OF TIFT AND COASTAL BERMUDA PLANTED IN A TIFTON SANDY LOAM IN MARCH, 1941, POUNDS PER ACRE

Cutting date	Tift Bermuda	Coastal Bermuda
May 20...............	602	1,361
July 11................	1,345	2,475
Aug. 5................	1,408	2,148
Oct. 5................	943	1,556
Total...............	4,298	7,540

SOURCE: *Ga. Coastal Plain Agr. Expt. Sta. Cir.* 10 (1943).

pressive performance for any grass hay. Suwannee appears to be most valuable in Florida. Other varieties and strains are being developed for lawn and turf purposes.

Cultural Practices

The addition of fertilizer to Bermuda grass greatly stimulates yields and improves the quality of the hay. Comparative tests in which treated plots were given 500 pounds per acre of 4–8–4 after the first cutting and 240 pounds of nitrate of soda after the second cutting are reported in Table 197.

TABLE 197. Acre Yields and Chemical Composition of Coastal and Tift Bermuda as Influenced by Fertilization

Strain and treatment	Yield of dry hay 3d cutting, lb. per acre	Chemical composition of hay cut, Aug. 18, 1942, %					
		Dry matter	Crude protein	Fat	Crude fiber	Cellu-lose	Ash
Coastal Bermuda:							
Unfertilized.......	637	40.1	6.22	2.33	29.3	32.1	4.79
Fertilized.........	2,500	37.7	7.18	2.31	30.5	31.6	4.50
Tift Bermuda:							
Unfertilized.......	318	43.9	6.86	2.66	30.1	33.7	4.62
Fertilized.........	1,735	37.6	8.59	2.21	31.0	34.0	4.85

SOURCE: *Ga. Coastal Plain Agr. Expt. Sta. Cir.* 10 (1943).

These fertilizer treatments increased the hay yields by 400 to 500 per cent and the crude protein content by 1 to 2 per cent. Other constituents remained essentially the same.

A comparison of the feed value of Bermuda with timothy and Johnson grass is given in Table 198. Bermuda compares very favorably, being considerably higher in protein and lower in fiber than either timothy or Johnson grass.

TABLE 198. Comparative Analysis of Various Hays, per Cent

Kind of hay	Protein	Fat	Crude fiber	Nitro-gen-free extract	Water	Ash
Johnson grass.......	7.22	1.90	30.0	44.1	9.7	7.12
Timothy............	7.75	2.25	28.7	43.2	10.2	7.88
Bermuda...........	10.88	2.14	23.0	46.4	10.1	7.60

SOURCE: *Tex. Agr. Expt. Sta. Cir.* 43 (1927).

Although no data are available, it is usually recommended that the grass be cut at an early stage, since it is of inferior quality when overripe. Under satisfactory growing conditions it can be cut twice a year when it is knee-high.

Very little seed is produced in the Southeast, but this enterprise is now under way in Arizona and southern California. Bermuda grass is spread and propagated primarily by stolons or rootstocks, either of these being planted on prepared seedbeds. Planting in hills and rows is widely practiced, and care must be taken to prevent the plant stolons or rootstocks from drying out. The growing of shade and intertilled crops or exposure of the rootstocks to winter cold by fall plowing is helpful in destroying the crop.

Production Statistics

No data have been gathered by the Census Bureau or U.S. Department of Agriculture on the acreages of these two grasses cut for hay in America. In 1919 C. V. Piper of the Office of Forage Crop Investigations estimated that 400 thousand acres each of Bermuda and Johnson grass were cut for hay. Bermuda grass averages 1 ton of hay per acre and Johnson grass 1¼ tons. The amount and acreage of hay from these two grasses, especially from Johnson grass, without doubt has increased considerably since 1919.

References

1. Burton, Glenn W.: Coastal Bermuda grass, *Ga. Coastal Plain Expt. Sta. Cir.* 10 (1943).
2. Piper, C. V., *et al.:* Our forage resources, U.S. Department of Agriculture Yearbook, 1923, pp. 311–414.
3. Piper, C. V.: Forage Plants and Their Culture, The Macmillan Company, New York, 1927.
4. Pollock, E. O.: Johnson grass in Texas, *Tex. Agr. Expt. Sta. Cir.* 43 (1927).
5. Sturkie, D. G.: The influence of various topcutting treatments on rootstocks of Johnson grass, *Jour. Amer. Soc. Agron.*, **22**:82–93 (1930).
6. Sturkie, D. G.: Experiments with hay crops in Alabama, *Ala. Agr. Expt. Sta. Cir.* 79 (1937).
7. Vinall, H. N.: Johnson grass: Its production for hay and pasturage, *U.S. Dept. Agr. Farmers' Bul.* 1476 (1926).

CHAPTER 20

SUDAN GRASS AND SORGO

Sudan grass and sorghum (sorgo) are relatively new crops in America. but already they occupy an important position. In the dry Great Plains region these crops have proved very valuable for hay, silage, pasture, and grain. More than 10 million acres are now being planted annually.

Both these crops are summer annuals that like warm weather. They are adapted to large areas over the country. Under good conditions they grow rapidly and yield well. Even in dry seasons there is more certainty of getting a crop with them than with many other forage plants. Sudan grass is chiefly a hay and pasture crop. The sorgos are very valuable for fodder and in silage production, since a preservative is not required to give a good-quality product.

SUDAN GRASS (*Sorghum vulgare* var. *sudanensis*)

The introduction of Sudan grass into America was the result of a systematic search by C. V. Piper of the U.S. Department of Agriculture for a grass that would be the counterpart of Johnson grass but of a less tenacious character. In 1909 he obtained 8 ounces of Sudan grass seed from R. Hewison, Director of Agriculture and Lands at Khartum, Sudan. A portion of this seed was sent to the forage-crop field station at Chillicothe, Texas. The new grass was received enthusiastically, and rapid seed increase and distribution followed.

ADAPTATION

The culture of Sudan grass spread quickly, especially in the Southwest, While the most intensive cultivation of the crop occurs there, it is now grown to some extent in nearly every state; it is most limited in the far northern states and along the southeastern and southern seaboard regions. Figure 44 shows its general regions of adaptation. Climatic and soil conditions together with the need for a hay and pasture crop of the nature of Sudan grass have played an important role in its present geographical distribution.

Region 1. A profitable hay crop is very much needed in this southern region. Two to three cuttings of Sudan grass may be made here annually, and yields range from 2 to 4 tons per acre.

Region 2. Sudan is well adapted to the clover-timothy belt, but must compete with the regular hay crops. It is most widely used here as a mid-summer supplementary hay and pasture crop.

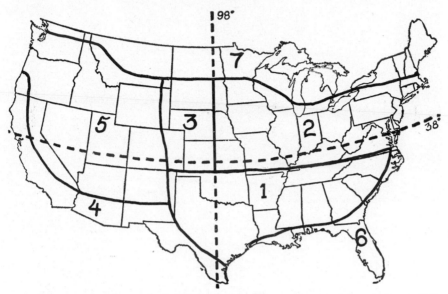

Fig. 44. Sudan grass regions in the United States. (*Bureau of Plant Industry, Soils and Agricultural Engineering, U.S. Department of Agriculture.*)

Region 3. Sudan grass competes primarily with alfalfa, sorghum, and the millets in this region. It makes a better quality of hay than the sorghums and is more widely adapted than alfalfa. Producing one to two cuttings a year, it yields 1 to 3 tons per acre.

Region 4. Sudan grass is grown best under irrigation in this area. When this is done, yields of 4 or more tons of good hay per acre are attained. It supplements alfalfa in livestock rations.

Other Regions. Only limited success is possible with Sudan in region 5. Factors such as low temperature, high altitudes, and low rainfall decrease the usefulness of the crop. In region 6 a severe foliage disease had handi-capped the crop, but new disease-resistant varieties, such as Tift, may increase the culture of the crop here. Because of the cool summer and short growing seasons in region 7 the crop has not proved profitable.

There are only two named varieties of Sudan grass: Tift and Sweet. Tift is highly resistant to leaf spot diseases and is adapted generally in the humid Central and Southeastern portions of the United States. Sweet Sudan is higher in sugar content and, therefore, more palatable than ordinary Sudan grass. It is less disease-resistant than Tift.

Fig. 45.   Cattle show a preference for sweet Sudan grass.   Common Sudan grass growing on either side of the two rows of sweet Sudan in the center. (*Texas Agricultural Experiment Station.*)

YIELDS

Since millet and sorgo grow best during the same summer period as Sudan grass, it is of interest to compare their performance in some of the great hay regions of the United States. Such data are given in Table 199.

TABLE 199.   COMPARISON OF SUDAN GRASS WITH MILLET AND SORGO IN AVERAGE YIELDS PER ACRE OF CURED HAY, TONS

Region	Sudan grass	Millet	Sorgo
Northern Great Plains.....	2.28	2.14	3.89
Central Great Plains.......	2.51	2.01	3.49
Southern Great Plains.....	4.03	1.25	5.34
Timothy and clover belt....	2.64	2.65	5.95

SOURCE: *U.S. Dept. Agr. Farmers' Bul.* 1126 (1922).

Millet yields as well as Sudan grass in the northern Great Plains and in the timothy-clover region, but is much inferior in the central and southern Great Plains. Sorgo invariably outyields both Sudan grass and millet, but it is more difficult to cure to a high-quality hay.

Because Sudan grass is an annual, it can be utilized in nearly any rotation. Except in those regions where other suitable hay or pasture crops are not as satisfactory, it is generally grown as a supplementary hay and pasture crop. It is used widely for this purpose in the more humid regions such as the clover-timothy belt. When other crops fail in this area or are not productive enough, Sudan grass can be sown in late May or June, and because of its fast growth and ability to endure heat and drought, it will provide July and August grazing or an early fall hay crop. That it is well received in many cropping sections is indicated by Table 200, where yield

TABLE 200. YIELDS OF SUDAN GRASS GROWN FOR HAY, TONS PER ACRE

Maryland, 3-year ave.	Texas, 13-year ave.	Kansas, 2-year ave.	California, 3-year ave.	
			Dry land	Irrigated
3.41	3.09	4.02	4.63	5.54

data are reported for states selected at random over the country. These yields, in general, are high and are indicative of the producing capacity of this crop over a wide area of the United States.

CULTURAL PRACTICES

Seeding. Sudan grass is a summer crop; it requires a warm soil for planting and high temperatures for most rapid growth. Some indication of favorable seeding dates in various sections of the country can be obtained from Table 201. Plantings are most successful when made in April and

TABLE 201. YIELDS PER ACRE OF SUDAN GRASS HAY FROM DIFFERENT DATES OF SEEDING IN VARIOUS SECTIONS OF THE UNITED STATES, TONS

Location of test	Apr. 1	May 1	June 1	July 1
Southern section..............	3.21	2.83	2.69	1.83
Middle section...............	1.14	2.15	2.28	1.66
Northern section.............	....	3.75	3.82	....

SOURCE: *U.S. Dept. Agr. Bul.* 981 (1921).

early May in Southern latitudes, May to early June in the Central area, late May and early June in more Northern latitudes. The latest period at which it seems wise to seed Sudan usually is 60 to 90 days before the first killing frost.

The rate and method of seeding vary with the moisture supply. Seeding is usually either in close drills or in spaced rows, with drilling preferred in the humid sections and row planting in the dry regions west of the 98th meridian. Actually the differences from a yield standpoint are not too significant. In the humid regions close drilling requires no cultivation, the plants have finer stems, and the hay is less dusty than where cultivation is practiced. Weeds are readily controlled by the vigorous growth of the Sudan. Row plantings in the dry regions suffer less from drought than close-drilled seedings. It is usually true that hay produced in rows is coarser and dustier than that from drilled fields.

The rate of seeding may range from 10 to 40 pounds of seed per acre. Close-drilled plantings naturally require more seed than row plantings. A summary of seeding rates as affecting yields is given in Table 202. In

TABLE 202. YIELDS PER ACRE OF HAY FROM DIFFERENT RATES OF SEEDING BROADCAST OR IN CLOSE DRILLS, TONS

Location of test	Seeding rate, lb.				
	10	15	20	25–30	35–40
Humid regions...............	....	2.91	2.95	3.02	2.87
Dry regions.................	....	3.37	3.32	3.19	3.22
Dry regions (irrigated)........	5.34	4.88	4.98	4.46	4.46

humid regions, 25 to 30 pounds or more seed is often sown per acre. In dry regions the use of 10 to 15 pounds of seed per acre is just as good as the higher seeding rates. Under most conditions Sudan grass tillers freely in thin stands; thus the final number of stems is greatly increased.

Use in Mixtures. In the humid sections it is a common practice to seed mixtures of Sudan grass with soybeans and occasionally cowpeas. Evidence is strongly in favor of the mixed plantings (see Table 203) and aside

TABLE 203. YIELDS PER ACRE OF HAY FROM SUDAN GRASS ALONE AND IN MIXTURES, TONS

Crop	Tennessee	Kentucky	Virginia	New Jersey
Sudan grass..................	1.70	4.60	1.46	2.53
Sudan and soybeans...........	2.13	5.70	2.29	2.77
Sudan and cowpeas............	1.72	5.30	1.72	....

from better yields they usually produce a higher quality hay. The Sudan grass itself is benefited by the legume, which causes an increase in its protein and ash content.

Harvesting. The stage at which Sudan grass is harvested affects both the yield and the quality. Data on stage of harvesting in Kansas indicate that cutting after the first heads appear and through the milk stage was

TABLE 204. EFFECT OF STAGE OF HARVESTING ON AVERAGE YIELDS OF SUDAN GRASS,
TONS PER ACRE

Stage cut	Kansas	Texas
Just before heading......	1.83	1.84
First heads appearing....	2.24	2.44
In full head.............	2.14	2.47
Seed in milk.............	2.31	2.12

SOURCES: *U.S. Dept. Agr. Farmers' Bul.* 1126 (1922); *Tex. Agr. Expt. Sta. Bul.* 396 (1929).

equally productive. Data from the Texas Station indicate the early to full-headed stages as being most satisfactory for yield. The stage of harvest also influences the number of cuttings made per year. Early cutting may permit one or more extra harvests. As a general rule, it is not profitable to mow Sudan grass before the heads appear. However, in the northern limits of the crop it is often cut the last two weeks in August, irrespective of maturity stage, so that it may be cured in good weather.

COMPOSITION OF HAY

The composition of Sudan grass at various stages of development must be considered along with yields to determine the best time for making hay. Actually this crop remains highly nutritious over a considerable period of time. This is probably a result of its ability to tiller freely, or, in other words, to send up new shoots as the old ones approach maturity. Based on

TABLE 205. COMPOSITION OF DRY MATTER OF SUDAN GRASS AT VARIOUS STAGES OF
GROWTH, PER CENT

Constituents	Before heading	Headed out	Full bloom	Half ripe	Ripe
Total dry matter.............	20.8	21.0	25.7	30.1	31.9
Protein.....................	8.8	9.8	6.6	5.1	4.3
Nitrogen-free extract.........	48.1	46.0	50.2	53.3	53.7
Crude fiber.................	33.0	36.0	32.3	33.0	33.8
Ether extract................	2.3	2.6	3.6	2.1	1.7
Ash........................	7.8	6.1	7.4	6.6	6.5

SOURCE: *Iowa Agr. Expt. Sta. Res. Bul.* 46 (1918).

protein and ash content together with total yields, the heading-out and full-bloom stages seem to give highest yields of superior-quality hay.

The presence of hydrocyanic acid in Sudan grass was discovered by Swanson, in Kansas, in 1919. The crop is dangerous under certain conditions of pasturing, but there are no known instances of poisoning from feeding it as hay. The content of HCN decreases as the crop approaches maturity. After Sudan grass reaches a height of 1 to 1½ feet, there is no longer any danger of HCN poisoning, even when it is used for pasture purposes.

On comparing with other hay crops, Sudan grass is found to be equal or superior to prairie hay and sorghum fodder. It ranks below alfalfa and other legume hays. This rating is upheld by chemical analysis as well as feeding trials and digestion coefficients. Tests at the Kansas Station (see Table 206) show that alfalfa gave higher milk production than Sudan grass.

TABLE 206. SUDAN GRASS HAY VERSUS ALFALFA HAY FOR MILK PRODUCTION

Items	Sudan grass	Alfalfa	Gain due to alfalfa
Milk produced, lb..........	4,022	4,112	90
Fat produced, lb.,......	168	178	10
Average body weight, lb....	1,053	1,077	24

SOURCE: *Kans. Agr. Expt. Sta. Bul.* 212 (1916).

The test ran for 60 days, and 1.5 pounds more milk per day per cow was produced as a result of feeding alfalfa hay. A feeding trial with stock cattle in Kansas[17] showed little difference among the various hay crops fed. The gain per day in pounds for those cattle fed Sudan grass hay was 0.670; kafir stover, 0.668; alfalfa, 0.658; and sorgo stover, 0.673.

SORGHUM (*Sorghum vulgare*)

Sorghum is believed to have been one of the earliest plants to be domesticated. Records indicate that sorghum originated in equatorial Africa, and the crop is said to have been grown by the Egyptians in 2200 B.C. Because of its early adoption for food purposes, numerous types have evolved.

The first sorgo brought to America was of Chinese origin, and the seed was planted on Long Island, New York, in 1853. In May, 1857, Leonard Wray brought sixteen varieties of sorgo to this country from Natal, Africa, and planted them in Georgia and South Carolina. These varieties, through selection and hybridization, formed the basis for the development of many of the present-day varieties of sorgo. The sorghums were first used for sugar and sirup purposes, but the settlement of the Great Plains states created a strong demand for drought- and heat-resistant forage crops. To a large extent sorghum replaces corn for silage in this area because it is more drought-resistant. The sorgos average 3 to 8 tons of silage annually per acre in the Plains region, where corn usually makes only 2 to 5 tons. More than 2 million acres of sorgo are now grown each year in

America, and about 5 million acres of grain and forage sorghum together are harvested annually for fodder and silage.

VARIETIES AND ADAPTATION

The many kinds of sorghum generally can be grouped into four classes. The sorgo class is a sweet forage sorghum used for hay, silage, or sirup. Another class, which is nonsaccharic, is used for grain production. The broomcorn type is grown for the panicle brushes that are used in making brooms. The grass sorghums are used primarily for hay and pasture.

TABLE 207. SORGO VARIETIES COMMONLY GROWN IN THE UNITED STATES

Varieties of first importance		*Secondary varieties*
Atlas	Orange	Freemont
Black Amber	Red Amber	Leotic
Gooseneck	Sourless	Sugar Drip
Honey	Sumac	Tricker
Kansas Orange	Waconia Orange	White African

SOURCE: *U.S. Dept. Agr. Farmers' Bul.* 1844 (1940).

The sorgos or forage sorghums possess stalks that are juicy and sweet, making them very palatable. The varieties may be grouped according to their popularity and general use. They vary greatly in drought resistance, maturity, productivity, and insect and disease resistance. The sorghum area has been divided into regions, as shown in Fig. 46, for convenience in

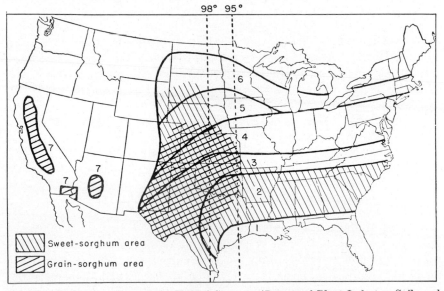

FIG. 46. Sorghum regions of the United States. (*Bureau of Plant Industry, Soils and Agricultural Engineering, U.S. Department of Agriculture.*)

indicating adapted varieties. Early varieties are grown in the north and late-maturing ones to the south.

Region 1. The Gooseneck and Honey sorgos are grown here, but Japanese sugar cane and Napier grass are said to be more productive for forage.

Region 2. The Sumac, Orange, Honey, Gooseneck, White African, Sugar Drip, Rex, Colman, and Sapling sorgos are grown in this area.

Region 3. The Atlas, Kansas Orange, Sourless, and Sumac sorgos are commonly grown here. In addition many grain sorghums are grown in this region for both grain and forage.

Region 4. West of the 98th meridian the varieties grown are Early Sumac, Leotic, and Sourless sorgos, as well as many grain sorghums. East of the 98th meridian Atlas, Kansas Orange, and Waconia Orange sorgos are most useful.

Region 5. In this area Black (Early and Minnesota) Amber, Early Sumac, Red Amber, Dakota Amber, Waconia Amber, Freemont, Atlas, and Kansas Orange are adapted. Also a number of grain sorghums are used for forage.

Region 6. The adapted varieties here are Black (Early and Minnesota) Amber, Dakota Amber, Red Amber, and Freemont sorgos, as well as several grain sorghums.

Region 7. This region grows Honey, Atlas, and Gooseneck sorgos and Hegari, a grain sorghum, for forage.

CULTURE

Time of Planting. The time of planting the sorgos varies with the latitude. Planting begins at an early date in the south and late in the season northward. A safe rule to follow is 2 weeks after corn-planting time. The sorghums require warm soils for seeding.

TABLE 208. TIME OF PLANTING SORGHUMS IN THE UNITED STATES

Southern states	Central states	Northern states
March–July 15	May 15–June 15	May 25–June 15

Seeding Methods. The method of seeding depends largely on the available moisture supply. Most of the sorghum crop grown in the semiarid regions is planted in rows so that it can be cultivated. Row plantings are made on the surface in the more moderate rainfall areas and by listing in the extremely dry areas. The planting is done with an ordinary corn planter using special sorghum planting plates.

Much of the silage sorgo is planted in rows, but sorgo planted for hay is often drilled if the moisture supply is great enough. This method produces a finer stemmed hay and requires no cultivation. In extremely dry

TABLE 209.   AVERAGE YIELD OF ROW AND DRILLED PLANTINGS OF SORGO ON THE
GREAT PLAINS, TONS PER ACRE

Location	Rows	Drilled
Hays, Kansas.............	3.15	3.82
Amarillo, Texas...........	4.51	3.36
Chillicothe, Texas.........	4.93	4.50
Average................	4.20	3.83

SOURCE: *U.S. Dept. Agr. Farmers' Bul.* 1158 (1930).

seasons close-drilled plantings do not attain satisfactory growth. Highest yields are usually obtained when the sorghum seed is planted relatively close together in cultivated rows, especially in the drier regions. This is due entirely to the response to moisture. A study in Nebraska gave data to show that close spacing in row plantings produced the highest yields and also the shortest plants with the finest stems, thus making a good quality of hay (see Table 210).

TABLE 210.   THE EFFECT OF DIFFERENT SPACINGS BETWEEN PLANTS, IN ROWS 42
INCHES APART, ON THE YIELD AND DEVELOPMENT OF ATLAS SORGO

Spacing, in.	Planting to heading, days	Stalks per plant	Stalks headed, %	Stalk diameter, in.	Stalk height, in.	Forage yield, tons per acre
2	82	1.24	30	0.72	53.3	3.41
4	82	1.33	37	0.74	53.7	3.08
6	81	1.52	40	0.75	54.0	3.06
8	80	1.62	55	0.84	56.7	2.93
12	80	1.97	72	0.96	57.0	2.56
18	81	2.29	69	0.95	58.0	2.16

SOURCE: *Nebr. Agr. Expt. Sta. Bul.* 329 (1940).

Seeding Rates. Close-drilling tests conducted at the Hays, Kansas, station showed that planting rates make little difference in the yield. Under farm conditions in the sorghum belt 3 to 4 pounds of seed are used per acre for row planting and 45 to 60 pounds for close drilling, but higher rates are used where more moisture is available.

TABLE 211. YIELDS OF FORAGE FROM RED AMBER SORGO SEEDED IN CLOSE
DRILLS AT DIFFERENT RATES AT HAYS, KANSAS

Planting rates, lb. per acre	15	30	45	60	75
Yields, tons per acre......	3.82	3.71	3.58	3.64	3.66

SOURCE: *U.S. Dept. Agr. Farmers' Bul.* 1260 (1924).

Time of Harvesting. The best time for cutting the sorghums for forage
is when the crop is fairly mature. Yields are usually highest when the
seeds are in the hard-dough stage. Up to a ton per acre more dry matter
can be produced by this late cutting practice than by early cutting before
heading, and the quality of the product is also better at the late cutting
stage. The composition and total yields of Red Amber sorgo cut at
different stages of maturity are shown in Table 212. The seed-ripe stage

TABLE 212. COMPOSITION OF HAY AND YIELD PER ACRE OF RED AMBER SORGO
WHEN CUT AT DIFFERENT STAGES OF MATURITY

Stage of maturity	Dry matter	Ash	Ether extract	Protein	Crude fiber	Nitrogen-free extract
Composition, %:						
Before heading...	100	11.92	2.18	12.75	39.97	33.18
Partially headed..	100	11.67	2.13	11.28	35.08	39.84
Bloom to dough..	100	10.84	2.19	11.03	27.97	47.97
Seed ripe........	100	9.66	1.95	8.94	24.44	55.01
Yield per acre, lb.:						
Before heading...	4,535	540	99	578	1,813	1,505
Partially headed..	4,963	579	106	560	1,741	1,977
Bloom to dough..	5,239	568	115	578	1,465	2,513
Seed ripe........	6,209	600	121	555	1,517	3,416

SOURCE: *U.S. Dept. Agr. Farmers' Bul.* 1260 (1924).

proved to be far superior to earlier harvestings. The yield of carbohydrate
was more than doubled and the crude fiber content actually decreased.
Late-cut sorgos are said to produce more palatable hay and hay that is
lower in hydrocyanic acid content. If used for fodder it cures more readily
in the shock, and when made into silage the mature sorghum makes a
higher quality produce with better keeping characteristics.

Young sorghum is higher in HCN content than more mature plants.
The rapid decrease in acid content with advancing age is shown in Fig. 47.
Young sorghum averages 2,000 p.p.m. of HCN; in the early dough stage it
is less than 1,400 p.p.m., and at the mature stage about 800 p.p.m. This

probably explains the reason for few if any poisonings ascribed directly to well-cured sorghum hay or silage.

Use as Silage or Fodder. The process of curing the forage products produced by the sorghum type of plant is relatively difficult. The proportion

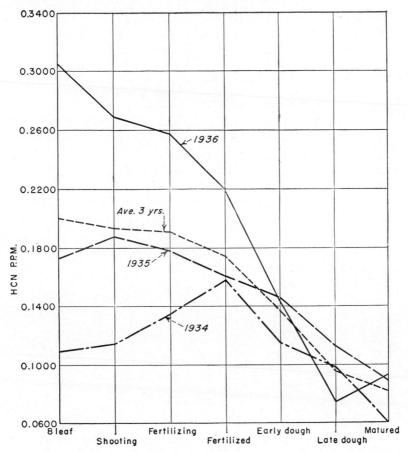

Fig. 47. Hydrocyanic acid content in green forage of 12 pure lines of sorghum and one strain of Sudan grass. (*South Dakota Agricultural Experiment Station.*)

of stalks to leaves is very high in the sorgos, and thus they cure slowly when being made into fodder. From 80 to 90 per cent of the plant, by weight, is usually stem. When cured in the field, the sorgos lose 50 to 60 per cent of their green forage weight. When air-dried to 10 per cent moisture, they lose 70 per cent of their original green weight.

The row or corn binder is commonly used to harvest fodder or silage crops. For fodder the bundles are usually stacked in the field to complete the curing process. Silage sorgo is hauled in immediately, chopped and

TABLE 213.   PER CENT OF STALKS AND LEAVES IN GREEN AND AIR-DRY
SORGO STOVER

Variety	Green stover		Air-dry stover	
	Stalks	Leaves	Stalks	Leaves
Kansas Orange........	87.7	12.3	83.1	16.9
Colman..............	88.0	12.0	85.3	14.7
Honey...............	90.6	9.4	86.4	13.6
Sumac..............	91.5	8.5	88.6	11.4
Saccaline............	95.1	4.9	92.2	7.8

SOURCE: *Tex. Agr. Expt. Sta. Bul.* 496 (1934).

placed in the silo.   The field chopper or silage cutter is becoming more
popular in harvesting the sorgos for silage.

Sorghum silage is said to be equal or superior to corn silage.   When used
as silage the feeding value of an acre of sorghum is about 50 per cent higher
than if fed as fodder.   Although the production of silage is increasing, most
of the crop raised in the sorghum region is still fed as fodder.

FIG. 48.   Harvesting sorghum for silage with a field chopper.   (*Allis Chalmers Manufacturing Co.*)

Sorghums usually are planted alone in the regions of deficient moisture,
but in more humid sections they may be mixed with such annual legumes as
cowpeas, velvet beans, and soybeans.   Such mixtures are suitable for silage
without adding a preservative, and with modern harvesting methods this
practice is becoming fairly popular.

References

1. Ahlgren, Gilbert H.: Supplementary hay crops, *N.J. Agr. Expt. Sta. Cir.* 465 (1943).
2. Boyd, F. T., O. S. Aamodt, G. Bohstedt, and E. Truog: Sudan grass management
   for control of cyanide poisoning, *Jour. Amer. Soc. Agron.*, **30:**569–582 (1938).

3. Cushing, R. L., T. A. Kiesselbach, and O. J. Webster: Sorghum production in Nebraska, *Nebr. Agr. Expt. Sta. Bul.* 329 (1940).
4. Franzke, C. J., Leo F. Puhr, and A. N. Hume: A study of sorghum with reference to the content of HCN, *S.Dak. Agr. Expt. Sta. Tech. Bul.* 1 (1939).
5. Gaessler, W. G., and A. C. McCandish: Composition and digestibility of sudan grass hay, *Iowa Agr. Expt. Sta. Res. Bul.* 46 (1918).
6. Hume, A. N., and Clifford Franzke: Sorghums for forage and grain in South Dakota, *S.Dak. Agr. Expt. Sta. Bul.* 285 (1934).
7. Hutcheson, T. B., E. R. Hodgson, and T. K. Wolfe: Sudan grass, *Va. Agr. Expt. Sta. Bul.* 212 (1916).
8. Karper, R. E., J. R. Quinby, and D. L. Jones: Sudan grass for hay, seed and pasture, *Tex. Agr. Expt. Sta. Bul.* 396 (1929).
9. Madson, B. A., and P. B. Kennedy: Sudan grass, *Calif. Agr. Expt. Sta. Bul.* 277 (1917).
10. Martin, J. H., and J. C. Stephens: The culture and use of sorghums for forage, *U.S. Dept. Agr. Farmers' Bul.* 1844 (1940).
11. Quinby, J. R., J. C. Stephens, R. E. Karper, and D. L. Jones: Forage sorghums in Texas, *Tex. Agr. Expt. Sta. Bul.* 496 (1934).
12. Schmitz, Nickolas: Sudan grass, *Md. Agr. Expt. Sta. Bul.* 194 (1916).
13. Swanson, A. F., and H. H. Laude: Sorghums for Kansas, *Kans. Agr. Expt. Sta. Bul.* 304 (1942).
14. Swanson, C. O.: Hydrocyanic acid in sudan grass and its effect on cattle, *Jour. Amer. Soc. Agron.*, **13**:33–36 (1921).
15. Thompson, G. E.: Sudan grass in Kansas, *Kans. Agr. Expt. Sta. Bul.* 212 (1916).
16. Vinall, H. N.: Sudan grass, *U.S. Dept. Agr. Farmers' Bul.* 1126 (1922).
17. Vinall, H. N., and R. E. Getty: Sudan grass and related plants, *U.S. Dept. Agr. Bul.* 981 (1921).
18. Vinall, H. N., and R. E. Getty: Growing and utilizing sorghums for forage, *U.S. Dept. Agr. Farmers' Bul.* 1158 (1930).
19. Vinall, H. N., R. E. Getty, and A. B. Cron: Sorghum experiments on the Great Plains, *U.S. Dept. Agr. Dept. Bul.* 1260 (1924).
20. Vinall, H. N., J. C. Stephens, and J. H. Martin: Identification, history and distribution of common sorghum varieties, *U.S. Dept. Agr. Tech. Bul.* 506 (1936).

CHAPTER 21

THE MILLETS

The millets have been losing popularity in the United States ever since Sudan grass was introduced. They have been unable generally to compete with this grass in yield, and they are not always considered as valuable for feeding. Nevertheless, the millets are still grown for supplementary hay crops because they possess several desirable characteristics. They are easy to grow, the seed is usually cheap, and a crop can be secured in 2 or 3 months.

Among the oldest of all cultivated crops, they were grown for food in China at an early date, and by 2700 B.C. they were a part of the Chinese religious ceremony conducted by the emperor. First distribution of millet seed in this country was made by the patent office in 1849. The crop spread rapidly and by 1899 there were 1,743,887 acres reported in the census. Recent records on acreage are not available.

Comparative trials with the millets have been conducted in many parts of the United States. One of the main reasons for the declining acreage of the crop is evident from the summary of yield records given in Table 214 for certain foxtail millets compared with proso millet and Sudan grass. Sudan grass, in general, proved superior in these tests, and such records as this probably explain the rapid rise of Sudan grass acreage.

TABLE 214. YIELDS OF FOXTAIL MILLETS COMPARED WITH THOSE OF PROSO MILLET AND SUDAN GRASS, TONS PER ACRE

Locality	Common	German	Kursk	Hungarian	Proso	Sudan grass
Great Plains:						
Northern.....	1.66	1.56	1.78	1.62	1.38	2.19
Central........	1.71	2.76	2.04	1.88	1.27	3.20
Southern......	....	2.12	1.27	1.37	....	3.74
Northern Mississippi Valley....	1.80	2.15	2.16	2.05	2.04	3.38
Northeastern Corn Belt..........	2.55	3.72	....	2.80	2.62	3.20
Southeastern states........	....	3.25	....	2.42	....	3.45

SOURCE: *U.S. Dept. Agr. Farmers' Bul.* 793 (1917).

212

Types and Varieties

There are many different millets, but only a few have attained any significance in this country. The more important ones are listed with their scientific names in Table 215. More than 90 per cent of the millet hay is said to be produced from the foxtail millets. Proso millet is seldom used for hay; it is grown mostly for its grain.

Fig. 49. Foxtail millet. (*New Jersey Agricultural Experiment Station.*)

TABLE 215. Groups of the Important Millets, Showing Common and Botanical Names

Common name	Botanical name
Barnyard or Japanese..............	*Echinochloa crusgalli* var. *frumentacea* (Roxb.) Wight.
Finger........................	*Eleusine coracana* (L.) Gaertn.
Foxtail........................	*Setaria italica* Beauv.
Pearl........................	*Pennisetum glaucum* (L.) R. Br.
Proso or hog....................	*Panicum miliaceum* L.

Source: *U.S. Dept. Agr. Farmers' Bul.* 793 (1917).

The millets probably are grown to some extent in every state. The most intensive cultivation occurs in the Great Plains states, where the crop is relatively successful. While the millets require warm weather for best growth, they grow well in the northern regions where summers are often hot and of short duration. The millets mature quickly and have a low water requirement, but they can be injured by severe droughts. From these they do not recover readily, and in this respect the sorghums and Sudan grass are superior.

Since the foxtail varieties are by far the most important for forage production, a tabulation of their characteristics is given in Table 216. The

TABLE 216. PLANT CHARACTERS OF THE PRINCIPAL VARIETIES OF FOXTAIL MILLET

Variety	Ave. period of growth, days	Size of stem	Size of head	Character of head	Color of bristles
Common......	69	Slender	Medium	Not lobed	Pale yellow
German......	87	Stout	Large	Distinctly lobed	Green to purple
Golden Wonder	..	Stout	Large	Distinctly lobed	Pale yellow
Gold Mine....	69	Medium	Medium	Not lobed	Pale yellow
Hungarian....	69	Slender	Small	Not lobed	Purple
Kursk........	64	Slender	Small	Not lobed	Purple
Siberian......	72	Medium	Medium	Not lobed	Purple
Turkistan.....	93	Stout	Large	Slightly lobed	Purple

SOURCE: *U.S. Dept. Agr. Farmers' Bul.* 793 (1917).

growing season differs with the variety, but the range is, in general, 60 to 90 days. Slender to heavy stems and small and large heads are to be found. Golden Wonder has such short bristles that they are barely detectable, while the bristles of other varieties are longer than the spikelets, making the heads appear bristly.

YIELDS OF HAY

Various millets were compared with other crops in Nebraska, the data being given in Table 217. The yields from the foxtail millets were about equivalent to Sudan grass in these tests, and the Pearl millet was superior. Proso or hog millet was very much lower in productivity. The sweet sorghum variety, Black Amber, gave a larger yield but required a much longer time to mature. The forage of Japanese and Pearl millet was described as coarse and unpalatable. It should be recalled that Pearl millet is adapted to the humid Southeast and under those conditions makes good forage while

TABLE 217. COMPARATIVE YIELDS OF ANNUAL FORAGE CROPS IN NEBRASKA

Crop	Average harvest date	Average height, in.	Average yield of hay per acre with 15% moisture content	
			Tons	Relative
Black Amber sorgo	Sept. 21	62	4.65	100
Sudan grass........	Sept. 21	76	3.25	70
Millets:				
Common........	Aug. 21	39	3.50	75
German.........	Aug. 29	42	3.47	75
Hungarian.......	Aug. 14	35	2.71	58
Siberian.........	Aug. 12	30	2.63	57
Hog or Proso....	Aug. 21	31	1.36	29
Japanese or barn-				
yard..........	Aug. 18	41	2.84	61
Pearl...........	Sept. 19	52	3.95	85

SOURCE: *Nebr. Agr. Expt. Sta. Bul.* 206 (1925).

Japanese millet is adapted for the northern humid areas of the New England states.

Another variety test reported from Michigan[6] shows great differences in productivity and quality of forage. The German and Common varieties were suggested for uplands in that state and the Hungarian for low, moist, muck soils. Japanese millet was considered too coarse and unpalatable for good hay.

Row plantings of the millets were compared with Sudan grass in Nevada[5] under dry-land conditions. The results showed that Siberian, Proso, and Kursk outyielded Sudan grass although the differences were small. Yields were in the range of 2 to 2½ tons of cured hay per acre. This study indicates the ability of the varieties to grow under the hot and dry conditions of the Southwest.

In the Northeast, data from Connecticut show superior yields for Japanese millet. It was recognized as difficult to cure, but its high productivity made it favored for hay. Japanese millet was found to mature later than Sudan grass and thus to make a better grass partner for soybeans. Mixtures of Japanese millet or Sudan grass with soybeans showed only small differences from a production standpoint, but they were inferior in yield to Japanese millet alone. Mixtures containing Japanese millet are not generally popular in the United States.

Rather complete variety test data have been reported from Hays, Kansas, and are given in Table 219. The numbered variety was superior for yield in these tests, followed by White Wonder and German. Kursk and Siberian were the earliest maturing varieties and also the least produc-

TABLE 218. TESTS WITH ANNUAL HAY CROPS AT STORRS, CONNECTICUT

Crop	Pounds per acre, 3-year ave.	Per cent rating, 3-year ave.
Millets:		
Japanese...............	7,184	100
Hungarian	5,235	72
Siberian...............	4,080	63
Golden................	4,540	62
Sudan grass..............	5,214	72
Wilson soybeans..........	4,631	65
Mixtures:		
Japanese and Ito San....	6,465	90
Japanese and Elton......	6,328	89
Japanese and Wilson....	6,071	85
Sudan and Wilson.......	6,006	84

SOURCE: *Conn. (Storrs) Agr. Expt. Sta. Bul.* 120 (1924).

TABLE 219. RELATIVE YIELDS AND AGRONOMIC DATA FOR MILLET VARIETIES GROWN AT HAYS, KANSAS

Variety	Relative yield, %	Average height, in.	Seeding to hay harvested, days	Seeding to maturity, days
S.P.I. 56398.............	117	35	67	85
White Wonder...........	111	39	69	87
German.................	107	36	70	93
Gold Mine..............	100	33	61	79
Hungarian..............	97	31	58	80
Siberian................	88	34	53	74
Common................	87	32	57	77
Kursk..................	86	31	54	74

SOURCE: *U.S. Dept. Agr. Tech. Bul.* 410 (1934).

tive. Hungarian and Gold Mine were intermediate in yields and maturity. White Wonder and S.P.I. were taller, coarser, and later than the other varieties and had a tendency to lodge.

Dry-land Experiments. Varieties were tested in Colorado by being grown on both fallow and Sudan grass stubble land over a period of 8 years. The Siberian, German, and Gold Mine varieties were most productive on either type of seedbed. In the same test, barnyard millet produced 3,027 pounds of hay on the fallowed land but only 820 pounds following Sudan grass. The low production on Sudan grass stubble land probably indicates a great dependence on the moisture supply in order to get high production. In the dry-land sections of the West the preceding crop has been shown to

TABLE 220. HAY YIELDS OF SIX VARIETIES OF FOXTAIL MILLET AND OF BARNYARD MILLET GROWN ON FALLOW AND SUDAN GRASS STUBBLE LAND AT AKRON, COLORADO

Variety	Fallow land		Sudan grass stubble land	
	Lb. per acre	% of Kursk*	Lb. per acre	% of Kursk*
Dakota Kursk.............	2,786	100	730	100
Siberian..................	3,308	119	814	112
German..................	3,218	114	903	111
Gold Mine................	3,169	114	806	110
Barnyard.................	3,027	113	820	64
White Wonder............	2,805	101	730	100
Hungarian................	2,601	93	747	102

SOURCE: *Colo. Agr. Expt. Sta. Bul.* 461 (1940).
  * Not all varieties grow each year. Data computed on the basis of years in which varieties compared with Kursk were grown.

TABLE 221. AVERAGE HAY YIELDS OF FOXTAIL MILLET ON STUBBLE LAND AND FALLOW AT AKRON, COLORADO, POUNDS PER ACRE

Test conducted from 1927 to 1930			Test conducted from 1931 to 1937	
Winter wheat stubble	Spring grain stubble	Fallow	Sudan grass stubble	Fallow
3,003	4,047	5,000	776	2,968

SOURCE: *Colo. Agr. Expt. Sta. Bul.* 461 (1940).

have a considerable influence along this line (see Table 221). Growing millet on fallowed soil has generally produced superior hay yields; seeding on Sudan grass stubble has proved unsatisfactory. Planting on winter wheat or spring grain stubble has resulted in reduced yields, but the extent of the reduction has not been great enough to rule the method out as impractical.

Time of Planting. Like Sudan grass or sorghum, millets must be seeded in warm soils for best results. In some Colorado tests, plantings made on May 15 resulted in highest yields of both hay and seeds. Other plantings made at 15-day intervals after that until Aug. 1 resulted in consistent yield reductions of both hay and seed. Seeding can be made, however, whenever 60 to 70 days of the growing season remain for the crop to develop.

The millets are usually seeded by drilling or broadcasting. From 20 to 30 pounds of seed are used per acre in the humid sections and 10 to 15 pounds in the drier regions. Regular haying methods are applied in mowing, curing, and storing the crop.

TABLE 222. HAY AND SEED YIELDS OF FOXTAIL MILLET SOWN ON CORN STUBBLE ON SIX DATES AT AKRON, COLORADO, 1930–1939

Seeding date	Hay		Seed	
	Acre yield, 10-year ave., lb.	% of May 15 yield	Acre yield, 10-year ave., bu.	% of May 15 yield
May 15.........	2,352	100	7.0	100
June 1.........	2,126	90	6.7	96
June 15........	1,985	84	5.1	73
July 1..........	1,464	62	5.7	81
July 15.........	895	47	4.9	79
Aug. 1..........	217	11	1.0	14

SOURCE: *Colo. Agr. Expt. Sta. Bul.* 461 (1940).

QUALITY OF HAY

Hay from the millets usually is considered inferior to that from timothy and some of the other tame grasses. However, chemical analyses for feed components indicate that millet is as good as Johnson grass or timothy for hay (see Table 223). It may be that lower palatability is responsible for

TABLE 223. FOOD ELEMENTS IN THE DRY MATTER OF MILLET, TIMOTHY, AND JOHNSON GRASS

Crop	Number of analyses	Average constituents, %				
		Ash	Crude protein	Fiber	Nitrogen-free extract	Ether extract
Millet................	40	8.82	9.85	30.08	48.22	3.03
Timothy.............	194	6.23	8.19	32.53	49.87	3.18
Johnson grass........	40	7.71	8.80	32.75	47.77	3.00

SOURCE: *U.S. Dept. Agr. Farmers' Bul.* 793 (1917).

the reputation millet hay has gained. The Connecticut Station[1] has indicated that Hungarian millet is considerably inferior to red clover as feed for dairy cattle. Many Western growers feel that the millets are equal or superior to the prairie hays as a roughage for growing stock.

A continuous ration of foxtail millet hay is not suggested for horses. The hay has an injurious effect, causing lameness, swelling of the joints, and softening of the bone texture, which increases the danger of breaking. It also increases kidney action and infusion of blood into the joints. The injury is caused by a glucoside known as "setarian," found in millet hay at all stages of growth, whether seeds are present or not. No such reaction occurs with other livestock.

The millets are used primarily as hay or grain crops. The forage-producing millets are used also to a limited extent for silage and pasture. For silage the foxtail millets are said to be inferior to the Japanese group. The silage from the foxtail varieties is usually light and dry, but apparently it is eaten readily by all forms of livestock. Before the complete mechanization of the American farm, millets were used widely for soilage purposes, with Japanese millet preferred. Unless superior varieties of millets are produced that can compete more successfully with Sudan grass, the millets will continue to decline in importance in the United States.

References

1. Brown, B. A.: Summer annuals for hay in Connecticut, *Conn. (Storrs) Agr. Expt. Sta. Bul.* 120 (1924).
2. Curtis, J. J., J. F. Brandon, and R. M. Weihing: Foxtail millet in Colorado, *Colo. Agr. Expt. Sta. Bul.* 461 (1940).
3. Getty, R. E.: Experiments with forage crops at the Fort Hays Branch Station, Hays, Kansas, 1913 to 1928, *U.S. Dept. Agr. Tech. Bul.* 410 (1934).
4. Kiesselbach, T. A., and Arthur Anderson: Annual forage crops, *Nebr. Agr. Expt. Sta. Bul.* 206 (1925).
5. Knight, C. S.: Forage and root crops, *Nev. Agr. Expt. Sta. Bul.* 86 (1917).
6. Megee, C. R.: Emergency hay and pasture crops, *Mich. Agr. Expt. Sta. Spec. Bul.* 150 (1926).
7. Piper, C. V.: Forage Plants and Their Culture, The Macmillan Company, New York, 1927.
8. Schoth, H. A., and H. H. Rampton: Sudan grass, millets and sorghums in Oregon, *Oreg. Agr. Expt. Sta. Bul.* 425 (1945).
9. Vinall, H. N.: Foxtail millet, *U.S. Dept. Agr. Farmers' Bul.* 793 (1917).

CHAPTER 22

CEREAL HAY CROPS

Such cereal crops as barley, oats, rye, and wheat are used for hay silage, and pasture as well as for grain. These cereals have certain advantages as forage crops. Their adaptation to soil and climate are well known in most localities, and they fit into regular rotation systems so that these need not be disturbed in any way. The cereal hays make good feed for all classes of livestock. Badly lodged cereal crops, originally intended for grain, can be harvested for hay or silage, thereby saving the crop. Small grains that are used as companion crops may be cut for hay, thus favoring the grass and legume planting.

The small grains are grown for hay most extensively in California and the Pacific Northwest, where the climate and topography are favorable. To some extent grain hay is produced in every state, depending on the live-stock population and the farm-rotation program. These crops are popular for mixing with such annual legumes as hairy vetch, crimson clover, and field peas.

The crop return of small grains grown for forage is about equivalent to the combined straw and grain when they are produced for the latter purpose. Generally, the hay from oats weighs slightly more than the grain and straw, from barley it is about the same, and from wheat and rye the weight is less. The nutrient value of the harvested material decreases as the crop matures, but the moisture content becomes lower and curing weather improves so that it is easier to produce good hay at the later stages of maturity.

There is considerable variation among the cereal hays as well as between the varieties within any particular species. There are differences in such characteristics as their adaptation to soil and climate, the best stage of maturity for harvesting and the composition of the hay. The seasons of best growth vary, and there are varieties that can be seeded in both fall and spring for all four of the small grains. There is a difference in the productiveness of these various hays which is greatly accentuated by the local adaptation. For instance, all the small grains are good for hay purposes in California, provided that a wise choice is made depending on the local soil and climatic conditions. In this state[3] it was found that wheat, oats, and rye are more productive than barley except in years when the moisture supply is inadequate; then barley is superior.

OATS (*Avena sativa*)

Oats make an excellent hay crop for those regions where the spring is cool and moist or the soil is deep and well supplied with moisture. They are adapted to a wide range of soils. Winter oats are sown in regions of mild climate, but where the winters are severe the spring oat varieties are used exclusively.

FIG. 50. Oats are the most popular of the small grains for hay.

Yields. Wide differences exist in the yielding ability of the many oat varieties, so that studies of this characteristic are important in evaluating them. Late- or medium-maturing varieties are most useful for hay since they usually produce higher yields than do the early ones. In addition late maturity brings the crop along at a time when the weather is more favorable for curing.

Another factor that affects the hay yield of oats is the stage at which they are cut, though only a few studies have been made on this subject. Studies of yields of oat hay at successive stages of maturity have been made in California,[3] Maine,[2] and South Carolina.[4] The greatest production was secured in California at the soft-dough stage, in Maine at the milk stage, and in South Carolina at the ripe stage. Differences in varieties and climatic conditions probably are responsible for this variation. General opinion would favor the California results as being most typical.

Quality. The time of cutting oats for hay affects not only the yield but also the quality of the product, and yet the variations are not so great as with many other hay crops. The chemical composition (Table 224) and the apparent digestibility vary at the different stages, but many of the

TABLE 224. EFFECT OF CUTTING TIME UPON PER CENT CHEMICAL COMPOSITION

Variety	Stage of development cut	Moisture	Ash	Protein	Fat	Crude fiber	Carbohydrates
California red oat	Blossom	8.3	5.3	8.4	1.8	31.6	44.6
	Milk	9.3	5.7	6.6	2.5	34.3	41.6
	Soft dough	10.0	3.7	6.1	2.5	29.7	48.0
	Ripe	8.0	5.3	5.7	1.9	33.4	45.7

SOURCE: *Calif. Agr. Expt. Sta. Bul.* 394 (1925).

differences are insignificant. The conclusion of an investigation in Maine with sheep[2] was that the nutrients in oat hay are most digestible when it is cut at the milk stage. Digestion trials with lambs were conducted in Washington,[6] using the Markton variety of oats harvested at different stages of maturity. Here it was found that the dry matter, protein, carbohydrates, and crude fat were all somewhat more digestible in the mature hay. Considering yield as well as quality, the milk or soft-dough stages seem to be the best for harvesting.

The changes in quality with the different stages are due in part to the changing proportion of plant organs. It was found in a study of Markton oats that at different stages the percentage of the total plant weight contributed by stems varied from 41.5 to 26.2 per cent; the percentage of leaves from 28.6 to 18.6, and the percentage of heads from 31.7 to 55.2 (see Table 225).

TABLE 225. PER CENT WEIGHT RELATIONSHIP OF LEAVES, STEMS, AND HEADS OF MARKTON OATS AT DIFFERENT STAGES OF MATURITY

Plant part	Stage of maturity		
	Milk	Dough	Ripe
Leaves................	28.6	20.9	18.6
Stems.................	41.5	27.8	26.2
Heads................	31.7	51.3	55.2

SOURCE: *Jour. Agr. Res.*, **54** (1937).

The ratio of heads increases rapidly with advancing age, and that of the leaves and stems decreases. When the organs of the Markton oat were analyzed at the dough stage (Table 226), the heads were found to be high

TABLE 226. PER CENT CHEMICAL COMPOSITION (ON WATER-FREE BASIS) OF
WHOLE PLANTS, LEAVES, STEMS, AND HEADS OF MARKTON OATS

Plant part, dough stage	Ash	Crude protein	Crude fiber	Nitrogen-free extract	Fat
Whole plant........	7.37	10.16	29.4	49.2	3.89
Leaves...........	11.74	10.20	31.7	41.8	4.55
Stems............	6.34	5.89	39.6	46.8	1.31
Heads...........	4.70	13.76	18.4	57.5	5.63

SOURCE: *Jour. Agr. Res.*, **54** (1937).

in protein and carbohydrates and low in fiber. The stems were the least nutritious part of the plant; the leaves at this stage were higher in protein than the stems and lower in fiber and carbohydrates.

BARLEY (*Hordeum vulgare*)

In general, spring oats are preferred to spring barley throughout the Northeastern hay-producing region owing to the feeling that higher yields and better hay can be secured from oats. However, barley is preferred to oats in the semiarid regions of the West because of its greater drought resistance. A difficulty is encountered when feeding barley hay to livestock because of the beard growth on the grain heads. This often causes sore mouths in animals forced to consume such hay. The use of smooth-awned types is helpful, and hooded varieties would eliminate this problem.

The growth rates of spring and winter barley were compared at Arlington Farm, Virginia,[5] from plantings made on Mar. 14. Both types matured in about 110 days, which indicates that a crop of barley hay can be produced in 3 to 3½ months from spring planting time.

Yields. There are variations in the productiveness of barley due to the type and variety. The graph in Fig. 51 shows the hay yields from various types of barley grown in the state of Washington. The hooded varieties, which are highly favored by livestock producers, averaged over 5,000 pounds of hay per acre. The two-rowed varieties produced more hay than the six-rowed, and the bearded ones were more productive than the hooded. In California, the Coast variety (a rough-awned type) is most widely grown for hay because of its greater productiveness. Comparative tests[3] were made which showed that this variety yielded 3,000 pounds per acre more than did the California Mariout, also a rough-awned type. The barley varieties cut for hay in the Northeastern states are the same as those used for producing grain. Variations in the proportion of leaves, stems, and heads are not great enough to make this an important factor in choosing a variety.

As with most hays, another factor affecting the yield of barley hay is the stage of maturity at which it is cut. At the various stages the difference in morphological composition contributes both to yield and quality varia-

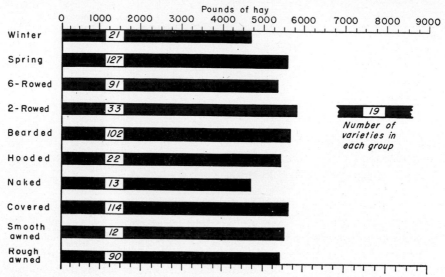

FIG. 51. The grouping of barley varieties according to plant characteristics are compared with pounds of hay. (*Washington Agricultural Experiment Station.*)

tions. The proportion of plant parts is shown for the various stages in Table 227, based on a study of Horsford barley grown in Washington. Stems decrease and heads increase with advancing maturity. The proportion of leaves remains fairly constant, and they make up only about 20 per cent of the total weight of the plant.

TABLE 227. PER CENT WEIGHT RELATIONSHIP OF LEAVES, STEMS, AND HEADS OF HORSFORD BARLEY AT DIFFERENT STAGES OF MATURITY

Plant part	Stages of maturity		
	Milk	Dough	Ripe
Leaves	22.79	20.74	20.87
Stems	36.84	29.96	15.21
Heads	40.37	49.30	63.92

SOURCE: *Jour. Agr. Res.*, **54** (1937).

Quality. The nutrient composition of the organs of barley at successive stages of maturity is found in Table 228. Crude protein is highest at the

TABLE 228. PER CENT CHEMICAL COMPOSITION (ON WATER-FREE BASIS) OF
WHOLE PLANT, LEAVES, STEMS, AND HEADS OF HORSFORD BARLEY

Plant part and stage	Ash	Crude protein	Crude fiber	Nitrogen-free extract	Fat
Whole plants:					
Milk..................	7.01	10.20	29.79	50.92	2.08
Dough................	7.13	8.32	22.64	59.90	2.01
Ripe.................	7.45	6.95	18.61	65.29	1.70
Leaves:					
Milk.................	14.04	8.14	28.82	45.09	3.91
Dough...............	16.77	10.09	26.56	42.73	3.85
Ripe.................	15.01	8.21	29.81	43.02	3.95
Stems:					
Milk.................	3.67	3.78	38.92	52.44	1.19
Dough...............	4.18	3.09	36.46	55.05	1.22
Ripe.................	6.07	2.18	47.86	43.05	0.84
Heads:					
Milk.................	6.29	13.29	17.13	61.67	1.66
Dough...............	5.59	10.16	11.84	70.89	1.52
Ripe.................	4.80	8.97	8.76	76.11	1.36

SOURCE: *Jour. Agr. Res.*, **54** (1937).

milk stage. Fiber remains almost constant in the leaves, but it increases in the stems and decreases in the heads with advancing age. The heads are richest in carbohydrates; the leaves are lowest in this factor. On the other hand, the leaves are highest in ash and fat content. The leaves and heads are considerably more nutritious than the stems. From a quality standpoint harvesting at the dough stage will give a superior hay product.

WHEAT (*Triticum vulgare*)

Wheat is usually considered inferior to oats as a hay crop. It is not used for this purpose in the Northeastern wheat regions nor in the prairie states, except when the grain price is low compared with that of hay or when the crop is heavily contaminated with weeds. In the Pacific Coast area where the grain hays are so significant, wheat is preferred to barley under conditions where the two can be grown equally well. Wheat is not considered so drought-resistant as barley and, therefore, not so adapted to the more arid sections. On the other hand, it is more winter hardy; it is well adapted for high altitudes; and it grows well on fertile soil provided the rainfall is adequate.

RYE (*Secale cereale*)

Rye is considered the least desirable of the small-grain hays. It is lower in palatability and higher in fiber content than the other cereals, and it is ready to cut so early in the season that weather conditions are usually unfavorable for curing hay. This crop, however, is well adapted to poor soils and cold climates where other cereals cannot be grown with a high degree of success. Under such conditions it should be considered useful.

Feeding Value. The feeding value varies with the stage of maturity at which rye is cut. The proportions of the plant parts as well as the chemical constituents change somewhat with the different stages of growth. As rye matures it becomes least palatable of all the cereal hays. The proportion of stems increases and that of the leaves decreases; the stalks become tough and the fiber content is high. According to a study of the chemical composition made in California,[3] the crude-fiber content was found to be lowest at the milk and soft-dough stages while the carbohydrates were highest then, and the protein decreased rapidly in the more mature stages. The data in Table 229 substantiate these conclusions. A study

TABLE 229. PER CENT CHEMICAL COMPOSITION (ON WATER-FREE BASIS) OF THE DRY MATTER OF ROSEN RYE PLANTS IN RELATION TO STAGES OF MATURITY

Stage	Ash	Crude protein	Crude fiber	Nitrogen-free extract	Fat
Half bloom.............	8.9	11.4	29.2	47.1	3.4
Full bloom.............	7.6	11.8	35.4	42.2	3.0
Dead ripe.............	6.1	5.4	32.2	54.3	2.0

SOURCE: *Jour. Agr. Res.*, **54** (1937).

of the protein content in Ohio[7] showed that it decreased from 8.5 per cent at the heading stage to 5.0 per cent at the mature stage. Also it was shown there that the protein content could be increased by adding nitrogen (see Table 230). Rye hay should be cut in the blossom stage or earlier to compare favorably with other cereal hays.

TABLE 230. RYE TOP-DRESSED WITH SULFATE OF AMMONIA IN APRIL AND ITS EFFECT ON PROTEIN CONTENT

Sulfate of ammonia, lb. per acre	Date of sampling and per cent of crude protein*	
	May 22	June 8
0	10.57	5.50
100	11.56	5.64
200	12.17	6.51
400	13.52	7.72

SOURCE: *Ohio Agr. Expt. Sta. Bul.* 543 (1934).
* Sample air-dry.

General Discussion

The relative palatability of the various cereal hay crops was studied in Washington with lambs. Data are given in Table 231. The rating shows Horsford barley at the dough stage to be the most palatable hay of those tested. Albit wheat in the milk stage rated second, and Markton

Table 231. Palatability Index of the Cereal Hay Crops Based on Experiments with Lambs

Cereal hay and stage	Feed-fed basis, %	Dry-matter basis, %	Cereal hay and stage	Feed-fed basis, %	Dry-matter basis, %
Albit wheat:			Markton oats:		
Milk........	108	109	Dough......	104	106
Dough......	100	100	Horsford barley:		
Ripe........	97	97	Milk........	85	86
Pacific Bluestem wheat:			Dough......	118	122
			Ripe........	94	96
Dough......	99	98			

Source: *Jour. Agr. Res.*, **54** (1937).

oats at the dough stage third. The ripe stages of wheat and barley were both inferior. These data indicate, in general, that the cereals are most palatable in the early stages of maturity.

The cereals are grown for hay in a manner similar to that for grain production. Hay yields are not increased markedly by heavier seeding rates since tillering is correspondingly reduced. The grains do respond to fertilizer, especially nitrogen from which strong increases in yield are often reported.

Regular haying techniques are used in curing and storing the hay. After cutting it is wilted in the swath, then put into windrows where curing usually is completed. In some areas the hay is placed in small shocks or haycocks where curing is completed before hauling to the mow or stacking. This latter method of curing is seldom used in arid climates; it has most merit where there is danger of rain or heavy dews.

No real attempt has been made in America to develop small-grain varieties particularly suited for hay or silage. Because of the great importance of these cereals for grain production their use for forage has had to take a secondary position except in the coastal area of the Pacific Northwest.

References

1. Barbee, O. E.: Barley production in Washington, *Wash. Agr. Expt. Sta. Bul.* 382 (1939).
2. Bartlett, J. M.: Oats as grain and fodder, *Maine Agr. Expt. Sta. Ann. Rpt.* (1901).

3. Hendry, Geo. W.: I. Cereal hay production in California, *Calif. Agr. Expt. Sta. Bul.* 394 (1925).
4. Keitt, T. E., and F. G. Tarbox: Changes in composition of the oat plant as it approaches maturity, *S.C. Agr. Expt. Sta. Bul.* 163 (1912).
5. Pope, Merritt N.: The growth curve in barley, *Jour. Agr. Res.*, **44**:323–341 (1932).
6. Sotola, Jerry: The chemical composition and nutritive value of certain cereal hays as affected by plant maturity, *Jour. Agr. Res.*, **54**:399–415 (1937).
7. Thatcher, L. E.: Cereal hays for Ohio, *Ohio Agr. Expt. Sta. Bul.* 543 (1934).
8. Wheeting, Lawrence C.: Cooperative field experiments with commercial fertilizer mixtures, *Wash. Agr. Expt. Sta. Bul.* 392 (1940).
9. Woll, F. W.: II. Feeding trials with cereal hays, *Calif. Agr. Expt. Sta. Bul.* 394 (1925).

CHAPTER 23

IDENTIFYING THE PLANTS

Nearly all the important forage crops belong to the grass (*Gramineae*) or legume (*Leguminosae*) families. No families of plants are of greater significance than these two. Several thousand species of grasses include the cereals such as corn, wheat, and oats and the numerous meadow, pasture, range, turf, and cover crop grasses. Many thousand species of legumes are also found, including such famous plants as alfalfa, soybeans, the clovers, and lespedezas. The legumes are used not only for forage but also for oil, as cover crops, for food and many other purposes.

The Grass Family

Members of this family possess certain characteristics which make it possible to distinguish them from other families. These are characters of the physical complex easily recognized by visual examination. Briefly they are as follows:

1. The root system is fibrous.
2. The stems are usually hollow, cylindrical, and with prominent nodes.
3. There are two vertical rows of alternate simple leaves with parallel veins.
4. The inflorescence is usually a spike or panicle; sometimes a raceme.
5. The flowers are composed of three stamens, two lodicules, a single pistil, and an outer covering consisting of lemma and palea.
6. The fruit contains a single seed fused to the ovary wall.
7. The leaves consist of a blade and a sheath.

The forage grasses are either annual or perennial, the annuals being of both the winter and summer type but possessing only fibrous roots. The perennials have not only fibrous roots but also either rhizomes or stolons. A few grasses possess both. As far as is known there are no biennial grasses.

Mature grasses may be distinguished by peculiarities of their inflorescences together with such characteristics as bulbs, rhizomes, stolons, leaves, and other organs. A simple key for the common grasses discussed in this book is here presented.

229

Key to Identifying Grasses

A. Inflorescences a single-terminal spike.

    1. Axis disjointing with spikelets attached. Three spikelets at each joint; the lateral ones sterile and reduced to awns in the case of two-rowed heads. *Barley*.

    2. Axis not disjointing; spikelets 1 to 3 at each joint, all alike.

        a. Ovate glumes, awned or pointed, sometimes toothed. *Wheat*.

        aa. Glumes narrow, awned or awnless, not toothed.

        b. Lemmas pubescent on keel, glumes one-nerved. Plants annual. *Rye*.

        bb. Lemmas smooth on keel, glumes several-nerved. Perennial. *Wheatgrass*.

        c. Spikes 4 to 6 cm. long, compressed and spikelets overlapping. *Crested wheatgrass*.

        cc. Spikes 10 to 25 cm. long, spikelets separate to overlapping. *Slender wheatgrass*.

B. Inflorescence a dense spikelike panicle.

    1. Enlarged or swollen base of stem. Jointing above glumes. Notched ligule. Perennial. *Timothy*.

    2. No enlarged base of stem. Panicle slightly less dense. Jointing below glumes; rhizomes. Perennial. *Meadow foxtail*.

    3. Panicle lobed, spikelets in clusters, very bristly, originating below the spikelet. Ligule a fringe of hairs. Annual. *Foxtail millet*.

C. Inflorescence a reduced panicle.

    1. Spikelets flattened and in clusters; stems round; rhizomes; blades very near sheath becoming pointed at tip. *Reed canary grass*.

    2. Spikelets clustered in one-sided inflorescence; stems somewhat flattened; leaves folded in the bud. *Orchard grass*.

    3. Spikelets two-flowered, distributed along entire panicle; branches whorled; long awn on lemma of staminate flower. *Tall oatgrass*.

D. Spreading panicle.

    1. Spikelets small and one-flowered; pyramidal panicle, branches whorled, rhizomes. *Redtop*.

    2. Large spikelets; two-flowered; branches whorled, usually long awns. Spring or winter annual. *Oats*.

    3. Spikelets in two's or three's; upper stalked and sterile; lower sessile and fertile. Strongly awned fertile spikelet.

        a. Stems size of a lead pencil or smaller; no rhizomes. Summer annual. *Sudan grass*.

        aa. Stems size of a lead pencil or smaller. Ligule hairy on top. Perennial by rhizomes. *Johnson grass*.

        aaa. Stems larger than lead pencil, juice sweet. Annual. *Sorgo*.

    4. Spikelets six- to eight-flowered extending to near base of branches.

Branches not whorled. Underside of leaf shiny. Auricles and rhizomes present. *Meadow fescue.*

5. Spikelets six- to ten-flowered. Branches whorled; inverted W near leaf tip; auricles absent; rhizomes present. *Bromegrass.*

Aids in Identification. The vegetative parts of the grass plant that are helpful in identification include the ligule, blade, collar, auricles, sheath, and bud shoot. The student should be able to recognize these characters and to use them with suitable keys in identifying any of the common hay grasses in the vegetative state.

Orchard grass   Brome grass   Reed canary   Timothy

Fig. 52. Grasses in the vegetative stage are difficult to identify.

Leaves are either rolled or folded in the bud shoot, and this forms a primary separation of grasses into two fairly large groups. The vernation can be determined by cutting a cross section of a shoot, just below the ligule of the uppermost leaf. It is also often possible to pull back the outermost leaves to observe the innermost one or in large grass species simply to observe the terminal blade of the bud shoot.

The presence or absence of auricles is readily noted. These are appendages that project from each side of the collar. They may vary in length and shape or may be rudimentary only. The auricles are often described as long, short, flat, blunt, clawlike, clasping, etc. Their presence or absence is normally consistent in any given species.

The ligule is also a prominent character valuable for identification. It is a thin often membranaceous outgrowth from the junction of the blade and the sheath. Such characteristics as length, shape of membranaceous types, margin conformations, presence or absence of hairs distinguish each species. A few species possess no ligule.

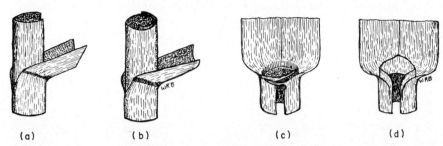

(a)   (b)   (c)   (d)

FIG. 53. Grass seedling characters: (*a*) folded leaf, (*b*) rolled leaf, (*c*) clawlike auricles and hairy ligule, (*d*) auricles absent, membranaceous ligule.

The blade is the free part of the leaf beginning above the collar or ligule. Most grass blades are long and flat, but a few are short or tightly rolled. Blades may be described as flat, V-shaped, bristlelike, involute and rolled, and involute. The tips may be tapering or boat-shaped and the surfaces glabrous or hairy and smooth or ridged. The blades of various species differ in degree of green color and in shiny or dull appearance.

The tubular basal portion of the leaf encircling the culm is called the sheath. These may be split, split to near base with margins overlapping, or almost completely closed. They vary in color, may be compressed or rounded, and may be glabrous or hairy.

THE LEGUME FAMILY

Legume plants produce and supply the major portion of the world's plant protein. This is utilized directly by man through eating the seed or grain, or indirectly by livestock feeding and subsequent consumption of livestock products.

Legumes are characterized by the following group of plant features, all of which are readily identified and observed by close examination.

1. The plants possess taproots either extreme or branching.
2. Nodules for nitrogen fixation are found on the roots of inoculated plants.
3. The leaves are compound, that is, composed of two or more leaflets. Venation is netted.
4. The flower is composed of five petals known as a standard, two wings, and a keel. It is said to be "papilionaceous" because of its butterfly

shape.   Two petals are fused to form the keel.   There are 10 stamens either all united or nine united and one free.

5. The fruit is a legume or pod opening along both dorsal and ventral sutures and may contain one to many seeds.

6. Seed normally without endosperm.

The legumes in general are not difficult to identify, especially in the flowering stage.   Showy flowers possessing variations in stipules, calyx lobes, and different leaf arrangements and markings characterize the group. A key to the principal genera as originated by Robbins is given below. Lespedezas were inserted.

Key to Principal Genera of Leguminosae[1]

A. Plants with tendril-bearing leaves.

    1. Calyx lobes prominent; stipules large, rounded, *Pisum* (pea).

    2. Calyx lobes not prominent; stipules mostly small, pointed.

        a. Style slender, bearded at the tip, *Vicia* (vetch).

        b. Style flattened, bearded along the inner side, *Lathyrus* (vetch-ling).

B. Plants without tendril-bearing leaves.

    1. Leaves palmately three-foliolate, flowers in heads, *Trifolium* (clover).

    2. Leaves palmately three-foliolate, flowers in axils of leaves, *Lespedeza.*

    3. Leaves pinnately three-foliolate, rarely five- to seven-foliolate.

        a. Flowers small, many in a cluster.

            (1) Flowers in slender, spike-like racemes, *Melilotus* (sweet-clover).

            (2) Flowers in short racemes, *Medicago* (alfalfa and other medics).

        b. Flowers medium to large, few in a cluster.   Pods smooth.

            (1) Keel of corolla spirally coiled, *Phaseolus* (bean).

            (2) Keel of corolla merely incurved, *Vigna* (cowpea).

        c. Pods hairy.

            (1) Twining plants, *Stizolobium* (velvet bean).

            (2) Erect or spreading, not twining, *Glycine* (soybean).

    4. Leaves pinnate, with two pairs of leaflets, *Arachis* (peanut).

Alfalfa and Sweetclover.   Alfalfa and sweetclover are readily confused because of their general similarity.   The leaflets of alfalfa are less broad than those of sweetclover, and the flowers are more clustered at the ends of the branches, whereas sweetclover has a spikelike raceme.   The fused sepals are longer and more pointed in alfalfa.   In the seedling stage sweet-clover can be distinguished from alfalfa by its smaller stipules compared

[1] Courtesy, W. W. Robbins, "Botany of Crop Plants," The Blakiston Company, Philadelphia, 1924.

with the larger ones possessed by alfalfa. Sweetclover leaves also have a bitter taste, and the plants can be distinguished on this basis.

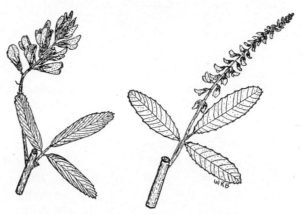

Fig. 54. A leaf and flower cluster of alfalfa (*left*) and sweetclover (*right*).

The Forage Clovers. There are many true clovers, but only four of them are significant as harvested forage crops, and accordingly the following key is limited to those crops.

Key to Important Hay Clovers (Trifoliums)
A. Plants hairy.
    1. Usually with white leaf marking; leaves elongated. *T. pratense* (red clover).
    2. Without leaf markings; leaves rounded. *T. incarnatum* (crimson clover).
B. Plants not hairy.
    1. Usually with white leaf marking; stoloniferous. *T. repens* (ladino clover).
    2. Without leaf markings; erect habit. *T. hybridum* (alsike clover).

Crimson clover has a bright scarlet seed head, but like red clover the plants are hairy. They do not have the white marking on the leaflets characteristic of red clover, nor are the leaflets as long and pointed. In addition to the white leaf markings red clover has hairy stems, leaves, and petioles. Ladino clover is completely glabrous, possesses stolons from which new leaves arise, and rooting occurs at the nodes.

Soybeans and Cowpeas. Soybeans and cowpeas are summer crops of annual duration only. The pods of the cowpea are long, and both pods and plants are smooth, whereas soybean plants and pods alike are hairy. Soybean leaves are trifoliolate, and they wither and fall as the plant matures. Leaves of the cowpea are also trifoliolate and usually larger than those of the soybean. The soybean has a determinate habit of growth, but the cowpea is of indeterminate habit and will continue growth until frost.

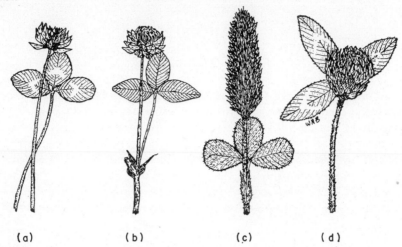

(a)   (b)   (c)   (d)

Fig. 55. Leaf and flower characteristics: (a) ladino clover, (b) alsike clover, (c) crimson clover, and (d) red clover.

Field Peas and Vetches. The stems of the field pea are hollow and the leaves pinnately compound, possessing one to three pairs of leaflets and one or more pairs of tendrils. Large showy stipules are present. The vetches are all vinelike plants excepting *Vicia faba*, which is an erect annual. The leaves are pinnately compound and tendril bearing. They, in general, possess five to eight pairs of leaflets per leaf. The weak nature of the stems is apparent.

References

1. Hitchcock, A. S.: Manual of the grasses of the United States, *U.S. Dept. Agr. Misc. Pub.* 200 (1935).
2. Nowosad, F. S., D. E. Swales, and W. G. Dore: The identification of certain native and naturalized hay and pasture grasses by their vegetative characters, *MacDonald Col. Tech. Bul.* 16 (1938).
3. Piper, C. V.: Cultivated grasses of secondary importance, *U.S. Dept. Agr. Farmers' Bul.* 1433 (1934).
4. Piper, C. V.: Forage Plants and Their Culture, The Macmillan Company, New York, 1927.
5. Piper, C. V.: Important cultivated grasses, *U.S. Dept. Agr. Farmers' Bul.* 1254 (1934).
6. Robbins, Wilfred W.: The Botany of Crop Plants, The Blakiston Company, Philadelphia, 1931.

CHAPTER 24

KNOW THE SEEDS

The ability to identify forage seeds together with knowledge of bushel weights and seeding rates is useful in seed production, processing, selling, buying, and planting. The detection and identification of associated weed and other crop seeds accurately and quickly are necessary when handling seeds and are desirable knowledge for producer, seedsman, and consumer. Most seeds can be identified by their external features alone. State seed-testing laboratories, seed houses, and state agricultural experiment stations will aid in identifying crop and weed seeds on receipt of suitable samples.

GRASS SEEDS

The fruits of grasses, commonly called "seeds," can easily be distinguished from other plant seeds. The grass "seed" has a small but readily recognized embryo partially enclosed by a relatively large endosperm. The seeds or fruits are enclosed by a lemma and palea, the palea often partly to completely covered by the lemma. Many grass fruits also possess a small stalk called a rachilla attached near the base of the glumes on the same side as the palea. Structural details are illustrated in Fig. 56.

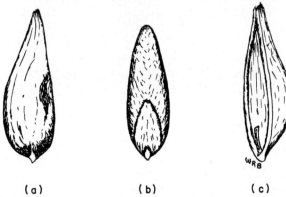

(a) (b) (c)

FIG. 56. Grass-seed characteristics: (a) palea, (b) caryopsis showing embryo, and (c) lemma with attached rachilla.

The characteristics of the rachilla regarding size, shape, length, and pubescence are further aids. The number of nerves on the back of the lemma is often helpful.

236

Certain of the grass seeds are extremely difficult to distinguish from related species. Of these, Johnson grass and Sudan grass, the wheatgrasses, domestic and perennial ryegrass, and the millets present the biggest problems. A summary of the differences between Sudan grass and Johnson grass may be found in Table 232. Thus seed of Johnson grass is smaller,

TABLE 232. A COMPARISON OF SEED CHARACTERISTICS OF JOHNSON AND SUDAN GRASS

Name	Size and shape of		Color of		Pedicels
	Spikelet	Fruit	Spikelet	Fruit	
Johnson grass	Smaller than Sudan, sharply pointed at apex, rounded at base	Greatest width above center, broad and blunt at apex, tapering toward embryo end	Mostly dark brown to black, occasionally buff	Amber, lustrous	Enlarged and cup-shaped at apex, sometimes hairy, frequently not
Sudan grass	Pointed at apex, tapering toward each end	Greatest width at center, tapering toward each end	Usually buff, sometimes brown or black	Dull, light to dark brown, greenish when immature	Ends jagged, not enlarged, sides usually hairy

SOURCE: *Iowa Agr. Expt. Sta. Res. Bul.* 334 (1944).

wider above the centers, and darker in color than Sudan grass seed. Magnifying glasses and dissecting microscopes are very helpful in identifying details of seed structures. To distinguish perennial ryegrass from the annual species the seed must be germinated and the seedlings exposed to ultraviolet light. The roots of the annual ryegrass fluoresce (appear violet) when placed under such light in a dark room and with a white filter-paper background. For the wheatgrasses a detailed examination of the characteristics of the rachilla, palea, and lemma must be made for identification.

Grass seeds may also be divided on the basis of size. Thus the seeds of barley, wheat, rye, oats, sorghum, Johnson grass, and Sudan grass may be considered large. Seeds of bromegrass, meadow fescue, tall oatgrass, and the wheatgrasses are intermediate in size and Bermuda grass, orchard, reed canary, meadow foxtail, redtop, and timothy are relatively small.

LEGUME SEEDS

The seeds of the legume family vary greatly in shape, size, and color, and these are the characters generally used for species identification. Legume

Fig. 57.   Differences in size and appearance of timothy (*left*) and bromegrass (*right*) seed.

seeds possess a strophiole and micropyle, these being close to the hilum but on opposite sides.   Another generally noticeable feature is the raphe. These characters are illustrated in Fig. 58.   Internally, legume seeds possess two cotyledons, an epicotyl, and a hypocotyl that can usually be identified as noted in the illustration of the soybean (Fig. 58).

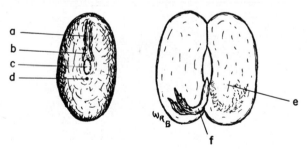

Fig. 58.   The parts of the legume seed: (*a*) raphe, (*b*) strophiole, (*c*) hilum, (*d*) micropyle, (*e*) cotyledon, and (*f*) embryo.

   Seeds of the legumes are readily classified as large, medium, or small. Of the large-seeded species the field pea, soybean, and cowpea are most important for forage.   There are many varieties of each of these crops. The variety influence is so general and so significant that it has been emphasized repeatedly.   As an example of variety differences the seed of Canadian Beauty field peas is somewhat larger than Golden Vine.   Both are relatively round and smooth.   The Kaiser variety has medium-sized seed, deeply dented, gray in color, and speckled with purple. Soybeans also vary in shape, size, and color. The seed, in general, is ovoid to elliptical and may be of solid or mixed colors. Thus seed of the Wilson variety is black, comparatively small, and elliptical in shape. Biloxi is larger and brownish, and Lincoln is yellowish to cream-colored and of medium size. Cowpeas are just as variable. The Black Crowder is a large irregularly shaped seed, and Iron variety is relatively small. Holstein is two-colored and fairly large. Seeds of the cowpeas may be marbled, spotted, or speckled, kidney-shaped, oblong, globose, etc. Even within this group of large-seeded legumes the size of the seed and the habit of growth of any particular variety influence the seeding rate. The larger the seed, the higher the bushel seeding rate per acre must be to give adequate plant populations.

The medium-sized legume seeds are represented by the vetches. Seed of this genus in turn varies in size, shape, color, and mottling and speckling.

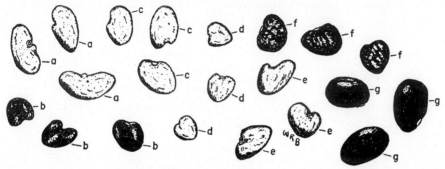

Fig. 59. Legume seeds: (*a*) alfalfa, (*b*) alsike, (*c*) sweetclover, (*d*) ladino clover, (*e*) red clover, (*f*) common lespedeza, and (*g*) Korean lespedeza.

Seeds of the clovers, alfalfa, and lespedeza are more difficult to distinguish than those of the larger seeded species. Here shape, size, and color become highly significant. Sweetclover seed can be identified not only by its shape but also by its associated sweet odor. Alfalfa seed is kidney-shaped compared with sweetclover (see Fig. 59). Alsike seed is darker colored than the other clovers, and ladino seed is extremely small. The lespedeza seeds are distinguished from each other by size and color. Common is relatively small, of dark purple color with irregular blotches, Korean is larger and uniformly dark purple in color. The sericea seed is light green and very small.

WEED SEEDS

The forage-crop seeds are often contaminated with weed seeds (see Fig. 60) that do considerable harm, depending on the kind present. The presence of persistent perennial weed seeds such as dodder or Canada thistle

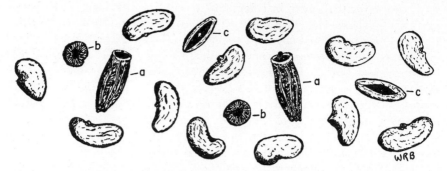

FIG. 60. Alfalfa seed showing contaminants: (*a*) Canada thistle, (*b*) lambsquarters, and (*c*) buckhorn.

TABLE 233. SUGGESTED ACRE SEEDING RATES, WEIGHTS PER BUSHEL OF SEED
AND NUMBER OF SEEDS PER POUND

Crop	Amount to seed* per acre, lb.	Weight per bushel, lb.	Seeds per pound†	Seeds per sq. ft. at seeding rates per acre, lb.				
				2	4	6	8	10
Alfalfa............	8–18	60	226,720	10	20	30	40	50
Barley............	50–80	48	13,600	0.6	1.2	1.8	2.4	3.0
Bermuda grass......	8–10	20–40	1,769,760	82	164	246	328	410
Bromegrass........	15–20	14	136,000	6	12	18	24	30
Canada field peas...	60–120	60	....	......	......	......	......	......
Clover, alsike.......	6–8	60	680,320	32	64	96	128	160
Clover, crimson.....	15–25	60	149,600	6	12	18	24	30
Clover, red........	8–12	60	272,160	12	24	36	48	60
Clover, ladino.......	4–8	60	680,320	32	64	96	128	160
Corn, silage........	8–14	56	....	......	......	......	......	......
Cowpeas...........	90–120	60	....	......	......	......	......	......
Crested wheatgrass..	12–20	..	192,800	8	16	24	32	40
Fescue, meadow.....	15–25	24	....	......	......	......	......	......
Johnson grass.......	20–30	28	122,400	6	12	18	24	30
Lespedeza..........	15–25	25	372,000	18	36	54	72	90
Millet.............	25–35	50	213,120	10	20	30	40	50
Oats..............	64–96	32	12,640	0.6	1.2	1.8	2.4	3.0
Orchard grass......	15–25	14	521,600	24	48	72	96	120
Peanuts...........	30–60	22	....	......	......	......	......	......
Redtop...........	8–10	14	4,989,600	230	460	690	920	1,150
Reed canary grass...	8–10	44–48	680,320	32	64	96	128	160
Rye..............	60–90	56	18,080	0.8	1.6	2.4	3.2	4.0
Ryegrass..........	25–40	20–24	280,500	12	24	36	48	60
Soybeans..........	60–90	60	3,168	0.14	0.28	0.42	0.56	0.70
Sudan grass........	30–35	40	54,240	2.6	5.2	7.8	10.4	13
Sunflower.........	8–12	24	....	......	......	......	......	......
Sweetclover........	8–15	60	258,400	12	24	36	48	60
Tall oatgrass.......	25–45	10	149,600	6	12	18	24	30
Timothy...........	8–10	45	1,133,920	52	104	156	208	260
Wheat.............	60–120	60	11,328	0.6	1.2	1.8	2.4	3.0
Vetch, hairy........	15–30	60	16,000	0.8	1.6	2.4	3.2	4.0

* *Hoard's Dairyman*, **87** (1942).
† *Iowa Agr. Expt. Sta. Res. Bul.* 334 (1944).

is of more concern than such annuals as ragweed or common mustard, because the former are more difficult to eradicate. Such seeds, by growing and spreading in areas formerly free of them, increase the cost of producing the crop and reduce the land value. The value of the crop and the quality are also less. Many states prohibit the sale of seed containing noxious weed seeds.

WEIGHTS AND SEEDING RATES

The legal bushel weights of the various forage-crop seeds are indicated in Table 233, together with generally suggested seeding rates and the number of seeds per pound. The range in seeding rates is considerable and in the national survey from which the data were assembled was found to depend on numerous factors. These included seedbed preparation, soil fertility, use of companion crops, season of planting, method of planting, seed prices, and climatic conditions. The seeding rates shown for certain crops, such as ladino clover and orchard grass, are too high. Many growers have been known to secure good stands by using 1 or 2 pounds of ladino seed or 6 to 8 pounds of orchard grass seed per acre.

It is interesting to consider rate of planting in relation to number of seeds per pound of any particular crop. In general, the larger the seed, the higher the pound rate of seeding (see Table 233) but the fewer the number of seeds planted per unit area. The number of seeds per pound of the various forages thus ranges from almost 5 million for redtop to as few as 3 thousand for soybeans. Seeds per square foot applied at the various acre seeding

TABLE 234. LIST OF SOME SEED-BORNE ORGANISMS DETECTABLE IN OR ON FORAGE SEEDS

Crop	Common name of disease	Causal organism	How carried by seed
Bromegrass.........	Scab	*Fusarium* sp.	Spores and mycelium on seeds
Millet.............	Smut	*Ustilago crameri*	Spores
	Downy mildew	*Sclerospora graminicola*	Spores
Redtop............	Ergot	*Claviceps* sp.	Black ergot bodies
Sorghum..........	Blight	*Helminthosporium* sp.	Mycelium
	Blight	*Fusarium* sp.	Mycelium
	Smut, covered	*Sphacelotheca sorghi*	Spores and smut balls
	Smut, loose	*Sphacelotheca cruenta*	Spores and smut balls
Soybean...........	Anthracnose	*Colletotrichum glycine*	Mycelium
Timothy..........	Scab	*Fusarium* sp.	Spores and mycelium
	Seedling blight	*Helminthosporium* sp.	Mycelium

SOURCE: *Iowa Agr. Expt. Sta. Res. Bul. 334* (1944).

rates give further information on density of seeding the many crops. In general, the smaller the seed, the greater the number of seeds needed to assure satisfactory stands.

SEED-BORNE DISEASES

Certain plant diseases are carried by infected seeds, but not much information is available for the forage crops in this respect. Those diseases which have been shown to be seed-borne are listed in Table 234 together with the causal organism. Soil-borne diseases such as "damping off" cause further inroads to forage stands under conditions favorable for their development. A measure of control can be secured through the use of organic mercury dusts which act as protectants and through the purchase of high-quality seed.

References

1. Etheridge, W. C., C. A. Helm, and B. M. King: A classification of soybeans, *Mo. Agr. Expt. Sta. Res. Bul.* 131 (1929).
2. Pieper, J. J., O. H. Sears, and F. C. Bauer: Lespedeza in Illinois, *Ill. Agr. Expt. Sta. Bul.* 416 (1935).
3. Piper, C. V.: Agricultural varieties of the cowpea and immediately related species. *U.S. Dept. Agr. Plant Industry Bul.* 229 (1912).
4. Piper, C. V.: Forage Plants and Their Culture, The Macmillan Company, New York, 1927.
5. Porter, R. H.: Testing farm seed, *Iowa Agr. Expt. Sta. Res. Bul.* P68 (1944).
6. Porter, R. H.: Testing the quality of seeds for farm and garden, *Iowa Agr. Expt. Sta. Res. Bul.* 334 (1944).
7. Seeding rates for crops, *Hoard's Dairyman*, **87**:168 (1942).
8. Vinall, H. N.: The field pea as a forage crop, *U.S. Dept. Agr. Farmers' Bul.* 690 (1915).

CHAPTER 25

HAY MIXTURES

The wide range of climatic and soil conditions existing in the United States requires a great variety of forage crops. In many situations a single species is grown, for example, alfalfa in the West or silage corn in the humid sections. On the other hand, certain mixtures of crops have been found to be of great value over large areas of the forage-producing regions where they are adapted. Growing crops in mixtures has a sound basis for popularity, or else this practice would have been discarded.

Selection of Mixtures

Mixtures usually consist of a grass or grasses with one or more legumes. Thus cowpeas and pole beans are sometimes grown with corn; cowpeas and soybeans are often planted with millet, Sudan grass, or sorgo. Timothy is mixed with red and alsike clover or alfalfa. Bromegrass and sweetclover or alfalfa are often grown together. Mixtures of oats with winter vetch or common field peas have been widely accepted.

Quality of Roughage. Obviously high-quality roughage is a first consideration. Grasses are easier to grow than legumes but are of lower feeding value. A mixture of a grass and a legume is a happy compromise. For example, when red clover is grown alone, the digestible protein content averages 7.8 per cent, as shown in Table 235. The same factor in timothy grown alone is only 4.2 per cent, and the mixture falls in between. Little difference exists on a total digestible-nutrient basis, but the clover and clover-grass mixture are over 40 per cent higher in mineral content. A

Table 235. Comparison of Clover, Clover-timothy Mixed, and Timothy Hay

Hay crop	Constituents, per cent		
	Digestible protein	Total digestible nutrients	Minerals
Red clover in bloom.........	7.8	53.4	6.2
Clover and timothy.........	5.2	50.5	6.2
Timothy..................	4.2	51.6	4.4

Source: Morrison, "Feeds and Feeding," Morrison Publishing Company, 1948.

TABLE 236. CHEMICAL COMPOSITION, POUNDS PER TON OF HAY

Crop	N	Protein	P	Ca	Mg
Alsike clover.................	47.0	294	4.2	26.2	10.6
Sweetclover..................	34.4	215	3.0	42.0	13.4
Alfalfa......................	55.0	344	3.6	25.0	9.8
Timothy.....................	19.6	122	3.0	5.6	3.6
Orchard grass...............	19.4	121	3.6	5.4	4.2

SOURCE: *Ill. Agr. Expt. Sta. Bul.* 518 (1946).

comparison of legume and grass hays was made in Illinois, a portion of the data being given in Table 236.   The legumes were far superior to the grasses in protein and mineral content, especially calcium.   By mixing a legume and grass the nutritive value of the resultant hay can be improved over that of a grass hay.   If, for example, alfalfa had been seeded with timothy in the above study and if each crop contributed 50 per cent by weight to the yield, then there would be 233 pounds of protein and 15.3 pounds of calcium per ton of hay.

The presence of the more nutritious leguminous plants is not the only factor involved in the quality of forage from a grass-legume mixture.   It has been found that often there is a favorable protein response in the grasses that are grown in mixtures with legumes.   The data in Table 237 indicate

TABLE 237.   PROTEIN IN GRASSES GROWN WITH AND WITHOUT A LEGUME

Crop	Protein in dry matter of grass	
	%	Lb. per ton
Timothy grown alone...........	9.00	162
Timothy grown with alfalfa......	9.69	174
Oats grown alone..............	7.93	159
Oats grown with peas..........	8.94	179

SOURCE: *Cornell Univ. Agr. Expt. Sta. Bul.* 294 (1911).

that the protein content of timothy was increased significantly by its association with alfalfa.   Similar results were secured for oats and peas at Cornell and also by Lipman[8] in New Jersey, working with corn, barley, wheat, and oats grown in combinations with winter vetch, soybeans, crimson clover, and peas.

In a series of analyses of mixtures Westgate and Oakley[13] showed that increases and losses of protein occurred.   The range was from a gain of

1.25 per cent protein in rye grown with sweetclover to a loss of 1.22 per cent in velvet grass growing with alsike clover. The variations in results were explained on the basis of different soils and climatic conditions, since the samples were collected in several states. In some cases the legume apparently supplied nitrogen to the grass, and in other cases there was competition between the two species for available soil nitrogen.

A study of timothy and clover mixtures in Virginia[6] showed that in the first year the clover did not have any effect on the protein content of the timothy. The plots on which this study was conducted were spaded up and reseeded in the fall to the same plants. In the second year the timothy with extra nitrogen in the soil profited by its legume associations, being 4.5 per cent higher in protein than the timothy grown alone. Corn and soybeans were studied at the same time in a similar manner. Corn grown alone averaged 1.73 per cent nitrogen, but when it was grown with soybeans it contained 2.05 per cent nitrogen in the dry matter.

Grasses have been shown to respond by more rapid leaf growth and better color when associated with legumes. Data collected in Ohio by Evans emphasize this. Table 238 summarizes the study on length of timothy

TABLE 238. AVERAGE LENGTH IN INCHES OF TIMOTHY LEAVES WHEN GROWN ALONE, WHEN IN MIXTURE WITH CLOVER, AND WHEN FERTILIZED WITH AMMONIUM NITRATE

Sample	Timothy grown alone	Timothy grown with clover	Ammonium nitrate
Timothy from lawn..............	0.94	1.14	....
Timothy from field..............	1.03	1.23	1.21
Average.......................	0.985	1.185	1.21

SOURCE: *Jour. Amer. Soc. Agron.*, **8** (1916).

leaves when grown alone and with clover. The clover essentially had the effect of stimulating leaf elongation in a manner similar to the ammonium nitrate fertilizer. The observation of Evans on the color of grasses growing alone and with clover are shown in Table 239. Clover in all cases tended to improve the greenness of the associated grass. This is a phenomenon commonly noted in mixtures of grasses and legumes.

Yields of Roughage. In addition to the quality of the roughage, another important consideration is total yield. Here again many mixtures display an advantage over straight seedings by showing an increase in dry-matter production. Studies in many states support this fact. Some comparative yield data on mixed plantings of clover and grasses are summarized in Table 240. In Tennessee, yields were increased 1½ to 2 times by the addition of alsike or red clover to the hay grass. Similar trends in

TABLE 239. PER CENT PROPORTION OF GREEN, PARTIALLY GREEN, AND BROWN LEAVES ON GRASS GROWING ALONE AND IN MIXTURE WITH CLOVER

Grass	Green	Partially green	Brown
Kentucky bluegrass:			
Alone........................	52	10	38
With clover...................	71	15	15
Creeping bentgrass..............			
Alone........................	29	28	44
With clover	42	25	33
Rhode Island bentgrass:			
Alone........................	31	30	40
With clover...................	47	24	29

SOURCE: *Jour. Amer. Soc. Agron.*, **8** (1916).

TABLE 240. COMPARATIVE YIELDS OF HAY FROM DIFFERENT PLANT COMBINATIONS, TONS PER ACRE

Hay crop	Tennessee*	New York†
Red clover and grasses........	3.31	1.33
Alsike clover and grasses.......	2.26	1.80
Grasses alone.................	1.41	1.14

* *Tenn. Agr. Expt. Sta. Bul.* 165 (1938).
† *Cornell Univ. Agr. Expt. Sta. Bul.* 424 (1923).

yield, though of less magnitude, were found in New York State.   In New Jersey[3] alfalfa-grass mixtures were compared with alfalfa alone.   The yields from the mixtures equaled those from the straight alfalfa seedings in the first two years and showed a real advantage as the alfalfa thinned out after the second year.

Not all grass-legume mixtures prove beneficial throughout the area where mixtures are generally employed.   Studies on mixing soybeans and cowpeas with corn were continued over a period of 6 years in Tennessee.[10] With both soybeans and cowpeas a reduction in the dry-matter yields of corn resulted, moisture apparently being the limiting factor.   The average yield for six crops of corn grown with soybeans was 32.3 bushels per acre compared with 49.9 bushels of corn grown alone, or 17.6 less bushels per acre.   The soybeans yielded 17.1 bushels per acre, but this did not compensate for the loss of corn yield.   When planted with cowpeas, the average corn yields were 27.1 bushels per acre compared with 39.4 for corn alone, or a difference of 12.3 bushels per acre.   A yield of 8.2 bushels of peas did not make up the difference here.   Mixing these crops is practiced with varying results in the regions of their adaptation. For silage the legume would contribute protein and increase this constituent. Decrease in the grain content, however, is undesirable from the standpoint of high-quality silage.

Fig. 61. An alfalfa-bromegrass mixture. (*Wisconsin Agricultural Experiment Station.*)

That legume partners influence the total growth of associated grasses is evident from general observations as well as controlled studies. An investigation[11] conducted in Indiana showed the greatest growth of both redtop and bluegrass when they were grown with red or white clover. Sweetclover was the least desirable of the partners tried, and alsike clover, alfalfa, and lespedeza had an intermediate effect on the two grasses. The reason for the differences in the effect on growth are not known, but it seems reasonable to suppose that competition for plant nutrients and moisture may vary between species, or that variation in nitrogen excretions from root nodules may stimulate grass growth accordingly. In general, a favorable relationship exists between the grasses and legumes, resulting in increased yield of dry matter and of total nitrogen content also.

Further data on dry-matter production as influenced by mixtures were presented by Äberg *et al.* (see Table 241). They found that the yield of bromegrass was lower when it was grown in association with orchard grass, timothy, and red clover than when grown alone, whereas there was an increase in yield when its partners were alfalfa and sweetclover. Both orchard grass and timothy proved to be better producers when grown in

TABLE 241. AVERAGE YIELD OF DRY FORAGE IN GRAMS PER PLANT FROM THREE CUTTINGS OF THREE GRASSES AND THREE LEGUMES GROWN ALONE AND IN ASSOCIATION

Crop	Associated crop					
	Brome-grass	Orchard grass	Timothy	Alfalfa	Sweet-clover	Red clover
Bromegrass.........	2.45*	1.17	1.41	2.79	2.65	1.63
Orchard grass.......	4.01	3.34*	3.44	4.37	4.24	2.92
Timothy...........	4.42	2.20	3.22*	4.67	4.76	2.80
Alfalfa............	9.37	4.80	5.91	6.81*	7.34	2.52
Sweetclover........	12.30	7.60	8.38	7.43	9.11*	2.73
Red clover.........	16.16	13.48	13.71	19.07	16.49	10.76*

SOURCE: *Jour. Amer. Soc. Agron.*, **35** (1943).
* A crop grown alone.

mixtures with alfalfa, sweetclover, and bromegrass. Red clover was favorably influenced in all associations compared with a straight seeding. It was also found in connection with this work that the mixtures which contributed to greater production of tops were also the better partners from the standpoint of root development. In general, the grasses responded favorably in association with legumes, both for yields of forage and for root development. Red clover was benefited most by association with other species, whereas sweetclover and alfalfa received the least benefit. Favorable response to grass-root growth with legumes was attributed to reduced competition between the fibrous rooted grasses and the tap-rooted legumes because different soil areas were occupied by each. Significant losses in dry matter for both members of any particular association did not occur in these studies. Where one species was depressed, the other responded by more vigorous growth.

Root Interactions. A study made at the Wisconsin Experiment Station[4] showed that there was a depression in yield when timothy and redtop were grown together. For example, timothy grown in pure culture averaged 0.577 gram per plant top, whereas when mixed with redtop the average was only 0.360 gram per plant. Similar results were secured with other grass mixtures studied. The root development followed the same pattern. In both cases the grasses in pure culture developed larger root systems than when grown in association with each other. Root interactions resulting in yield depressions are indicated as being responsible.

Data from Cornell field trials in which timothy and redtop were sown alone and in mixtures are not in agreement with the Wisconsin greenhouse findings. In this test the yield was actually greater with the mixture of redtop and timothy than with the straight seedings. A second test at

TABLE 242. YIELD OF HAY FROM TIMOTHY AND REDTOP ALONE AND IN COMBINATION

Crop	Average yield of dry matter, lb. per acre		
	1st year	2d year	Average
Timothy..................	2,598	2,112	2,355
Redtop...................	2,395	2,091	2,243
Timothy and redtop........	2,872	2,360	2,616

SOURCE: *Cornell Univ. Agr. Expt. Sta. Bul.* 424 (1923).

Cornell[14] resulted in timothy alone outyielding redtop alone and also the timothy-redtop mixture. Apparently the grass mixture relationship is complicated by many environmental factors, and this makes it most important to study mixtures in order to determine their adaptations to local conditions.

That root interactions do occur within a species seems evident from work on bromegrass, as given in Table 243. When grown in sand containing

TABLE 243. DRY WEIGHTS OF BROMEGRASS PLANTS GROWN WITH NUTRIENT SOLUTIONS IN SAND CONTAINING VARIOUS AMOUNTS OF DEAD BROMEGRASS ROOTS

Dead oven-dried roots per 2-gal. crock, grams	Dry weights per plant, grams		
	Roots	Tops	Plants
0 (check)...............	0.207	0.486	0.696
7......................	0.146	0.336	0.482
25.....................	0.039	0.056	0.095

SOURCE: *Jour. Amer. Soc. Agron.*, **33** (1941).

varying amounts of dried bromegrass roots the growth of the plants varied inversely with the quantity of dried roots present. When 25 grams of dead roots was added to the sand in 2-gallon crocks, the resulting bromegrass yield was only 0.095 gram per plant. With no dead roots added the average plant weight was 0.696 gram. The presence of inhibiting growth substances is suggested, but nitrogen deficiency has been shown to be a limiting factor here. It is well known that bromegrass reaches a sod-bound condition where thick stands appear to thin out for a few years, and root toxicity as related to nitrogen may be responsible.

Other Factors. In choosing hay mixtures a spreading type of legume seems best suited to grow with a bunchgrass and a sod-forming grass with a nonspreading legume. Thus ladino clover fills in around orchard grass, and bromegrass fills in around alfalfa. This relationship is an especially important one for field plantings where long-time stands are desired.

The time of maturity of grasses and legumes to be grown together is of significance in the making of quality hay. A grass that matures ahead of an associated legume will yield an inferior product if harvest is delayed until the legume has reached the proper stage of maturity. Grasses maturing later than the legume are preferred since this implies extra quality. For example, orchard grass is usually considered too early for red clover, and such a mixture will not give the best-quality hay. Timothy is somewhat late for alfalfa, but bromegrass is an excellent partner for this legume from a maturity standpoint and otherwise.

Perennial grasses normally should be sown with perennial legumes. This ensures a longer life of a balanced grass-legume stand. Timothy is often sown with the clovers, because the seed is cheap and stands are easy to secure. When the clovers disappear, straight timothy is harvested for hay, or the field is put back through the rotation. Annual grasses and legumes are seeded together on the basis of seasonal adaptation. The choice of associated crops often depends on the length of rotation desired.

No perennial grasses have been discovered that will grow back vigorously after spring harvest and give an additional cutting or two. Such a grass, if it had other desirable characters, would be very useful for haymaking. The fibrous grass-root system appears advantageous for growing with the tap-rooted legumes. Complete occupation of soil areas is secured by such a compatible arrangement, and this makes for more thorough utilization of soil zones.

ADVANTAGES OF MIXTURES

Certain other advantages are credited to grass-legume mixtures, but scientific data have not been presented in all cases to substantiate such claims. These observations, together with the advantages previously discussed, are covered in the following summary:

1. The productive period of the field is prolonged. As legumes thin out, the grass often takes over.
2. Grasses tend to prevent winter heaving of legumes by providing a protective vegetative mulch of aftermath.
3. Good mixtures yield nearly as well as straight legumes and usually outyield pure stands of grass.
4. Legumes grown with a grass have an effect similar to that of fertilizing the grass with nitrogen. Growth, vigor, and protein content of the grass are increased by this favorable association.
5. The chances of obtaining a full stand are increased, as thin spots may be occupied by the grass.

6. Erosion dangers are decreased by the denser soil coverage provided.
7. Encroachment by weeds is reduced to a minimum.
8. The organic matter content of the soil increases over a period of years, primarily because of the grass root systems.
9. Grass hastens the curing process in making hay.
10. Dairy cattle consume more of the mixture because it is more palatable than is the grass or legume alone.

It appears that grass-legume mixtures are highly desirable in that they generally contribute one to the other in some manner that is advantageous. The choice of grasses and legumes is one of local implication rather than broad principle. Nevertheless, such plantings as alfalfa-bromegrass, red clover–timothy, Sudan grass–soybeans and lespedeza–Bermuda grass are widely accepted in the several forage regions. The use of such mixtures seems fully justified.

References

1. Äberg, Ewert, I. J. Johnson, and C. P. Wilsie: Associations between species of grasses and legumes, *Jour. Amer. Soc. Agron.*, **35**:357–369 (1943).
2. Ahlgren, Gilbert H.: Supplementary hay crops, *N.J. Agr. Expt. Sta. Cir.* 465 (1943).
3. Ahlgren, Gilbert H., Howard B. Sprague, and Firman E. Bear: Growing alfalfa in New Jersey, *N.J. Agr. Expt. Sta. Bul.* 718 (1945).
4. Ahlgren, H. L., and O. S. Aamodt: Harmful root interactions as a possible explanation for effects noted between various species of grasses and legumes, *Jour. Amer. Soc. Agron.*, **31**: 982–985 (1939).
5. Benedict, H. M.: The inhibiting effect of dead roots on the growth of brome grass, *Jour. Amer. Soc. of Agron.*, **33**:1108–1109 (1941).
6. Ellett, W. B., H. H. Hill, and W. G. Harris: The effect of association of legumes and non-legumes, *Va. Agr. Expt. Sta. Tech. Bul.* 1 (1915).
7. Evans, Morgan W.: Some effects of legumes on associated non-legumes, *Jour. Amer. Soc. Agron.*, **8**:348–357 (1916).
8. Lipman, Jacob G.: The associative growth of legumes and non-legumes, *N.J. Agr. Expt. Sta. Bul.* 253 (1912).
9. Lyon, T. L., and J. A. Bizzell: A heretofore unnoted benefit from the growth of legumes, *Cornell Univ. Agr. Expt. Sta. Bul.* 294 (1911).
10. Mooers, C. A.: Influence of cowpea crop on yield of corn, *Tenn. Agr. Expt. Sta. Bul.* 137 (1927).
11. Roberts, James L., and Frank R. Olson: Interrelationships of legumes and grasses grown in association, *Jour. Amer. Soc. Agron.*, **34**:695–701 (1942).
12. Snider, H. J.: Chemical composition of hay and forage crops, *Ill. Agr. Expt. Sta. Bul.* 518 (1946).
13. Westgate, J. M., and R. A. Oakley: Percentage of protein in non-legumes and legumes when grown alone and in association in field mixtures, *Jour. Amer. Soc. Agron.*, **6**: 210–215 (1914).
14. Wiggans, R. G.: Studies of various factors influencing the yield and the duration of life of meadow and pasture plants, *Cornell Agr. Expt. Sta. Bul.* 424 (1923).

CHAPTER 26

MULTIPLE–PURPOSE MIXTURES

The tendency in America is toward planting mixtures of hay crops that are adapted also for other purposes such as pasture, grass silage, or seed production. Then if the hay crop proves larger than needed, the extra acreage can be turned to some other purpose. The planting of multiple-purpose mixtures thus ensures greater uniformity of feed supply through diversifying crop usage. As shown in Chap. 25, a grass-legume combination produces a larger yield of forage which is higher in feeding value than grass alone. Legumes grown alone are shorter lived than the mixtures, permit more soil erosion, and are more conducive to bloat if used for pasture. In some areas of the country lack of adapted grasses or legumes makes it desirable to plant only one or the other.

Climatic and soil conditions are responsible chiefly for the choice of mixtures in the various hay regions. Economic factors requiring flexible farm rotations further contribute to the choice of crops.

Massachusetts. Thus in Massachusetts, where the clovers are widely adapted, they are the primary choices in any mixture. Alfalfa gets first choice on the few more favorable soils, but clovers usually are included in all mixtures. Four mixtures adapted to Massachusetts are given in Table 244. Hay and silage can be made from these mixtures with aftermath grazing. The addition of ladino strengthens the pasture possibilities, thus broadening the usefulness of the mixtures.

TABLE 244. FORAGE-CROP SEED MIXTURES FOR MASSACHUSETTS

For well-drained soils:

1. Red clover 6 lb., alsike clover 3, timothy 6, redtop 1, and ladino clover 1 if hay land is to be pastured.
2. Alfalfa 6 lb. per acre, together with red clover 6, timothy 6, and ladino clover 1 (if desired).

For wet soils:

1. Red clover 3 lb., alsike clover 5, timothy 5, redtop 2, and ladino clover 1 if hay land is to be pastured.
2. Alfalfa 12 lb. per acre, together with red clover 3, timothy 3, and ladino clover 1 (if desired).

SOURCE: Massachusetts State College, Extension Leaflet 221 (1944).

New York. In New York State a half-dozen mixtures are suggested for hay and other purposes. Two of these are given in Table 245. Mixtures

TABLE 245. HAY MIXTURES FOR NEW YORK STATE

For well-drained fertile, sweet soils:

Alfalfa 8 lb., timothy 6. If used partly for pasture 8 lb. of smooth bromegrass seed may be substituted for the timothy.

For wet soils:

Red clover 3 lb., alsike 5, timothy 5, and redtop 3. If mixture is to be used for more than 2 years, substitute 1 lb. of ladino for 2 lb. of alsike.

SOURCE: New York Dairy Farm Service Letter, 1944.

are chosen according to soil conditions, the desired life of the stand, or the primary purposes for which it is to be used. The addition of bromegrass and ladino to these mixtures increases their value for pasture purposes.

New Jersey. Four mixtures are recommended for pasture purposes in New Jersey, and at the same time it is suggested that they are useful for hay and silage. They are given in Table 246. Ladino clover, bromegrass,

TABLE 246. MULTIPLE-PURPOSE MIXTURES SUGGESTED FOR NEW JERSEY

For productive well-drained soils:

1. Alfalfa 10 lb., together with smooth bromegrass 10, or orchard grass 6, or timothy 8 for spring sowing or 4 for summer or fall sowing.
2. Alfalfa 5 lb., red clover 3, ladino clover ½, together with smooth bromegrass 10, or orchard grass 6, or timothy 8 for spring sowing or 4 for summer or fall sowing.

For poorly drained soils:

Ladino clover 1 lb., alsike clover 3, reed canary grass 8, and timothy 4 for spring sowing or 2 for summer or fall sowing.

For sandy or shaly soils:

Ladino clover 1 lb., red clover 5, orchard grass 6, and timothy 4 for spring sowing or 2 for summer or fall sowing.

SOURCE: *N.J. Agr. Expt. Sta. Cir.* 492 (1945).

and orchard grass are considered especially valuable for pasture. Alfalfa and the other clovers increase the value of these mixtures for hay or grass silage.

North Carolina. Mixtures are often used for combination hay and pasture in North Carolina.[7] These are said to increase the yield, improve the palatability, and give variety in feeding. Thus small grains are mixed with annual legumes for fall-sown mixtures. Vetch, crimson clover, and Austrian peas are valuable components in these mixtures. Summer-sown mixtures consisting of Sudan grass and soybeans or sorghum and cowpeas are also used for hay, silage, or pasture. Two semipermanent sod mixtures

Fig. 62. A 4-year old sod of ladino clover and bromegrass. (*New Jersey Agricultural Experiment Station.*)

for North Carolina are given in Table 247. Orchard grass is important in both.

Table 247. Hay and Aftermath Grazing Mixtures Used in North Carolina

1. Orchard grass 10 lb., redtop 5, tall oat grass 4, red clover 6, and alsike clover 3 lb. per acre.
2. Orchard grass 10 lb., redtop 4, red clover 5, alsike clover 2, and lespedeza 7 lb. per acre.

Source: *N.C. Agr. Ext. Cir.* 237 (1939).

Table 248. Mixtures Primarily for Hay or Rotation Pasture in Ohio

Seeding number	Composition of mixture and seeding time
1	Alfalfa 6, medium red clover 4, timothy 3 (fall) or 6 (spring)
2	Alfalfa 4, medium red clover 6, timothy 3 (fall) or 6 (spring)
3	Alfalfa 4, medium red clover 4, alsike clover 2, timothy 3 (fall) or 6 (spring)
4	Alfalfa 2, medium red clover 6, alsike clover 2, timothy 3 (fall) or 6 (spring)
5	Medium red clover 6, alsike clover 3, timothy 3 (fall) or 6 (spring)
6	Alsike clover 4, timothy 2 (fall) or 4 (spring), redtop 2 (fall) or 4 (spring)
7	Alfalfa 7, alsike 3, timothy 3 (fall) or 6 (spring)
8	Alfalfa 10, timothy 3 (fall) or 6 (spring)
9	Alfalfa 10, orchard grass 6
10	Alfalfa 6, red clover 4, orchard grass 6
11	Alfalfa 10, smooth bromegrass 5 to 10
12	Alfalfa 6, red clover 4, smooth bromegrass 5 to 10
13	Add 1 to 2 lb. of ladino clover to any hay mixture recommended for the same situation or replace alsike clover in a mixture with 1 to 2 lb. of ladino

Source: *Ohio Agr. Expt. Sta. Ext. Bul.* 261 (1945).

Ohio. A great many mixtures are suggested for Ohio. A few of those recommended primarily for hay or rotation pasture are given in Table 248. Mixtures 1, 8, 9, and 11 are valuable for soils of good drainage and high lime content. Numbers 2, 3, 10, and 12 are particularly valuable for soils with a fair amount of lime and good to fair drainage. Seedings 4 and 5 can be used with limited success on lime-poor but fairly well-drained soils. Mixtures 3, 7, 9, and 11 are considered valuable for soils of poor to moderate drainage and adequately supplied with lime. Numbers 4 and 5 are recommended for medium to poorly drained soils of average lime content and 5 and 6 for inadequately drained and lime-deficient soils. Ladino clover is suggested as a replacement for alsike clover in any mixture containing it. It is possible to use seeding 5 for seed as well as hay and silage. With this planting, mixed red and alsike clover seed can be harvested from the second cutting in the first and second years, and timothy can be harvested after the second year. Other Ohio mixtures can be used similarly with greater or less success.

Michigan. Alfalfa is considered the most important legume grown in Michigan and bromegrass one of the most suitable grasses. Mixtures of the two are widely grown in that state, and even for short rotations they are preferred over red clover and timothy. Studies[11] comparing the hay yields obtained in the first year following seeding show that alfalfa and bromegrass outyielded timothy and red clover by as much as 2,745 pounds of cured hay per acre. Pasture tests in Michigan proved the superiority of the bromegrass–alfalfa mixture to a straight alfalfa seeding. The data as given in Table 249 show a 300-pound milk production advantage annually for 3

TABLE 249. GRAZING RETURNS PER ACRE FROM STRAIGHT ALFALFA AND A MIXTURE OF ALFALFA-BROMEGRASS AS MEASURED BY DAIRY COWS RECEIVING SUPPLEMENTARY GRAIN AND SOME SILAGE, AVERAGE OF 3 YEARS

Items	Alfalfa-brome	Alfalfa
Milk production, lb.	3,933	3,606
Butterfat production, lb.	179	165
Concentrates fed, lb.	845	822
Pasture days.	145	124
Net T.D.N. from pasture.	1,549	1,371

SOURCE: *Mich. Agr. Expt. Sta. Cir. Bul.* 189 (1944).

years for the mixture and a 21-day annual increase in pasturing. Tests on grazing sheep, also conducted by the Michigan Station,[11] confirm the superiority of this mixture. Sheep gained 53 more pounds per acre on alfalfa-brome mixed than on straight alfalfa. Mixtures of orchard grass and alfalfa or straight orchard grass were much inferior.

Wisconsin. Bromegrass is considered to be very valuable for hay, pasture, or silage in Wisconsin as well. It is suggested for growing in rotations where the crop is used 3 or more years for forage purposes. The yields from some crops of this type grown at Madison are given for comparison in Table 250. Bromegrass and alfalfa outyielded all the other seedings

Fig. 63. Multiple-purpose sods ensure complete use of all forage. (*New Jersey Agricultural Experiment Station.*)

TABLE 250. YIELDS OF DRY FORAGE IN WISCONSIN, POUNDS PER ACRE

Seeding	1940	1941	1942	1943	Average
Bromegrass and alfalfa....	6,772	8,509	8,331	6,420	7,508
Timothy and alfalfa......	7,465	8,270	5,363	1,980	5,770
Alfalfa*................	7,264	7,854	4,605	740	5,116
Bromegrass.............	4,922	4,314	3,478	2,946	3,915
Timothy...............	6,402	4,177	3,328	1,353	3,818

SOURCE: *Wis. Agr. Ext. Cir.* 344 (1944).
* Stand seriously reduced by wilt disease in 1942 and 1943.

tried. It was not so productive in the first year as timothy and alfalfa mixed or alfalfa alone, but second-, third-, and fourth-year yields were superior to all others. The mixture is recommended for well-drained fertile soils. Other mixtures, such as red clover and timothy, are suggested where the conditions are less favorable.

Wyoming. The mixtures indicated as suitable for Wyoming are compounded chiefly on the basis of moisture supply. These mixtures are given in Table 251. The conditions in this state are such that seedings of single

TABLE 251. FORAGE MIXTURES AND CROPS SUGGESTED FOR PLANTING IN WYOMING, POUNDS PER ACRE

Crop	Alone	Mixture
Wet-land meadows:		
Timothy	6	3
Redtop	6	3
Alsike clover	5	3
Slender wheat	6	3
Well-drained fertile soils:		
Western wheat	6	3
Brome	6	3
Sweetclover (yellow)	8	5
Alfalfa	8	5
Dry fields (or where one light irrigation might be possible):		
Western wheat	10	3
Crested wheat	8	3
Brome	8	3

SOURCE: *Wyo. Agr. Ext. Cir.* 91 (1945).

species are appropriate, depending on grower preferences. Drought-resistant species are most desirable. For very dry conditions no legume is added to the mixture, but reliance is placed on the dry-land grasses.

South Dakota. Mixtures of grasses are preferred in South Dakota because they are helpful in overcoming the hazards of seeding and the varying climatic and soil conditions. To meet climatic variations, cool- and warm-season mixtures are suggested. The so-called cool-season grasses start growth early in the spring, have a dormant period in midsummer, and resume growth in early fall. The warm-season mixtures begin growth in late spring and give fair growth during summer provided that adequate moisture is available. On the basis of seeding tests and other information[6] the following is a suggested cool-season mixture for southeastern South Dakota: smooth bromegrass 12 parts, alfalfa 4 parts. A warm-season mixture for the same area is big bluestem 15 parts, switchgrass 3 parts, and side-oats grama 2 parts. In central and western South Dakota a recommended cool-season mixture is western wheatgrass 3 parts, crested wheatgrass 4, feather bunchgrass 2, and yellow sweetclover 1 part.

Nebraska. The effect of introducing legumes into native meadows has been studied in Nebraska. Data from such a test were collected over a 4-year period where sweetclover was the legume introduced. It was found that the forage yield was 112 per cent more than from an area where the native grasses had only a very small proportion of sweetclover. Similar results were secured where alsike, mammoth and medium red clover, as well

TABLE 252.   EFFECT ON YIELD OF THE INVASION OF SWEETCLOVER IN NATIVE NEBRASKA MEADOWS

Clover content by weight, %		Yield per acre (15% moisture), lb.		Increase due to clover	
Heavily invaded area	Slightly invaded area	Heavily invaded area	Slightly invaded area	Lb.	%
66.2	6.3	5,268	2,485	2,783	112.0

SOURCE: *Nebr. Agr. Expt. Sta. Res. Bul.* 60 (1932).

as timothy and redtop, had invaded the native swards. Interestingly enough, yields of the native vegetation were reduced by the associated legumes in many cases, probably by competition for moisture, light, and space. Alsike clover caused a 39 per cent reduction, whereas white clover caused no loss at all.

Nevada. In northeastern Nevada, soils vary from moist to very dry. Accordingly, mixtures have been selected to meet the varying soil and climatic conditions and also to give quality and productivity to any resulting stands. A few mixtures suggested for hay and second-growth pasture for Nevada are found in Table 253. Alfalfa and the clovers play an important

TABLE 253.   SEED MIXTURES FOR HAY AND SECOND-GROWTH PASTURE IN NEVADA

Medium to good soil (moist with good drainage):
  Alfalfa 7 lb., meadow fescue 5, orchard grass 3, and timothy 3.

Medium to good soil (wet with fair drainage):
  Timothy 4 lb., redtop 3, meadow fescue 6, alsike clover 2, and mammoth red clover 2.

Poor to medium soil (wet with poor drainage):
  Timothy 5 lb., redtop 5, reed canary grass 3, and alsike clover 4.

Semidry bench land:
  Crested wheatgrass 5 lb., bromegrass 5, and sweetclover 5.
  SOURCE: *Nev. Agr. Expt. Sta. Bul.* 154 (1940).

role on the moist soils; the dry-land grasses and sweetclover replace these on semidry soil. All the hay mixtures will produce adequate growth for pasturing if irrigation water can be supplied.

Colorado. Extensive hay and pasture tests in southwestern Colorado[9] indicate the value of alfalfa in that section. The combination of alfalfa and brome was superior to all other seedings tried. A mixture recommended for nonirrigated land in southwestern Colorado is alfalfa 2 or 3 pounds, bromegrass 6 to 8 pounds, and crested wheatgrass 5 to 7 pounds per acre. The mixtures are used for grazing or for making hay as desired.

The widespread planting of mixtures adapted to any of several uses indicates their recognized value in the United States. Alfalfa is more widely planted than any other hay species. Bromegrass and timothy also are widely disseminated. Crested wheatgrass is popular over much of the northern prairie states. In most instances, except under very dry conditions, legumes are seeded with grasses to secure maximum performance and benefits.

References

1. Ahlgren, H. L., and F. V. Burcalow: Brome grass and alfalfa, *Wis. Agr. Ext. Serv. Cir.* 344 (1944).
2. Boyd, George: Cultivation and renovation of native and alfalfa meadows, *Wyo. Agr. Ext. Cir.* 91 (1945).
3. Branch, F. H.: A production program for Massachusetts dairymen, *Mass. Agr. Ext. Leaflet* 221 (1944).
4. Cox, H. R., and G. H. Ahlgren: Improved pastures from better grasses and legumes, *N.J. Agr. Expt. Sta. Cir.* 492 (1945).
5. Fleming, C. E., and C. A. Brennen: Possibilities and limitations in the use of irrigated land for forage production in northeastern Nevada, *Nev. Agr. Expt. Sta. Bul.* 154 (1940).
6. Franzke, C. J., and A. N. Hume: Regrassing areas in South Dakota, *S.Dak. Agr. Expt. Sta. Bul.* 361 (1942).
7. Gaither, E. W., and E. C. Blair: Making hay in North Carolina, *N.C. Ext. Cir.* 237 (1939).
8. Keim, F. D., A. L. Frolik, and G. W. Beadle: Studies of prairie hay in North Central Nebraska, *Nebr. Agr. Expt. Sta. Res. Bul.* 60 (1932).
9. Koonce, Dwight: High altitudes forage investigations in southwestern Colorado, *Colo. Agr. Expt. Sta. Bul.* 490 (1946).
10. Ohio State University, Department of Agronomy: Choosing and sowing meadow and pasture seedings, *Ohio Agr. Ext. Bul.* 261 (1945).
11. Rather, H. C., and C. M. Harrison: Alfalfa and smooth brome grass for pasture and hay, *Mich. Agr. Expt. Sta. Cir. Bul.* 189 (1944).
12. Serviss, George H.: Dairy Farm Service Letter, New York College of Agriculture, 1944.

CHAPTER 27

SOIL–IMPROVEMENT PRACTICES

The successful production of forage crops is often dependent on factors in the soil environment. These may include the use of lime, fertilizer and manure, seed inoculation, drainage, or irrigation. The practices of liming and fertilizing are widespread in the podsolic and lateritic soil regions, and inoculation of certain legume seeds is generally accepted. Drainage and irrigation are limited in scope, yet significant where needed.

LIME

Certain forage crops are especially sensitive to soil acidity, whereas others are capable of growing readily under a wide pH range. Thus alfalfa and sweetclover are known as lime-loving plants (see Table 254). Red

TABLE 254. CROPS GROUPED ACCORDING TO THEIR TOLERANCE OF ACIDITY

Very sensitive to acidity, pH 6.5–7.0	Will tolerate slight acidity, pH 6.0–6.5	Will tolerate moderate acidity, pH 5.5–6.0
Alfalfa	Bermuda grass	Alsike clover
Barley	Corn	Cowpeas
Beets	Crimson clover	Lespedeza
Hubam clover	Field peas	Meadow fescue
Peanuts	Ladino clover	Millet
Rutabaga	Orchard grass	Oats
Saltgrass	Red clover	Redtop
Sugar beet	Ryegrass	Rye
Sunflower	Sorghums	Soybeans
Sweetclover	Timothy	Sudan grass
	Wheat	Vetch

SOURCE: *Ohio Agr. Expt. Sta. Bul.* 177 (1936).

clover, field peas, orchard grass, and timothy will tolerate slight acidity and alsike clover, meadow fescue, and the lespedezas are examples of acid-tolerant plants. Most legume hays prefer neutral to mildly acid soils, whereas the grasses are generally more tolerant.

In addition to correcting soil acidity, lime also supplies to the plant the important nutrients calcium and magnesium. Crops take up large quantities of calcium; the amounts vary with the type of crop. Legumes absorb five or more times as much calcium as grasses. In a 5-year rotation study[10] in Ohio including corn, oats, wheat, clover, and timothy, total calcium removed was as high as 240 pounds per acre. Almost half this quantity was found in the clover; this attests to the high calcium requirement of legumes.

Lime-deficient Regions. Lime is deficient in the whole general region lying eastward of a line from central Texas to northern Minnesota, as shown in Fig. 64. There are, of course, islands or smaller regions within this area in which sufficient lime is present in the soil. Most farmers within this region must consider the lime requirements of the crop being produced if they are to achieve maximum production and efficiency. Attention must be given to the quantity of lime required, its place in the rotation, and the method of application.

Crop Response to Lime. Field tests which involve the measurement of crop responses to known applications of lime are good indicators of the value of liming. Many such tests have been conducted, and a few which are representative are presented here. In Minnesota, fields having increasing degrees of acidity were selected for a lime study using alfalfa as the test plant (see Table 255). A positive correlation between degree of acidity

TABLE 255. YIELDS PER ACRE OF ALFALFA ON REPRESENTATIVE DEMONSTRATION TRACTS IN MINNESOTA, TONS

Field	Acidity		Unlimed land	Limed land	Increase from lime
	At surface	At 12–15 in.			
A	None	Medium	5.18	4.83	0.00
B	Slight	None	3.10	3.34	0.24
C	Slight	Slight	3.16	3.80	0.64
D	Slight	Medium	2.08	2.81	0.73
E	Medium	Slight	1.58	3.35	1.77
F	Medium	Medium	1.51	2.71	1.20
G	Medium	Strong	1.33	2.78	1.45
H	Strong	Medium	2.21	3.01	0.80
I	Strong	Strong	1.56	3.58	2.02
J	Strong	Strong	1.32	4.06	2.74

SOURCE: *Minn. Agr. Ext. Serv. Spec. Bul.* 107 (1926).

and crop response to lime is apparent. The stronger the acidity, the more marked the response from liming. In a 15-year study in Ohio[8] the unlimed soil developed a moderately acid condition, whereas liming maintained a satisfactory pH for good crop growth and yields of hay were more

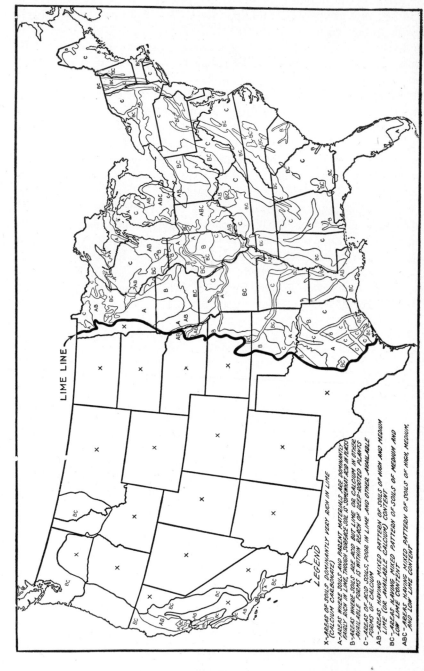

than doubled. Data from Vermont[9] also indicate increases in alfalfa hay yields with increasing satisfaction of the lime requirement, but these investigators also point out that excessive liming may cause a strong yield depression.

Even with a crop such as lespedeza, which is tolerant of soil acidity, more vigorous growth may result from liming. Thus a study in Virginia with Korean lespedeza (see Table 256) shows the increased response to fertilizer on limed soil. Yields of lespedeza were increased by more than 1 ton per acre by the addition of lime.

TABLE 256. THE EFFECT OF SUPERPHOSPHATE AND MURIATE OF POTASH ON THE YIELD OF KOREAN LESPEDEZA HAY ON LIMED AND UNLIMED SOILS

Fertilizer treatment	Yield of cured hay per acre, tons	
	Limed	Unlimed
No fertilizer..........................	2.00	0.80
100 lb. muriate of potash............	2.10	0.89
300 lb. 16% superphosphate.........	2.50	1.20
300 lb. 16% superphosphate and 100 lb. muriate of potash................	3.50	2.24

SOURCE: *Va. Agr. Expt. Sta. Bul.* 292 (1933).

Graphic results from liming forage crops as compiled by the National Lime Association are shown in Fig. 65. This graph shows the strong response of legumes, especially alfalfa, but also indicates that grasses are

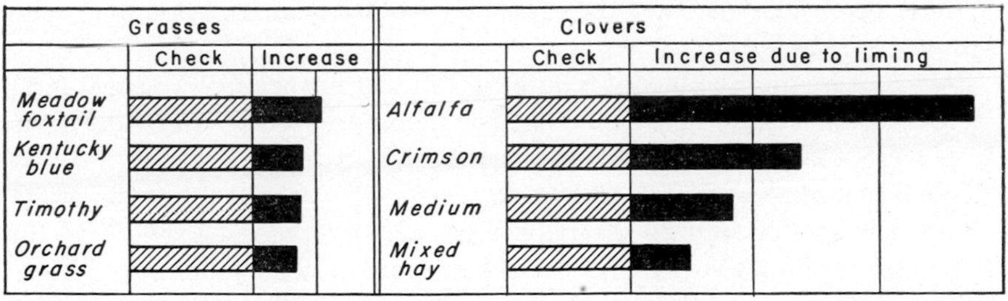

FIG. 65. Response of grasses and clovers to liming on an acid soil. (*National Lime Association.*)

benefited. In general, it has been shown that addition of sufficient lime to the soil for good crop growth is an economical practice resulting in higher yields of better quality forage.

Soils in the humid regions vary in their lime requirements from 1 to 5 tons per acre. Even on very acid soils, however, it is seldom desirable to add more than 2 tons of lime in any given year. For such heavy applications it is best to spread half the quantity on top of the soil before plowing and to broadcast the rest on top of the plowed ground and disk it in. Since lime changes the pH rather slowly, it should be applied 6 to 12 months in advance of seeding legumes and in sufficient quantity to meet the needs of the hay crop during the rotation. Top-dressing hay land with lime is not considered satisfactory, but some benefit from such a practice results, especially if lime is badly needed.

Since liming results in increased yields, greater removal of plant nutrients occurs and thus sufficient fertilizer must be added to prevent soil exhaustion. Thus, although applications of lime alone under many conditions will increase forage yields, this response will decrease with each succeeding harvest. Liming should go hand in hand with the addition of manure or complete fertilizer mixtures. Marked stimulation from lime alone was found in New York tests[5] with increases also from fertilizer alone. Combining the two treatments gave further increase in yields and proved most satisfactory.

Fertilizer Treatments

The addition of plant nutrients as fertilizer is common practice in the lateritic and podsolic soil regions of America and the practice is spreading to other areas. The most reliable method of determining fertilizer response by forage crops is through applied field tests. Obviously, fertility supplies in the various soils vary the country over, and no specific conclusions are possible.

In fertilizing hay crops two distinct problems are involved: (1) application at time of seeding and (2) top-dressing established stands. Neither of these problems has received adequate attention in America, but some data are available.

Fertilizer in the Seedbed. The best time to incorporate mineral fertilizers into the soil is when the seedbed is being prepared. In Ohio[16] fertilizers were applied at the time of planting wheat in the fall, and residual effects on an alfalfa-mixed hay crop were studied. The application of 300 pounds per acre of an 0–20–0 fertilizer gave an average increase of ½ ton of hay per acre for 3 years. An 0–14–6 mixture added at the rate of about 400 pounds per acre increased hay yields by ¾ ton per acre, and a 2–14–4 mixture added at the same rate also gave an increase of ¾ ton per acre. Thus, the substitution of 2 per cent nitrogen for 2 per cent potash gave no increased yields. These results are the average of tests conducted in seven Ohio counties and indicate good returns for fertilizer applied.

The influence of potash and phosphate fertilizers on the growth of timothy, alfalfa, soybeans, and legume-grass mixtures was studied in New Jersey.[2] Phosphate fertilizer was applied at the rate of 300 pounds of 16 per cent superphosphate per acre and potash as 50 pounds of muriate. Eight-year average yields for plots treated with phosphate only averaged about 1 ton of cured hay per acre. When both phosphate and potash fertilizers were applied, the yields were nearly 2 tons per acre. Legumes showed greater response to potash than the grasses, and the writers indicated that besides increased yields the life of alfalfa fields could be prolonged by adding potash.

Fɪɢ. 66. Drilling fertilizer into the seedbed in advance of planting. (*Cooperative G.L.F. Exchange.*)

Tests such as these have greatly stimulated the practice of adding commercial fertilizer at the time of seeding down. Concentrated commercial fertilizers are often used now in such ratios as 0–20–20, 4–12–8, 5–10–5, and 5–10–10. Rates of application may vary from 200 to 600 or more pounds per acre. In the older soil regions the use of complete fertilizers is gaining in popularity, since a small quantity of nitrogen tends to stimulate young grass and legume seedlings to a vigorous start.

Top-dressing Established Stands. The practice of adding fertilizer on top of sod ground is generally accepted as a desirable treatment. The formation of a sod naturally prevents placing fertilizer down in the soil where it would be readily available to crop roots.

Results of top-dressing experiments on alfalfa as conducted by the Arkansas Experiment Station are given in Table 257. All fertilizer treatments increased yields over the check plots. The complete fertilizer was superior to the superphosphate or potash alone, and manure gave the highest yield. The manure treatment also favored maintaining the stand, 87 per cent of the plants remaining under this treatment at the end of 7 years.

TABLE 257. EFFECT OF TOP-DRESSING FERTILIZER ON YIELDS OF ALFALFA

Treatment	7-year ave. yield, lb. per acre	Average stand at end of experiment, %
Check..........................	4,063	28
300 lb. 16% superphosphate........	4,962	38
120 lb. 50% muriate of potash......	4,500	58
400 lb. 4–12–4....................	5,615	60
10 tons manure...................	8,787	87

SOURCE: *Ark. Agr. Expt. Sta. Bul.* 447 (1944).

In Washington, tests[3] were conducted on oat hay, alfalfa, and red clover, using manure with phosphate and nitrogen reinforcements. Manure was added at the rate of 5 or 6 tons per acre, and 3 pounds of soluble nitrogen and 8 pounds of phosphoric acid was added per ton of manure. The fertility-treatment data show that greater yields resulted for the three hay crops with the addition of fertilizer. Manure alone on alfalfa increased the yield by $\frac{1}{2}$ ton per acre; on red clover, $\frac{1}{10}$ ton; and on oats, $\frac{3}{10}$ ton per acre. The addition of soluble nitrogen or phosphoric acid further stimulated yields.

Studies on the value of top-dressing alfalfa with mineral fertilizers, manure, and complete mixtures were conducted in Ohio.[16] Weeds and dry weather interfered with these tests, and top-dressing under such conditions was not profitable. Applications of 300 pounds of mineral fertilizer per acre gave yield increases ranging from as little as 24 pounds per acre up to 490 pounds. This indicates that top-dressing does not always pay but is dependent on crop response as influenced by climate and initial fertility supplies in the soil.

In Rhode Island a 5-year study of top-dressing a mixture of alfalfa, red and alsike clover, timothy, and redtop shows the value of potash (see Table 258). Reducing the potash from 100 to 50 pounds per acre reduced the legume content from 49 to 3 per cent and the yield from 2.95 to 1.82 tons. When the potash was reduced to 25 pounds, a yield of only 1.17 tons per acre was obtained. Potash is generally recognized in the Northeast hay region as the most important fertilizer for stimulating legume hay yields and increasing the persistence of the crop. Top-dressing with phosphate fertilizers usually does not give as marked responses.

TABLE 258. THE EFFECT OF VARYING AMOUNTS OF POTASH ON THE YIELD AND COM-
POSITION OF LEGUME-GRASS HAY

Treatment $N–P_2O_5–K_2O$ lb. per acre	Average yield, tons per acre	Average, %	
		Legumes	Grasses
20– 80– 100	2.95	49	51
20– 80– 50	1.82	3	97
20– 80– 25	1.17	2	98

SOURCE: *Jour. Amer. Soc. Agron.*, **39** (1947).

Applying Nitrogen Carriers. Soluble nitrogen fertilizers are very effective in stimulating the growth of grass hays in humid regions. In a 9-year study in New York[6] on timothy the application of 160 pounds of nitrate of soda increased yields by 1,332 pounds of cured hay per acre over check plots. The application of 320 pounds of muriate of potash returned an extra 1,017 pounds of hay, whereas combining this mineral treatment with nitrogen gave an increase of 2,247 pounds per acre. The check plots received no fertilizer during the 9 years of this study.

In New Jersey[14] soluble nitrogen fertilizers gave strong increases in early-cut timothy hay (see Table 259). Early spring applications are usually

TABLE 259. EFFECT OF SOLUBLE NITROGEN FERTILIZERS ON YIELD OF TIMOTHY

April treatment	*Average yield per acre, lb.*
No treatment	1,779
135 lb. of calcium cyanamide	2,637
125 lb. of nitrate of soda	3,431
10 tons of manure	2,187

SOURCE: *N.J. Agr. Expt. Sta. Bul.* 644 (1938).

practiced. Deferring the nitrogen application until 10 to 20 days before harvesting has given increased protein content of the hay, but this does not permit time for maximum yield response of the crop.

Use of Manure. The application of manure to hayfields appears to be a justifiable practice. Light rates of 5 to 6 tons per acre are used. Manure is considered especially valuable for top-dressing new seedings to offer winter protection and to stimulate their growth in the seedling year.

MINOR ELEMENTS

Of the minor elements, boron in particular has been shown to be significant in forage production in America. In addition manganese deficiencies have occurred on soybeans, oats, and peas especially in the Southeastern states, and iron has been reported deficient in very limited areas on sorghum, corn, and lespedeza. There are some investigations under way in which molybdenum and copper are being tested. Deficiencies of minor elements would be expected to become problems first on the long-cultivated soils of the Eastern states.

FIG. 67. Top-dressing a hay field with barnyard manure. (*New Idea, Inc.*)

TABLE 260. Effect of Application of Borax on Yield of Alfalfa Hay at Chatham, Virginia, Pounds per Acre

Borax applied per acre, lb.	Amount of limestone applied per acre		
	4 tons	2 tons	1 ton
	Hay yield, lb.		
15.................	1,243	1,299	796
0..................	586	670	682
Increase due to borax.......	657	629	114

Source: *Va. Agr. Expt. Sta. Bul.* 336 (1941).

Responses to boron have been reported for alfalfa and the clovers. An example of data from such tests is found in Table 260. Small applications of borax gave very marked yield increases. These were most pronounced when adequate lime was added to the soil so that lack of this material did not limit alfalfa growth. The minor element problem will become of increasing significance in crop production in eastern America.

Removal of Plant Nutrients

Large quantities of the major plant-food elements are removed by the hay and forage crops, and these point to the need for replacement through sound fertilizer programs. Data on the percentage of the nutrients present in crops are found in Table 261. The data are given in terms of percentages

TABLE 261. Average Percentages of Nitrogen and Minerals Found in Forage Crops*

Crop	Ca	N	P	K	S	Mg
Alfalfa	1.445	2.243	0.211	1.811	0.209	0.246
Alsike clover	1.232	2.052	0.204	1.641	0.095	0.254
Barley hay	.....	1.330	0.227	1.871	.....	.....
Cowpeas	1.757	2.939	0.260	1.684	0.192	0.963
Field pea	1.006	2.344	0.240	1.333	0.120	0.231
Johnson grass	1.079	1.060	0.205	0.094	0.176	0.277
Lespedeza	0.427	1.940	0.450	1.720	0.106	0.166
Millet	0.260	1.091	0.199	1.382	0.070	0.137
Oat hay	0.326	1.373	0.350	.....	.....	0.184
Prairie hay	.....	0.822	0.059	0.482	.....	0.249
Red clover	1.530	.....	0.299	1.862	0.134	0.435
Rye hay	.....	1.032	0.199	1.576	0.120	.....
Saltmarsh	.....	.....	0.192	0.813	.....	0.169
Sorgo	0.493	1.057	0.119	1.106	0.090	0.314
Soybean	1.386	2.629	0.236	1.115	0.185	0.478
Sweetclover	1.303	2.403	0.217	1.347	0.139	0.314
Sudan grass	0.435	1.075	0.201	1.826	0.134	0.303
Timothy	0.274	1.039	0.158	1.037	0.116	0.068
Timothy and clover	0.268	1.349	0.169	1.371	0.217	0.098
Velvet bean	1.671	2.537	0.201	2.202	.....	.....
Vetch (common)	1.273	2.766	0.332	2.213	0.115	0.241
Wheat hay	0.387	0.641	.....	.....	.....	.....
White clover	1.317	.....	0.266	1.270	0.180	.....

* From data compiled by J. H. Stallings.

and can be easily converted into pounds per ton of hay by multiplying each value by 20. Legume hays invariably run higher than grass hays in minerals, and thus they are a particularly good source of minerals for livestock. These elements accumulated in the forage crops are in part returned to the soil through manure, but large quantities are sold off the farm as meat, wool, milk, and other products.

Inoculation

Inoculation is required for best results with most legumes raised for hay, excepting perhaps the clovers. Different types of legume bacteria exist, and these have been placed into seven important groups by bacteriologists. Cross-inoculation occurs within each group. The groups are as follows: (1) alfalfa and sweetclover, (2) the true clovers, (3) vetch and peas, (4) garden and navy beans, (5) lupines, (6) cowpeas and lespedeza, and (7) soybeans.

From the Mississippi River westward soils are well stocked with alfalfa bacteria. The spread of sweetclover along railroads and roadsides and the planting of alfalfa and sweetclover by farmers in the East have given wide distribution to the alfalfa strain of nodule bacteria there. Nevertheless, inoculation is usually considered essential. The clovers of the genus *Trifolium* are widely distributed in the Northeastern part of the United States. Practically all the soils in that section are well supplied with nodule bacteria. This is true also of the Southeastern section of the United States, where crimson, white, and hop clover are widely grown. Inoculation is seldom necessary.

The vetch strain of nodule bacteria is present in many localities where wild vetches and garden peas, field peas, and crop vetches have been grown. Many soils in the Middle West and East, however, are deficient in this organism. On the Pacific Coast the soils are well supplied with vetch bacteria. Inoculation is usually desirable and safest.

Neither the garden and navy bean nor the lupine groups have any forage significance. The nodulating bacteria for cowpeas and lespedeza are spread widely throughout the South due to the extensive growing of these crops, and inoculation usually is not practiced. Since soybeans have been grown for relatively few years in the United States, it is best to inoculate the seed before planting.

Method and Value of Inoculation. The most practical method of inoculating legume seeds is by the purchase of artificial cultures which are mixed with the seed before planting. Such cultures are cheap, effective, and easy to apply. The nodule bacteria working symbiotically with the host legume fix soil-air nitrogen in such a way that it can be utilized by the plant. Thus it is usually unnecessary to apply nitrogen fertilizers to legume crops. Legumes in general take about as much nitrogen from the air as is removed in the tops when cut for hay. Thus, plowing under a legume crop or returning manure to the field should give a favorable nitrogen balance.

Effect of Lime. The addition of lime to acid soils normally makes conditions more favorable for fixation of nitrogen by the nodule bacteria. Tests conducted in Wisconsin[4] indicate better fixation by increased nitrogen content in the hay from the inoculated alfalfa compared with no inoculation. In two cases out of three the yields of dry matter were also increased by inoculating.

Results of studies in Florida on nodule formation with decreasing soil

TABLE 262. MEAN NUMBER OF NODULES ON FOUR CLOVERS AT DIFFERENT pH VALUES

Soil reaction, pH		Average 4 clovers
Initial	At end of experiment	
3.71	4.34	0.59
4.26	4.77	1.97
4.59	4.77	1.89
5.94	5.58	2.74
6.33	7.03	19.04
6.50	6.59	12.75
7.05	7.35	13.34

SOURCE: *Fla. Agr. Expt. Sta. Bul.* 417 (1945).

acidity are given in Table 262. The legumes studied were California bur, black medic, sweetclover, and white dutch. Rapid improvement in nodulation occurred at pH 6.33 in these tests, and higher pH values showed no further increase. The function of lime with legumes is in part to make conditions favorable for the nodule bacteria to multiply and to function efficiently.

DRAINAGE

Soils can be improved by draining wet areas. Whether or not such extra investment pays depends on land values, crop productivity, and farm prices. Nearly all legume crops require good soil drainage and aeration for maximum growth. Alsike clover and ladino are fairly tolerant of wet soils, red clover is less so, and alfalfa is very exacting in its demands for good aeration. Corn requires a well-drained soil, but most of the hay grasses are tolerant of moist soil conditions. Studies with alfalfa in Ohio, data for which are given in Table 263, show that severe winter heaving of this crop occurs when drainage is poor. The same can be said for sweetclover and

TABLE 263. EFFECT OF TILE ON ALFALFA YIELDS ON A POORLY DRAINED SOIL

Condition	Yield per acre, tons				
	1919	1920	1921	1922	Average, 4 years
Untiled...........	2.85	3.19	2.49	2.14	2.67
Tiled.............	3.79	3.33	4.63	3.41	3.79

SOURCE: *Ohio Agr. Expt. Sta. Bul.* 540 (1934).

to a lesser extent for the true clovers. Drainage improves soil aeration, increases microbial activity, and helps to raise the soil temperature. Better utilization of lime and plant nutrients results.

IRRIGATING

Irrigation is widely practiced in many of the hay-producing sections of the arid West. Irrigation may be brought about by wild flooding, by farm and main ditches, flooding from field laterals, or several other methods outside the province of the present subject. Data on yield increases are

Fig. 68. Irrigating alfalfa in Washington. (*Soil Conservation Service, U.S. Department of Agriculture.*)

given in Table 264. An increase in acre production from 1.80 to 2.46 tons per acre from irrigating for the various hay crops is evident. These long-time averages, presented by the Oregon Station, are sound evidence in favor of irrigation where inadequate moisture is strongly limiting hay production. Further studies by the Oregon Station indicate the average quantity of water applied giving maximum returns per acre. Water added per pound of dry matter produced varied from 504 pounds for red clover to 657 pounds for grass hay.

The improvement of the soil is fundamental to growing the forage crops. The regions of lime and fertility shortages are closely related to the podsol and lateritic soil regions of America. Drainage is required on a small percentage of this land. In the West on the aridic soils, irrigation is probably the most promising means of increasing hay yields.

TABLE 264. COMPARISON OF FORAGE YIELDS FROM SUPPLEMENTAL IRRIGATION INVESTIGATIONS IN OREGON

Crop	Average irrigation, in.	Yield per acre, tons		Gain per acre	
		Dry	Irrigated	Total Tons	Tons per Inch
Alfalfa.................	10.50	3.62	5.83	2.21	0.21
Red clover.............	8.15	4.17	6.25	2.08	0.26
Alsike.................	8.44	1.92	4.01	2.09	0.25
Grass..................	11.20	3.33	5.13	1.80	0.16
Corn..................	5.80	6.47	8.93	2.46	0.42

SOURCE: "Supplemental Irrigation," Johns-Manville Publication, 1946.

References

1. Alway, F. J., and C. O. Rost: Liming for alfalfa in Southeastern Minnesota, *Minn. Agr. Ext. Serv. Spec. Bul.* 107 (1926).
2. Blair, A. W., and A. L. Prince: Potash saves alfalfa, clover and soybeans. Better Crops with Plant Food, Reprint FF–8, American Potash Institute, Washington, D.C.
3. Dunn, L. E., and L. C. Wheeting: Utilization of barnyard manure for Washington soils, *Wash. Agr. Expt. Sta. Bul.* 395 (1941).
4. Graul, E. J., and E. B. Fred: The value of lime and inoculation for alfalfa and clover on acid soils, *Wis. Agr. Expt. Sta. Res. Bul.* 54 (1922).
5. Gustafson, A. F.: Liming New York soils, *Cornell Ext. Bul.* 78 (1924).
6. Gustafson, A. F.: Meadow improvement through seeding, fertilization, and management, *Cornell Ext. Bul.* 181 (1929).
7. Hutcheson, T. B., and R. P. Cocke: Effects of boron on yield and duration of alfalfa, *Va. Agr. Expt. Sta. Bul.* 336 (1941).
8. Jones, Earl: Liming Ohio soils, *Ohio Agr. Ext. Bul.* 177 (1936).
9. Midgley, A. R., and V. L. Weiser: Need and use of lime on Vermont soils, *Vt. Agr. Expt. Sta. Bul.* 371 (1934).
10. Nelson, Martin: Maintenance of alfalfa stands, *Ark. Agr. Expt. Sta. Bul.* 447 (1944).
11. Ohio State University: Liming and lime requirements of the soil, *Ohio Agr. Expt. Sta. Bul.* 306 (1916).
12. Slipher, John A.: The uses of lime on the farm, *Nat. Lime Assoc. Bul.* 176, Washington, D.C.
13. Smith, F. B., R. E. Blaser, and G. D. Thornton: Legume inoculation, *Fla. Agr. Expt. Sta. Bul.* 417 (1945).
14. Sprague, H. B., and Arthur Hawkins: Increasing the protein content of timothy, *N.J. Agr. Expt. Sta. Bul.* 644 (1938).
15. Supplemental Irrigation, Johns-Manville Publication, 1946.
16. Willard, C. J., L. E. Thatcher, and J. S. Cutler: Alfalfa in Ohio, *Ohio Agr. Expt. Sta. Bul.* 540 (1934).

CHAPTER 28

SEEDBED PREPARATION

Of all crops, the small-seeded legumes and grasses require a seedbed of the highest quality. A good seedbed should be firm and free of weeds and trash, should contain adequate moisture, and should have a fine but granular structure to prevent severe crusting. Small seeds are usually unable to produce seedlings capable of overcoming the handicap of a cloddy soil or a soil of loose and open structure. Such conditions often result in too deep coverage of the seed and in rapid drying and death of the root hairs due to excess soil air.

Cultural Practices

The preparation of a superior seedbed for forage seeds requires accurate knowledge and considerable skill. The cost will vary depending on the number of operations required such as plowing, disking and harrowing, applying fertilizer, and cultipacking. Methods for obtaining the desired results vary greatly also, depending on the previous crop, soil type, moisture conditions, and the species of forage crop to be planted.

Plowing. In some rotations, plowing is practical only for turning under sod crops preparatory to planting corn. Many growers, however, plow before seeding each crop. Where plowing is used as the first step in making the seedbed, an immediate consideration is depth. For forage crops, no advantage from deep plowing is evident (see Table 265). In the Pennsyl-

TABLE 265. Effect of Depth of Plowing on Forage Yields

Crop	Location	Yields, lb. per acre	
		Ordinary plowing	Deep plowing
Alfalfa*........................	Pennsylvania	2,716	2,774
Clover and timothy*..............	Pennsylvania	4,537	4,483
Clover†........................	Ohio	5,300	5,060
Legumes‡......................	South Dakota	4,614	4,473

* *Jour. Amer. Soc. Agron.*, **11** (1919).
† *Ohio Agr. Expt. Sta. Bul.* 362 (1922).
‡ *S.Dak. Agr. Expt. Sta. Bul.* 344 (1940).

vania study, plowing at 7½ inches was as valuable as a 12-inch depth in producing alfalfa, and clover and timothy. Similar results are evident for the Ohio study on red clover. The South Dakota experiment covers 24 years of work on the legumes red clover, sweetclover, and soybeans. Again no advantage from deep plowing could be found. Tests on sub-soiling, deep tillage, and dynamiting were compared with normal plowing at 7 inches in Illinois.[11] Seed yields of sweetclover were as good with 7-inch plowing as with 14-inch subsoiling or tilling. From these experiments it appears that normal plowing depths are satisfactory in preparing a seedbed for the forage crops.

Harrowing. On stubble ground, plowing is often omitted because an adequate seedbed can be prepared with greater speed and economy by disking and harrowing. The surface of stubble fields is usually open and receptive to this type of treatment. Sometimes planting is made directly onto stubble fields with no prior preparation whatsoever.

A comparison of methods for the preparation of a seedbed for alfalfa on wheat-stubble ground is given in Table 266. It is evident from these data

TABLE 266. YIELD OF ALFALFA HAY AS INFLUENCED BY METHOD OF SEEDING IN WHEAT STUBBLE

Job method	Yield of field-cured hay, lb. per acre			
	1941	1942	1943	Average
Disked, harrowed; alfalfa seeded in August and covered by harrowing..................	2,800	11,280	11,700	8,590
Disked, harrowed, cultipacked; alfalfa seeded in August and covered by harrowing......	2,600	12,610	11,780	9,000
Disked, harrowed, cultipacked; alfalfa seeded in August and covered by cultipacking....	2,480	12,170	11,020	8,560
Disked, harrowed; alfalfa seeded in August and covered by cultipacking................	2,400	11,810	11,240	8,480
Plowed (Aug. 1), disked, harrowed; alfalfa seeded and covered by harrowing.........	2,520	12,090	12,060	8,890
Plowed (Aug. 1), disked, harrowed, culti-packed; alfalfa seeded and covered by har-rowing...............................	2,400	13,130	10,460	8,660

SOURCE: *Va. Agr. Expt. Sta. Bul.* 393 (1946).

that disking and harrowing were as effective as plowing in preparing a satisfactory seedbed for alfalfa. In South Dakota the type of seedbed most satisfactory for some western grasses was studied.[2] On the basis of grass survival double-disking oat stubble was as satisfactory as early plow-ing, and both methods were superior to seeding on unprepared oat- and corn-stubble ground. Drilling proved superior to broadcasting on all types of seedbeds. Planting by drilling grass seed directly into grain stubble is very useful in the drier areas of the plains, since soil blowing can be reduced to a minimum by this technique.

Firming the Seedbed. A firm seedbed appears to be especially important for forage plantings. The firmness helps the seeds and seedlings to obtain moisture from the soil. To secure such a condition, early preparation is

Fig. 69. The cultipacker is an excellent implement for firming the seedbed.

desirable. This permits the soil to settle and firm prior to seeding. In addition such implements as the roller and cultipacker are valuable, especially for August seedings.

The importance of the cultipacker as an aid to firming the seedbed may be noted in Table 267. By cultipacking prior to seeding followed by a

TABLE 267.   COMPARISON OF METHODS OF SUMMER SEEDING, COLUMBUS, OHIO

Method of seeding	Plants per square yard		
	Alfalfa	Red clover	Timothy (not counted)
Sown with grass-seed attachment on a grain drill...................	103	0	Very few
Sown broadcast after cultipacking and covered lightly with harrow........	182	38	Few
Same as above, but mulched with straw or manure immediately after seeding	198	137	Many

SOURCE: *Ohio Agr. Expt. Sta. Bul.* 588 (1937).

light harrowing it was possible to establish an additional 79 alfalfa seedlings per square yard of seeded area. In this test cultipacking made the difference between 38 red clover plants per square yard and a complete stand failure. Many workers favor cultipacking before planting August seedings. In the Virginia tests, however (see Table 266), cultipacking either before or after seeding appeared to be equally effective.

Mulching. Manure or straw mulches are sometimes used to increase the chances of securing good stands. This is especially common with seedings made in winter grains in late winter on frozen soil. Light top-dressings of manure or straw ranging from 1 to 5 tons per acre are the more common rates.

An indication of the value of manure as a mulch was obtained in certain Ohio experiments.[12] By applying one-half of the manure treatment to the corn and plowing the other half under for the wheat, succeeding crops of clover hay averaged 3,373 pounds per acre compared with control plots averaging 2,984 pounds. When one-half the manure was applied to the corn and one-half top-dressed on the wheat crop, the following clover yields average 4,274 pounds per acre, or an increase of 1,439 pounds over the control plots. Data on the use of straw for mulching winter wheat may be found in Table 268. Small increases from mulching at the 1-ton rate

TABLE 268. EFFECT ON CLOVER AND ALFALFA FROM MULCHING WINTER WHEAT WITH STRAW

Amount of mulch per acre, tons	Time of application	Yield, lb. per acre	
		Clover hay	Alfalfa hay
0	. . . .	4,710	5,550
1	Sept. or Oct.	4,790	5,820
1	Dec. or Jan.	5,100	6,140
2	Sept. or Oct.	4,640	6,140
2	Dec. or Jan.	4,360	5,870

SOURCE: *Ohio Agr. Expt. Sta. Bul.* 588 (1937).

are evident for the clover and alfalfa. At the 2-ton rate yields of clover were depressed, but a continued stimulation to the alfalfa was found. The straw mulch helps to prevent excessive straw growth of the winter grains and reduces the injurious effects of spring and summer droughts. It is doubtful that mulching with straw is as effective as manure on a field basis.

Mulches are particularly valuable in conserving soil moisture near the surface. This means that the beneficial effects of mulches would be most pronounced in dry seasons. They would also be more valuable for August than for fall or spring plantings.

Summer Fallowing. In the dry-land areas of the West, summer fallowing is practiced to conserve moisture before seeding down to forage and other crops. The moisture supply is so critical in this area that crop failures would often result without adequate conservation practices. In a Nebraska test[5] alfalfa seeded on land fallowed for 2 years before planting averaged 3.80 tons per acre; on land fallowed for 1 year, 3.33 tons; and without fallow, only 2.87 tons per acre. Even more striking data probably could be secured farther west where moisture is more limiting.

Labor Costs

The cost of preparing a superior seedbed is a factor of prime consideration. Each operation requires labor, machinery, and power and adds to the investment per ton, bale, or acre of hay produced. While it is desirable to keep these costs to a minimum, this must not be done at the sacrifice of a superior seedbed.

Requirements for Hay and Silage. A general idea of the location of costs in preparing a seedbed for a hay planting can be obtained by examining the data in Table 269. A total of 328 farms was included in these New

TABLE 269. HOURS OF LABOR PER ACRE AND PER TON FOR HAY GROWN IN NEW HAMPSHIRE

Labor	Hours per acre			Hours per ton		
	Man	Horse	Tractor and truck	Man	Horse	Tractor and truck
Plowing...............	0.40	0.661	0.071	0.27	0.448	0.048
Fitting................	0.37	0.611	0.067	0.25	0.414	0.045
Seeding...............	0.16	0.243	0.002	0.11	0.165	0.001
Manuring.............	1.09	2.000	0.003	0.74	1.358	0.002
Fertilizing............	0.04	0.057	0.002	0.02	0.039	0.001
Total...............	2.06	3.572	0.145	1.39	2.424	0.097

SOURCE: *N.H. Agr. Expt. Sta. Bul.* 273 (1933).

Hampshire studies, and therefore the data should be fairly representative for the New England states. To produce 1 ton of hay required about 1.4 man-hours, 2.4 horse-hours, and 0.1 hour of truck or tractor use. The most time was required for applying manure and for plowing and fitting the seedbed.

In comparison the production of a ton of corn silage was about equally time-consuming. For this purpose 1.2 hours of man-labor, 1¾ hours of horse-labor, and ¼ hour of tractor or truck labor was required. On an acre basis, however, hay required only one-fifth of the time compared with corn silage, since it is not necessary to plow and prepare a seedbed each year for the hay crop.   This latter is especially significant, since an acre of hay will produce almost as much dry matter as an acre of corn in the area where these studies were made.   Obviously, seedbed operations that tend to reduce labor and power requirements in the production of forage crops are very desirable.

Distribution of Crop Costs.   The cost of preparing a seedbed should not be charged entirely to the hay crop unless it is seeded alone.   In the normal establishment of a hay crop it is often seeded in wheat, barley, or oats, except with late summer seedings or under dry-land conditions.   When this is done, cost of seedbed preparation should be borne jointly by the crops concerned.   Studies in Oregon on this point are given in Table 270.   The

TABLE 270.   MAN-HOURS AND HORSE-HOURS PER ACRE FOR OPERATIONS UPON ALFALFA SEEDED ALONE AND WITH GRAIN

Operations	Seeding alone, hr.		Seeding with grain,* hr.	
	Man labor	Horse labor	Man labor	Horse labor
Fertilizing, manuring...........	0.3	0.8	0.2	0.3
Plowing......................	2.3	5.3	0.2	0.7
Disking, rolling, harrowing.......	3.0	9.3	0.5	1.6
Leveling, bordering, ditching.....	1.4	2.2	0.7	2.5
Spreading straw...............	0.1	0.2	...	...
Seeding......................	1.0	2.7	0.5	1.0
Irrigating....................	3.4	...	1.3	...
Harvesting...................	4.5	6.6	0.8	1.2
Total.....................	16.0	27.1	4.2	7.3

SOURCE: *Oreg. Agr. Expt. Sta. Bul.* 241 (1928).

* Only labor charged to the alfalfa is shown.

cost of seeding alfalfa alone was about four times as great as when it was seeded with a grain companion crop.   Such data emphasize the economy of seeding the hay crop with a small grain, thus distributing the cost of seedbed preparation and thereby reducing the cost of producing each bale, ton, or acre of hay.

References

1. Abell, M. F.: Roughage production in New Hampshire, *N.H. Agr. Expt. Sta. Bul.* 273 (1933).
2. Franzke, C. J., and A. N. Hume: Regrassing areas in South Dakota, *S.Dak. Agr. Expt. Sta. Bul.* 361 (1942).

3. Hume, A. N.: Depth of plowing and crop yields, *S.Dak. Agr. Expt. Sta. Bul.* 344 (1940).

4. Hutcheson, T. B., M. H. McVickar, and T. J. Smith: Alfalfa production in Virginia, *Va. Agr. Expt. Sta. Bul.* 393 (1946).

5. Kiesselbach, T. A., Arthur Anderson, and J. C. Russel: Subsoil moisture and crop sequence in relation to alfalfa production, *Jour. Amer. Soc. Agron.,* **26:**422–442 (1934).

6. Noll, C. F.: Deep versus ordinary plowing, *Ann. Rept.* Pennsylvania State College, No. 18, pp. 34–47, 1912.

7. Ohio Agricultural Experiment Station: Deep plowing, ordinary plowing and subsoiling, Forty-first Annual Report, 1921, pp. 10–12.

8. Piper, Charles V.: Forage Plants and Their Culture, The Macmillan Company, New York, 1927.

9. Selby, H. E.: Cost and efficiency in producing alfalfa hay in Oregon, *Oreg. Agr. Expt. Sta. Bul.* 241 (1928).

10. Sewell, M. C.: Tillage: A review of the literature, *Jour. Amer. Soc. Agron.,* **11:** 269–290 (1919).

11. Smith, Raymond S.: Experiments with subsoiling, deep tilling, and subsoil dynamiting, *Ill. Agr. Expt. Sta. Bul.* 258 (1925).

12. Thatcher, L. E., C. J. Willard, and R. D. Lewis: Better methods of seeding meadows, *Ohio Agr. Expt. Sta. Bul.* 588 (1937).

CHAPTER 29

SELECTED SEED

The most practical and economical method of increasing crop yields is through the use of high-quality seed of adapted varieties. In spite of good seedbed preparation, incorporation of abundant lime and fertilizer into the soil, and best seeding methods and rates, the results will be inferior and disappointing unless good adapted seed is used. It has been estimated conservatively that a 15 to 20 per cent increase in crop productivity can be brought about by the widespread use of pure seed of the most satisfactory varieties. Poor seed, on the other hand, lowers yields and may cause weedy fields and even crop failures.

There are fewer varieties of most forage crops from which to choose than is the case with cereal, vegetable, and other crops. On the other hand there is a large choice of plant species for use, at least in the humid sections. There are numerous varieties of alfalfa, red clover, soybeans, sorghums, sweetclover, and cowpeas. However, with crops such as alsike clover, ladino, the lespedezas, orchard grass, bromegrass, and others, there are only a few varieties available. Intensive work by plant breeders is under way on a great number of forage crops to develop more productive varieties that are resistant to plant diseases and better suited to climate and soil.

Importance of Varieties

Since productiveness is often a first consideration in the growing of hay or silage crops, the importance of selecting the right variety cannot be overemphasized. This does not mean that one or more varieties can be recommended universally. The response of varieties varies the country over due to the many different soil and climatic conditions. It is necessary to study the results of variety tests conducted under local conditions in order to make a wise choice.

Alfalfa. For example, in Table 271 alfalfa varieties were compared on the basis of yields and persistence in the states of New Jersey and Kansas. In New Jersey the Atlantic variety outyielded Dakota Common by ⅓ ton of cured hay annually for the 3-year period reported. Almost a perfect stand of Atlantic remained at the end of 3 years compared with a loss of nearly one-fourth the stand of Dakota Common. Obviously, the choice of variety to grow in New Jersey is highly significant. In the Kansas test, the Buffalo variety was found superior to the other varieties in both yield

TABLE 271. COMPARATIVE STANDS AND YIELDS OF HAY FROM ALFALFA VARIETY TESTS CONDUCTED IN NEW JERSEY AND KANSAS OVER A PERIOD OF 3 YEARS, DRY-MATTER YIELD PER ACRE

Variety	New Jersey*		Kansas†	
	Average yield, tons	Final per cent stand	Average yield, tons	Final per cent stand
Atlantic......................	2.65	97	....	..
Kansas Common..............	2.54	93	3.40	25
Grimm......................	2.39	90	3.16	12
Dakota Common..............	2.30	78	3.38	6
Buffalo......................	....	..	3.51	95

* *N.J. Agr. Expt. Sta. Bul.* 718 (1945).
† *Kans. Agr. Expt. Sta. Bul.* 328 (1945).

and persistence. This was attributed to its resistance to the alfalfa wilt disease.

Red Clover. Extensive failures of red clover plantings occurred during the period following the First World War. Tests conducted in Kentucky (Table 272) show the wide differences between varieties. Good stands

TABLE 272. YIELDS AND PER CENT STANDS OF RED CLOVER VARIETIES IN KENTUCKY

Clover group	Percentage stand		Yield per acre, lb.
	Dec. 1, 1927	Apr. 2, 1928	
Kentucky 101..........	95	87	4,170
Southern.............	98	50	2,850
Central..............	100	53	2,786
Northern.............	97	22	617
Northwestern.........	94	Failure	.....
French..............	93	Failure	.....
Italian..............	95	Failure	.....

SOURCE: *Ky. Agr. Expt. Sta. Bul.* 318 (1931).

were found in the fall that they were planted, but by the following spring some varieties were already a complete failure. Of those varieties which did persist, Kentucky selection 101 was superior to all others. Loss of stand was attributed to heavy winterkilling. Differential response to climate and soil was evident among the varieties which survived the winter.

Soybeans. Varieties of annual hay legumes are just as responsive to soil and climate as are the biennial and perennial legumes. Data on 10 soybean

TABLE 273. COMPARATIVE YIELDS OF 10 SOYBEAN VARIETIES GROWN FOR HAY IN ILLINOIS

Variety	Average yield per acre, tons	Per cent of check	Variety	Average yield per acre, tons	Per cent of check
Macoupin.........	2.74	132	Wilson-Five.......	2.49	120
Mansoy...........	2.68	129	Kingwa...........	2.29	111
Manchuria........	2.66	128	Dunfield..........	2.11	102
Peking...........	2.60	126	Illini (check)......	2.07	100
Virginia..........	2.55	123	Ilsoy.............	1.67	81

SOURCE: *Ill. Agr. Expt. Sta. Bul.* 462 (1940).

varieties tested for hay over a 3-year period in Illinois are given in Table 273. The Macoupin variety produced 32 per cent more hay than Illini, while Ilsoy produced 19 per cent less. Since fine stems and leafiness are factors in making good soybean hay, these should also be considered.

Silage Corn. Another example of the importance of choosing the right variety is evident in the selection of a silage corn for growing in Wisconsin. Here the dairy industry makes the production of good silage essential, although the growing season is rather short. This means that relatively early-maturing varieties normally were the least productive, and the point was made that full use of the growing season would result in increased

TABLE 274. PERFORMANCE TRIALS WITH HYBRID CORN USED FOR SILAGE IN WISCONSIN

Variety or hybrid number	Maturity, days	Average increased yield of grain over Wisconsin 25, %	Yield of silage, tons per acre
Wisconsin 25..................	85	....	7.6
Early Minn. 404...............	95	32.9	9.4
Wisconsin 456.................	100	12.8	9.7
Golden Glow 531..............	105	14.9	12.4
Murdock 696..................	120	32.4	16.6

SOURCE: *Wis. Agr. Ext. Serv. Spec. Cir.* 1941.

yields. Also other factors must be considered in the choice because hybrid field corn varieties vary widely in lodging and disease resistance, stalk breakage, and grain quality. The large number of corn hybrids, many of which are known by number only, is confusing to the layman; this and varying conditions from one locality to the next make a local recommendation by competent authorities very valuable.

Factors in Seed Quality

Having selected the right variety, the crop producer must be sure that the seed purchased is pure and viable. Seed purity consists of several factors, among which trueness as to variety is highly significant. In the case of most of the hay grasses and legumes entering into trade channels, it is difficult to determine varieties. Seed-certification agencies are helpful in labeling and maintaining varietal identification and assisting the seed trade in many ways. However, less than 1 per cent of the forage-crop seed consumed is certified.

Freedom from Impurities. Other impurity factors, such as the presence of weed seeds, seeds of other farm crops, and inert matter, also reduce the value of forage seeds. If noxious weed seeds such as Canada thistle or quackgrass are found, there is a direct threat to farm value. Weed seeds persist in the soil for many years and are a continuous cause of expense. Most states have laws which require labeling of all seed sold to farmers or between farms. The label must give the kind of seed and in some cases the variety. Noxious weed seed content must be stated on the tags, and in some states other weed seeds and inert matter must be reported. Inert matter consists of chaff, plant refuse, dirt, stones, injured seeds, and other materials. This class of undesirable materials does no real harm to the farm where seeding occurs, but it is an unnecessary expense to the buyer.

Germination. The percentage germination of any lot of seed must be reported also on seed labels. Germination of some forage seeds, together with purity required for high quality, is found in Table 275. A high per-

TABLE 275. Purity and Germination of Forage Seeds of High Quality

Name of seed	Purity, %	Minimum germination, %	Name of seed	Purity, %	Minimum germination, %
Alfalfa.........	99	90	Meadow fescue....	97	90
Alsike clover.....	99	90	Meadow foxtail..	75	70
Bromegrass......	85	85	Millets..........	99	95
Common vetch...	98	95	Orchard grass....	85	85
Crested wheat-			Red clover......	98	85
grass.........	90	85	Redtop........	98	98
Crimson clover...	99	95	Tall oatgrass.....	80	80
Hairy vetch......	98	95	Timothy........	98.5	90
Ladino clover....	98	80			

centage of germination is desired in all seeds, but naturally this varies due to many factors among which are the age of the seed, seed size and maturity, presence of hard seeds, exposure to frost, type of seed, and sometimes the method used in harvesting.

Increasing age of seed usually results in decreasing viability. This is exactly what occurred in the study reported in Table 276. Alfalfa was shown to maintain high germination powers even at the end of 10 years' storage. Some seed lose their viability more rapidly than others. The

TABLE 276. VIABILITY OF VARIOUS FORAGE SEEDS STORED IN PAPER BAGS IN A DRY AIRY ROOM DURING 10 YEARS

Kind of seed	Percentage of germination						
	1 year	2 years	3 years	4 years	6 years	8 years	10 years
Alfalfa................	94	91	87	75	71	66	59
Alsike clover............	73	64	51	37	7	5	3
English ryegrass.........	72	70	66	60	28	9	1
Italian ryegrass..........	67	62	61	55	39	15	4
Meadow foxtail..........	13	11	9	7	5	1	0
Orchard grass...........	46	47	44	44	29	12	5
Red clover..............	90	90	88	84	68	16	3
Tall fescue..............	83	80	72	68	42	18	1
Tall oatgrass............	70	66	59	43	12	2	0
Timothy................	95	90	90	88	79	39	1

SOURCE: From Piper, "Forage Plants and Their Culture," rev. ed., copyright, 1924 by The Macmillan Company, and used with their permission.

hay grass and legume seeds, however, are fairly good compared with other crops in maintaining considerable percentage viability. Old seed with lowered germination must be seeded at higher rates than new seed in order to secure similar results.

The plumpness and color of the seed affect the germination and quality. These facts are brought out in Utah studies with alfalfa reported in Table 277. Hard seeds were induced to germinate by scarifying them. The shriveled seeds were highly inferior in germinating ability. Brown and dark-green seeds were also very inferior, while those seeds of true color and light green were best.

Hard Seed. A large portion of hard seeds are found ordinarily in the clovers, alfalfa, and *Lespedeza sericea*. Although these seeds are viable, they do not sprout readily but delay in germinating even under favorable conditions. From 10 to 50 per cent of the seeds of these legumes are usually hard. This condition can be reduced by scarifying the seed. In some respects hard seeds are desirable since they ensure a live seed supply in the soil, available for later germination. If these seeds are not scarified, extra seed must be sown to make up for those which do not germinate quickly.

TABLE 277. PERCENTAGE OF GERMINATION OF NORMAL AND SCARIFIED ALFALFA
SEED, TOGETHER WITH THE RELATIVE VALUES OF THE VARIOUS COLOR SEPARATES
COMPARED WITH UNSEPARATED BULK SEED (CHECKS = 100)

Color separate	Total germination		Weak and moldy		Healthy and vigorous			
	Normal	Scarified	Normal	Scarified	Normal	Scarified	Mean	Relative
Unseparated check.....	55.8	54.3	5.0	5.3	50.8	48.9	49.5	100
True color...........	59.4	75.0	4.0	11.9	55.4	63.2	60.5	122
Light green..........	49.2	68.4	5.6	15.9	43.6	52.5	49.5	100
Light brown..........	31.2	46.6	7.6	13.7	23.6	33.9	30.5	62
Dark green...........	34.8	35.0	8.0	10.8	29.8	24.2	26.1	53
Dark brown..........	18.2	28.5	3.6	7.7	14.6	21.0	18.9	38
Shriveled green.......	25.6	27.5	9.8	10.0	15.8	17.5	16.9	34
Shriveled brown......	7.6	16.9	1.8	5.3	5.8	11.6	9.7	20
Mean...............	32.3	42.6	5.3	10.7	26.9	32.0	30.3	61
Relative............	100.0	132.0	16.0	35.0	84.0	97.0	94.0	

SOURCE: *Jour. Amer. Soc. Agron.*, **24** (1932).

Harvesting and Storage.　　Maturity of seed at the time of harvesting has
a significant effect on germination.　　For example, sorghum seed harvested
in the milk and soft-dough stage is lower in viability than more mature seed
(see Table 278).　　Frost affects seed viability, as was shown in the same
study.　　A heavy frost before harvesting the seed in the milk and soft-dough

TABLE 278. SUMMARY OF RESULTS OF GERMINATION TESTS WITH SAMPLES OF SOR-
GHUM SEED SELECTED FROM THE FIELD AT DIFFERENT STAGES OF MATURITY

Stage of maturity when selected	Selected before frost		Selected after frost	
	Number of samples	Ave. per cent of germination	Number of samples	Ave. per cent of germination
Milk..................	12	68	2	3
Soft dough.............	12	81	12	28
Hard dough...........	12	87	4	81
Fully mature..........	12	90	1	81

SOURCE: *Kans. Agr. Expt. Sta. Bul.* 225 (1921).

stage greatly reduced the germination power of these seeds. The more mature sorghum seed was reduced in viability by frost but less so than that at earlier maturity stages.

The germination of some seeds is affected by the method of harvesting. A study of this point was made in Iowa with timothy seed, some of which were combined and the others threshed. The results are given in Table 279. The germination of the threshed seed was 95 per cent compared with

TABLE 279. GERMINATION OF COMBINED AND THRESHED TIMOTHY SEED

Method of harvesting	No. of lots	Percentage		Total pure seed	Percentage germination		
		Hull-less	Unhulled		Hull-less	Unhulled	Mixed
Threshed.....	9	29.3	68.3	97.6	91	96	95
Combined....	8	58.0	38.0	96.0	70	96	78

SOURCE: *Iowa Agr. Expt. Sta. Res. Bul.* 334 (1944).

only 78 per cent for that combined. Those seeds which lost their hulls in combining were especially lowered in germinating capacity.

Most seeds maintain their viability in storage best if the temperature is kept at 50°F. or less and if the relative humidity of the atmosphere is less than 50 to 60 per cent. Protection is necessary against the chalcis fly, weevils, the grain moth, and rodents.

Certified Seed. There is much to be said for the use of seed of known origin, genetic purity, and high quality. The purchase and use of certified seed gives added assurance that such a product is being used from which maximum yields of good quality can be obtained. The seed purchaser is thus afforded a measure of protection at a very small increase in price. Greater production and more general use of such seed should be encouraged.

FEDERAL REGULATIONS

The Federal Seed Act of 1939 regulates interstate shipment of seeds and also seed importations. Thus seed moving between states must be labeled to show (1) germination percentage, (2) date of germination test, (3) name of each kind of seed present in excess of 5 per cent, (4) lot number, (5) origin of alfalfa and red clover and other seeds as may be designated by the Secretary of Agriculture, (6) per cent by weight of all weed seeds, (7) names and number of noxious weed seeds per ounce in accordance with the regulations in the state for which the seed is destined, (8) other crop seeds, (9) inert matter, (10) per cent hard seed if any, (11) full name and address of shipper or consignee, and (12) code designation if any is used. The Act further states that screenings cannot be shipped in interstate commerce

unless labeled "screenings for processing — not for seeding." Seed for
screening or processing must be shipped as "seed for processing." All
these provisions are helpful to the seed consumer as a protection against
purchasing a product of unknown quality.

Further protection to purchasers of seeds classified as indistinguishable is
secured through the Federal Seed Act in the case of imported seed of alfalfa
and red clover. Alfalfa and red clover seed produced in foreign countries
other than the Dominion of Canada is considered unadapted for planting
in the United States. Thus alfalfa and red clover seed must be stained
according to its origin if produced outside the United States as follows:

1. Seed of alfalfa and red clover grown in any foreign country other than
   the South American countries and the Dominion of Canada must be
   stained 10 per cent red.
2. Seed from any of the countries of South America must be stained 10
   per cent orange-red.
3. Seed from the Dominion of Canada must be stained 1 per cent violet.
4. If the seed is (*a*) of unestablished origin, (*b*) of such an origin as to
   require different colors, or (*c*) foreign seed mixed with seed grown in
   the United States, it must be stained 10 per cent red.

References

1. Ahlgren, Gilbert H., Howard B. Sprague, and Firman E. Bear: Growing alfalfa in
   New Jersey, *N.J. Agr. Expt. Sta. Bul.* 718 (1945).
2. Burlison, W. L., C. A. Van Doren, and J. C. Hackleman: Eleven years of soybean
   investigations, *Ill. Agr. Expt. Sta. Bul.* 462 (1940).
3. Fergus, E. N.: Adaptability of red clover from different regions to Kentucky, *Ky.
   Agr. Expt. Sta. Bul.* 318 (1931).
4. Getty, R. E.: Forage crops in western Kansas, *Kans. Agr. Expt. Sta. Bul.* 225 (1921).
5. Grandfield, C. O., and R. I. Throckmorton: Alfalfa in Kansas, *Kans. Agr. Expt.
   Sta. Bul.* 328 (1945).
6. Middleton, Gordon K.: Size of Korean lespedeza seed in relation to germination
   and hard seed, *Jour. Amer. Soc. Agron.*, **25**:173–177 (1933).
7. Neal, N. P.: Wisconsin corn hybrids, *Wis. Agr. Ext. Serv. Spec. Cir.*, March, 1941.
8. Piper, Charles V.: Forage Plants and Their Culture, The Macmillan Company,
   New York, 1927.
9. Porter, R. H.: Testing farm seed, *Iowa Agr. Expt. Sta. Ext. Bul.* P68 (1944).
10. Porter, R. H.: Testing the quality of seeds for farm and garden, *Iowa Agr. Expt.
    Sta. Res. Bul.* 334 (1944).
11. Stewart, George, and J. W. Carlson: The quality of alfalfa seeds as affected by color
    and plumpness, *Jour. Amer. Soc. Agron.*, **24**:146–155 (1932).
12. U.S. Department of Agriculture, Office of Marketing Service: Rules and Regulations
    under the Federal Seed Act, Service and Regulatory Announcement 156, March,
    1940.

CHAPTER 30

SEED PLACEMENT

Plant populations are controlled by seeding rates, seed distribution, and satisfactory placement methods. The number of plants in a given area affects both yield and quality. Proper coverage of the seed is required to secure good stands of uniform distribution. With the small-seeded grasses and legumes, extra care is needed to ensure shallow planting.

Hay seeds undoubtedly were first sown by hand. This was an arduous and imperfect method, often resulting in failures and disappointments. Later the horn and cyclone seeders came into use and proved an aid to uniform seeding, especially in the humid sections where a heavier seeding rate is employed. The wheelbarrow seeder later effectively implemented broadcast seedings which can be covered by harrowing or cultipacking or through the action of frost in honeycombed ground. The use of the grass-seeding attachment on the grain drill and the development of the culti-packer seeder completely mechanized seeding.

Depth of Seeding

The optimum depth for the seeding of hay crops is often overlooked or relegated to a secondary position. Hay crops are sown regularly along with small-grain companion crops, and since the seeds of the latter are sown 1 to 3 inches deep, the grass and legume seeds sometimes are covered simultaneously to similar depths. Since these seeds are smaller than those of the grain crops, such deep coverage makes it impossible for them to establish a stand. The small seeds do not possess the required food reserves, nor is it morphologically possible for them to grow up through 2 or 3 inches of soil.

Studies on depth of planting in relation to emergence for various forage seeds have been conducted by several experiment stations. Results of work in Wisconsin are given in Table 280. Shallow plantings are shown to be best; there is progressive reduction in emergence with increasing depth of planting. The work was conducted on a Carrington silt loam type of soil. Other studies[8] conducted on a Miami silt loam and a Brookston silty clay loam in Ohio with the same seeds gave similar results. Depths of ¼ to ½ inch were most favorable. One inch was too deep for maximum emergence irrespective of the crop species. Surface seeding was tried also and found inferior to the shallow plantings. On a Cumberland silt loam soil in

TABLE 280. EFFECT OF DEPTH OF SEEDING ON PER CENT OF STAND OBTAINED IN RELATION TO NUMBER OF SEEDS SOWN

Crop	Depth of seeding				
	Surface	½ in.	1 in.	1½ in.	2 in.
Alfalfa........................	66	64	53	45	19
Alsike clover..................	47	53	49	9	4
Bromegrass....................	66	78	69	51	24
Red clover....................	58	56	62	22	14
Redtop........................	64	64	33	2	0
Sweetclover...................	51	51	45	26	14
Timothy.......................	90	80	81	39	12

SOURCE: *Hoard's Dairyman*, **83** (1938).

Tennessee, the best emergence was obtained with four varieties of lespedeza when the seeds were planted at depths of ¼ to ½ inch. Deeper plantings resulted in reduced stands. Tests conducted in Minnesota[9] on five soil types using about the same species as those in Table 280, showed the ½-inch depth of planting superior to 1, 2, or 3 inches.

The depth of planting for 16 prairie grasses and alfalfa was studied in South Dakota[3] under prairie conditions on a heavy clay soil. Shallow drilling at a depth of ¼ to ½ inch proved most satisfactory. Broadcasting on the surface of the soil or seeding deeper than ½ inch gave poorer stands in all cases.

Size of Seed. The size of seed undoubtedly influences the response to different depths of planting. The larger the seeds, the better their ability to overcome the handicap of deep seeding. Studies in Minnesota[9] indicate a high degree of correlation between seed size and emergence from increasing depths of planting. Other studies at Knoxville, Tennessee,[8] were made with crimson clover seed that had been separated according to size, and they showed that the larger seeds were more likely to come up when planted too deeply.

Rapidity of Emergence. The depth of planting also affects the time required for seedlings to emerge. A study of Sudan grass (see Table 281) indicates that over 50 per cent come-up was obtained at the end of 14 days even when planted 5 inches deep, but 80 per cent emergence was found at the end of 5 days when the planting depth was 1 inch. This study showed that the best depth for planting Sudan grass is 1 to 2 inches.

Even though the soybean has large seeds it has the disadvantage of having to push its large cotyledons up through the soil as it emerges, and therefore deep planting would be expected to reduce come-up. This is exactly

TABLE 281. EMERGENCE OF SEEDLINGS OF SUDAN GRASS PLANTED IN
CUMBERLAND SILT LOAM, TENNESSEE

Depth of planting, in.	Percentage of viable seeds that produced emerged seedlings within number of days indicated after planting					
	3	4	5	6	10	14
1	20	72	80	80	84	90
2	0	64	74	80	84	92
3	0	24	44	58	68	74
4	0	2	24	36	44	56
5	0	0	14	30	46	56

SOURCE: *Jour. Amer. Soc. Agron.*, **35** (1943).

the case, as shown by Moore.[8] The percentage emergence in this study
was much higher in the sandy soil than in the clay soil, regardless of depth
of planting. Planting at 1 to 3 inches gave the best emergence in the sandy
soil, whereas the 1-inch depth was superior for the clay soil. The rapidity
of emergence was also greater in the sandy soil, and it bore an inverse
relationship to the depth of planting.

Effect of Mulching. The use of a soil mulch might be expected to
encourage come-up, especially when moisture may be limiting and soil
crusting is common. Such a study was conducted by Moore[8] on a Cumberland silt loam soil, all seedings being made in the middle of April. Mulching was shown to be beneficial at all depths of seeding and more helpful
at deeper than at optimum depths. Since mulching helps to conserve
moisture it would be most valuable during periods of extreme dryness.
Although mulching produced better stands from deeper depths, the most
satisfactory placement for the small seeds tested was a depth of ¼ to ½ inch.

RATE AND PLACEMENT

The number of seeds sown per unit area will usually influence the yield
and quality of any hay crop. The placement of a larger or smaller number
of seeds per acre is also of significance from the standpoint of seed economy,
moisture and nutrient utilization, and seeding techniques. A test run in
Virginia (see Table 282) showed that seeding rate had little influence on the
yield of alfalfa or of alfalfa–orchard grass mixtures. However, this might
well be explained on the basis of increased growth per plant at the reduced
seeding rates resulting in coarser stems and lower quality hay, but giving
similar total yields. Extremely low or high rates were not tried, or other
and less similar data might have been secured.

Fig. 70.　Alfalfa and grass-seeding equipment in Idaho.　A harrow is followed by a double roller and two drills.　(*Soil Conservation Service, U.S. Department of Agriculture.*)

TABLE 282.　EFFECT OF SEEDING RATE ON TOTAL YIELD OF HAY IN VIRGINIA

Pounds of seed sown per acre		Yield of field-cured hay per acre, lb.		
Alfalfa	Orchard grass	1940	1941	Average
10	..	4,760	7,920	6,340
20	..	4,980	8,800	6,890
30	14	5,360	7,960	6,660
20	14	6,400	8,200	7,300
10	14	6,060	6,920	6,490
5	10	5,500	7,500	6,500

SOURCE: *Va. Agr. Expt. Sta. Bul.* 393 (1946).

TABLE 283.　YIELDS OF ALFALFA HAY GROWN ON UPLANDS IN ROW WIDTHS OF 6 TO 42 INCHES, KANSAS

Cutting	Yield of hay, tons per acre, for row widths named						
	6	12	24	30	36	42 single	42 double
First only..........	0.89	0.84	0.85	0.83	0.83	0.77	0.85

SOURCE: *U.S. Dept. Agr. Tech. Bul.* 410 (1934).

Growing alfalfa in rows of varying widths was studied in Kansas over a 13-year period.　The results are given in Table 283.　Row widths varied from 6 to 42 inches, and the data show no real yield differences for any spacing treatment.　Production was dependent on total moisture available. The 6-inch planting was preferred since it gave the better quality hay.

Plant spacing within rows greatly influenced yields of forage with Pink kafir. These data are given in Table 284. The closer spacings gave the

TABLE 284. RESULTS OF WITHIN-ROW SPACING EXPERIMENTS ON YIELDS OF PINK KAFIR, KANSAS

Row and plant spacings	Average row space per stalk, in.	Average height of plants, in.	10-year ave., tons
40-in. rows:			
6 in........................	5.7	59	3.44
12 in........................	8.4	57	3.10
18 in........................	11.2	55	2.86
24 in........................	13.9	55	2.53
Alternate 40- and 80-in. rows:			
4 in........................	4.1	61	3.04
8 in........................	6.3	60	2.75
12 in........................	8.0	58	2.54
16 in........................	10.1	57	2.23

SOURCE: *U.S. Dept. Agr. Tech. Bul.* 410 (1934).

highest yields, indicating that there was more complete moisture utilization here than with the wider placements. Different spacings within 80-inch rows gave similar results, but the data are not given here.

A rate of seeding test in Kansas[4] with red amber sorgo indicates no significant yield differences at seeding rates of 15 to 75 pounds per acre or with row spacings of 16 inches compared with 8 inches. Moisture was the limiting factor and not seed, even with a drought-resistant species such as sorghum. A better quality forage was obtained at the closer spacing.

An alfalfa seeding test conducted in western Oregon showed no significant difference in yields with various seeding rates whether drilled or broadcast. The seedings reported in Table 285 were made under ideal conditions.

TABLE 285. YIELDS OF ALFALFA IN OREGON WHEN SEEDED AT DIFFERENT RATES AND BY DIFFERENT METHODS

Method of seeding	Rate of seeding per acre, lb.	3-year ave. acre yields, tons
Broadcast.........	10	5.58
	15	5.31
	20	5.57
Drilled...........	8	5.30
	12	5.17
	16	5.51

SOURCE: *Oreg. Agr. Expt. Sta. Bul.* 246 (1929).

Evidently even the lowest seeding rates produced stands fully able to utilize available space, moisture, and plant nutrients.

Low seeding rates are highly important on the nonirrigated soils of the West. Studies of seeding alfalfa in Idaho on such soils are given in Table 286. Low rates resulted in good yields per acre. Much higher rates are

TABLE 286. RELATION OF METHOD OF SEEDING TO ACRE YIELDS OF GRIMM ALFALFA

Method of seeding	Rate per acre, lb.	Average acre yield of dry hay, tons
36-in. rows...........	1–2	2.09
24-in. rows...........	2–3	2.80
Drill...............	6	3.15
Drill...............	8	2.71

SOURCE: *Idaho Agr. Expt. Sta. Bul.* 120 (1920).

required for maximum returns in more humid areas. In the study above the highest yield was secured from drilled plantings using 6 pounds of seed per acre. Row plantings at the low seeding rates did not fully utilize the available moisture.

METHODS OF SEEDING

The necessity of covering forage seeds lightly under dry-land conditions has been emphasized by various tests. Drilling was compared with broadcasting the seed of a mixture consisting of western and crested wheatgrass and bromegrass on different types of seedbeds in South Dakota. The data are given in Table 287. The four types of seedbeds used were unpre-

TABLE 287. AVERAGE PER CENT EMERGENCE AND SURVIVAL OF CRESTED WHEATGRASS, WESTERN WHEATGRASS, AND BROMEGRASS AS DETERMINED BY SEEDING METHOD IN SOUTH DAKOTA

Condition	Late fall		Early spring	
	Drilled	Broadcast	Drilled	Broadcast
Emergence........	55	22	41	14
Survival.........	53	26	27	7

SOURCE: *S.Dak. Agr. Expt. Sta. Bul.* 361 (1942).

pared oat stubble, unprepared clean corn stubble, plowed oat stubble, and disked oat stubble. Drilling was superior to broadcasting on all of them from both fall and spring seedings.

Fig. 71. Mixing bromegrass seed with fertilizer as a planting aid. (*New Jersey Agricultural Experiment Station.*)

Drilling, row planting, and broadcasting were studied as methods for seeding, as is shown in Table 288. Drilling in both cases was superior to broadcasting and far better than the row plantings at 6 and 4 pounds per acre.

TABLE 288. COMPARATIVE FORAGE YIELDS FROM BLACK AMBER SORGO AND SUDAN GRASS WHEN PLANTED BY VARIOUS METHODS, 8-YEAR AVERAGE, NEBRASKA

Seeding method	Amount of seed planted per acre, lb.	Plant height, in.	Forage yield per acre (15% moisture content)	
			Tons	Relative
Black amber sorgo:				
Drilled.........	93	66	5.19	100
Broadcast......	93	72	4.42	85
Cultivated rows..	6	93	3.42	66
Sudan grass:				
Drilled.........	31	74	3.42	100
Broadcast......	31	74	3.15	92
Cultivated rows..	4	83	2.77	81

SOURCE: *Nebr. Agr. Expt. Sta. Cir.* 52 (1935).

The practice of planting legume seeds in late February or March on the top of ground planted to wheat or barley is common in the clover-timothy belt. This does not permit drilling because the soil is either frozen or too wet. Under these conditions broadcasting gives good results, since the alternate freezing and thawing at this season works the seed into the soil to a satisfactory depth. Such seedings made in April can usually be drilled if desired. Data from Ohio[12] show that broadcasting in late April compared

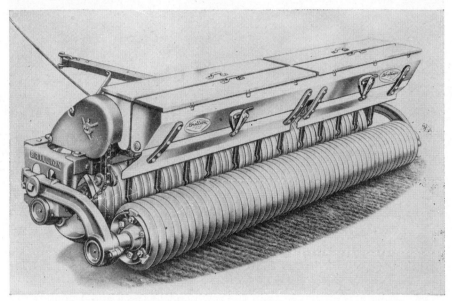

Fig. 72. A combination soil packer and seeder. (*Brillion Iron Works.*)

with drilling resulted in a reduction of alfalfa yields by a ton per acre. Broadcasting seedings in March and early April were as satisfactory as drilling later. A similar study with sweetclover sown in late April and early May, too late for frost action, indicated that covering the seed either by drilling or broadcasting and harrowing was superior to other methods tried.

On soil newly prepared for the planting of a grain crop or in making a late summer seeding in the humid East, broadcast plantings are best for the small-seeded grasses and legumes. The problem is to prevent too deep coverage rather than to secure adequate coverage. If a grain drill with grass-seed attachment is used for planting, the seed should be broadcast on the surface of the ground behind the disks or hoes and covered by a light harrowing or by cultipacking.

A good method of seeding on a newly prepared seedbed is to cultipack the soil first, broadcast the seed, and then cover it by a second cultipacking or a light harrowing. This method ensures a firm seedbed together with shallow placement of the seed. It is especially valuable for late summer seedings where moisture supply and a firm seedbed are very important. A recently developed and most satisfactory implement for this method of seeding is the cultipacker seeder. It has a grass-seed box between two iron rollers. Seed falls between these with a good degree of accuracy. The first roller firms and furrows the soil, and the second splits the furrows down the middle so that the seeds are covered at varying depths up to ½ inch or slightly more.

Seed placement plays a significant role in hay and silage production. Good stands of high-quality materials are dependent on proper depth of covering, on row width, and on spacing within the rows. The method used will vary in the different forage regions depending on the climatic and soil conditions, the season of the year, and the crop species chosen for planting.

References

1. Ahlgren, H. L.: Better seeding practices, *Hoard's Dairyman*, **83**:137, 144 (1938).
2. Bonnett, R. K.: Forage crops for the non-irrigated lands of Idaho, *Idaho Agr. Expt. Sta. Bul.* 120 (1920).
3. Franzke, C. J., and A. N. Hume: Regrassing areas in South Dakota, *S.Dak. Agr. Expt. Sta. Bul.* 361 (1942).
4. Getty, R. E.: Experiments with forage crops at the Fort Hays Branch Station, Hays, Kansas, *U.S. Dept. Agr. Tech. Bul.* 410 (1934).
5. Hutcheson, T. B., M. H. McVickar, and T. J. Smith: Alfalfa production in Virginia, *Va. Agr. Expt. Sta. Bul.* 393 (1946).
6. Kinney, E. J., Ralph Kenny, and E. N. Fergus: Practices in seeding meadow and pasture crops, *Ky. Ext. Bul.* 232 (1935).
7. Lyness, W. E., and T. A. Kiesselbach: Annual fodder and silage crops for Nebraska, *Nebr. Agr. Expt. Sta. Cir.* 32 (1935).
8. Moore, R. P.: Seedling emergence of small-seeded legumes and grasses, *Jour. Amer. Soc. Agron.*, **35**:370–381 (1943).
9. Murphy, R. P., and A. C. Arny: The emergence of grass and legume seedlings planted at different depths in five soil types, *Jour. Amer. Soc. Agron.*, **31**:17–28 (1939).
10. Schoth, Harry A., and George R. Hyslop: Alfalfa in Western Oregon, *Oreg. Agr. Expt. Sta. Bul.* 246 (1929).
11. Stitt, R. E.: The effect of depth of planting on the germination of soybean varieties, *Jour. Amer. Soc. Agron.*, **26**:1001–1004 (1934).
12. Thatcher, L. E., C. J. Willard, and R. D. Lewis: Better methods of seeding meadows, *Ohio Agr. Expt. Sta. Bul.* 588 (1937).

CHAPTER 31

COMPANION CROPS

Companion crops are used often in seeding down to biennial or perennial hay crops. The advantage of this practice is that it brings in a return in the same year. Since most companion crops are small grains, they may be pastured, cut for hay, or used for grain. Protection against weed competition is afforded young seedlings by the companion planting. On the other hand, the associated grain crops are severe competitors, since they tend to shade the hay seedlings and compete with them for moisture and nutrients.

This type of planting is most popular with spring and fall seedings, although good stands of both hay grasses and legumes can be secured when planted at these times without the companion crop if the seeding is done early enough. Studies in Canada on spring plantings as given in Table 289

TABLE 289. RELATION OF METHOD OF SPRING SEEDING TO SUBSEQUENT ACRE YIELD, ONTARIO AGRICULTURAL COLLEGE

Crops	Yield per acre, tons	
	With oats	No companion crop
Orchard grass............	4.44	3.73
Meadow fescue...........	3.66	3.64
Timothy................	3.27	4.28
Common red clover.......	3.61	4.18
Alsike clover.............	2.47	2.79
Alfalfa.................	4.03	4.17
Average 3 grasses.........	3.79	3.89
Average 3 clovers.........	3.37	3.71

SOURCE: From Piper, "Forage Plants and Their Culture," rev. ed., copyright, 1924 by The Macmillan Company, and used with their permission.

show little difference between the two methods. Yields of the grasses and legumes were slightly better in nearly all instances without the companion oat crop. However, the differences were not great enough to offset the value of the oat crop; in fact, they indicate the desirability of planting hay crops with a grain crop. These tests were conducted in Ontario, where

Fig. 73. Clipping back small grains often encourages legume growth. Top photograph: wheat clipped (*left*), not clipped (*right*). Bottom photograph: alfalfa on clipped area (*left*), unclipped area (*right*). (*Ohio Agricultural Experiment Station.*)

moisture is more abundant than in the Plains states and therefore not so likely to limit yields.

Factors in Success

Competition from the grain crops can be controlled to some extent by following good cultural practices and by selecting the most suitable companions. Clipping or grazing the grain crops or cutting them for hay is effective in reducing injury from shade and inadequate moisture. In case the grain lodges, the hay seeding can be saved only by mowing promptly for hay.   Early planting of spring-sown companion crops and reducing the seeding rate for the associated small grain are important in ensuring a satisfactory hay stand the following year.

Choice of Companions.   Where grain crops are sown with hay seedings, great care must be taken to choose only the most suitable species and varieties.   The factors to look for are early maturity, lodging resistance, and an open type of growth.   Lodging in a grain crop invariably results in heavy loss of hay seedlings and, if severe enough, in a crop failure.   An early maturing variety is removed from competition more quickly, thus giving the hay seeding a better opportunity to develop.

The choice of a companion grain crop is particularly important in the Great Plains states.   Hay crops are seldom sown with wheat in that area. The early and rapid growth of the wheat in the spring depletes the soil moisture so rapidly that hay seedings have little chance of surviving. Spring oats and barley, with their less vigorous spring growth, are much more favorable.   The same relationship is evident in the humid areas, but here competition for moisture is less of a factor.

Spring-sown hay crops are usually planted with spring wheat, barley, or oats as companion crops   Winter varieties of any of these grain crops can also be used for spring planting, but normally are not.   A 3-year test in Ohio compared the merits of spring-sown winter wheat with oats as companion crops for red clover and alfalfa.   Oats was clearly inferior to wheat with both legumes (see Table 290).   The wheat-clover combination gave

TABLE 290.   COMPARISON OF COMPANION CROPS FOR ESTABLISHING RED CLOVER
AND ALFALFA

Crop	Yield of hay, pounds per acre		
	Sown alone	Sown in spring-sown winter wheat	Sown in oats
Red clover......................	4,280	4,620	3,710
Alfalfa........................	4,240	4,280	3,700

SOURCE: *Ohio Agr. Expt. Sta. Bul.* 588 (1937).

the highest hay yields in this test.   Alfalfa sown alone was just as successful as with the wheat.   Winter wheat sown in the spring does not produce grain, and this reduces its value for companion purposes.

Spring seedings of sweetclover were made alone, with oats, and with barley in Kansas.   The moisture supply and weeds were primary considerations in these tests.   The results of these plantings made on fallow ground and following legumes or sorghum are given in Table 291.   Based on final

TABLE 291. SUMMARY OF TESTS FOR STAND OF SWEETCLOVER GROWN WITH AND WITHOUT A COMPANION CROP IN KANSAS

Preceding crop		Record of tests	Barley		Oats		No companion	
			Early stand	Final stand	Early stand	Final stand	Early stand	Final stand
Fallow...........	Good	7	8	7	5	5	5	
	Poor	1	0	0	2	0	0	
Legumes.........	Good	6	1	4	1	5	3	
	Poor	2	7	4	7	6	8	
Sorghum.........	Good	9	10	9	10	5	5	
	Poor	1	0	1	0	0	0	

SOURCE: *U.S. Dept. Agr. Tech. Bul.* 410 (1934).

stands, barley appears to be slightly superior to oats, but both were inferior to no companion crop. As a general rule barley is more valuable for companion purposes than oats since it possesses a more open type of growth and matures at an earlier date.

Alfalfa was sown alone and with a number of spring-seeded crops at some of the prairie stations. Yield records for the year following planting are given in Table 292. Alfalfa seeded alone gave the best results at all

TABLE 292. AVERAGE HAY YIELDS PER ACRE OF ALFALFA WITH AND WITHOUT A COMPANION CROP AT THREE STATIONS IN THE NORTHERN GREAT PLAINS REGION, POUNDS

Method of sowing	Redfield, S.Dak.	Sheridan, Wyo.	Moccasin, Mont.
Alfalfa alone.........	3,046	1,444	2,189
Alfalfa with wheat....	2,552	.....	2,017
Alfalfa with oats......	2,526	.....	2,061
Alfalfa with barley....	2,332	1,182	152
Alfalfa with flax......	.....	.....	2,020

SOURCE: *U.S. Dept. Agr. Dept. Bul.* 1244 (1924).

stations, which suggests the questionable value of any companion crop in this region. Complete alfalfa failures resulted in some instances where companion crops were used. Flax was as good a companion as any of the small grains.

Attempts have been made to use soybeans and Sudan grass as companion crops for semipermanent hay seedings. Strong growth of these crops during midsummer combined with increased competition for moisture and sunlight has usually resulted in failure of the sod crop. Light seeding rates of these crops and early harvest for hay increase the chances of a successful seeding, but even then results are uncertain. When soybeans are allowed to mature grain, companion forage seedings have seldom succeeded. It appears best to wait until the soybeans and Sudan grass have been harvested for hay or grain and then to prepare a seedbed and plant the hay mixture.

Fig. 74. Winter barley used as a companion crop for red clover in New Jersey. (*New Jersey Agricultural Experiment Station.*)

Corn has been suggested as a companion crop for hay seedings. Long-time tests at several experiment stations indicate successful hay plantings in corn less than 50 per cent of the time. Hairy vetch has been established more successfully in corn in Ohio tests; alfalfa was next, and the clovers followed. Corn stubble and uneven surfaces further complicate this procedure and, in general, point to its inadvisability.

Grass-legume Mixtures. In the humid regions of the country it is a common practice to seed winter grain crops with a hay grass in the fall and then to broadcast legume seeds early in the following spring to be covered by frost action. Later spring seedings of the legumes are made, but this requires covering by drilling or harrowing. Results of a study of this type of seeding are given in Table 293. Timothy was seeded in the fall with wheat as a companion crop, and alfalfa was added in early spring. The difference in hay yields favors seeding without wheat. Where timothy was not included, the difference is again in favor of seeding alfalfa without wheat, but it is not significant enough to eliminate the grain crop.

TABLE 293. AVERAGE YIELDS OF HAY FROM TIMOTHY AND ALFALFA MIXED AND ALFALFA ALONE SEEDED WITH AND WITHOUT WHEAT, POUNDS PER ACRE

Crop	Seeded alone	Seeded with wheat
Alfalfa...........................	8,583	8,243
Alfalfa with timothy..................	9,763	9,090

SOURCE: *Ohio Agr. Expt. Sta. Bul.* 588 (1937).

Rate and Time of Seeding. A study of the rate and time of seeding oats as a companion crop with alfalfa sown in the spring was made at the Ohio Agricultural Experiment Station (see Table 294). In general, light seeding

TABLE 294. EFFECT OF THE RATE AND DATE OF SEEDING OATS AS A COMPANION CROP FOR ALFALFA

Oats, rate of seeding per acre, pecks	Alfalfa plants per square yard		
	Early seeding	Medium seeding	Late seeding
4	101	74	112
8	108	88	104
12	92	88	101
16	72	88	78

SOURCE: *Ohio Agr. Expt. Sta. Bul.* 588 (1937).

rates were most favorable to the alfalfa stand, and as rates were increased reduction in stand occurred. Results of a similar study with sweetclover during two dry years are given in Table 295. There is a very close correlation between reduced seeding rates of oats and increased stands of sweetclover.

TABLE 295. EFFECT OF RATE OF SEEDING A COMPANION CROP OF OATS ON THE STAND OF SWEETCLOVER IN DRY YEARS

Oats, rate of seeding per acre, pecks	Sweetclover plants per square yard	
	First year	Second year
4	101	121
8	76	100
16	64	96

SOURCE: *Ohio Agr. Expt. Sta. Bul.* 588 (1937).

Spacing Grain Rows. The effect of spacing winter barley on the succeeding crops of lespedeza was studied in Oklahoma. There was only a small difference in hay yields of the lespedeza, this being in favor of the 14-inch planting (see Table 296). Abnormal amounts of moisture fell during the

TABLE 296. EFFECT OF SPACING WINTER BARLEY ROWS ON SUCCEEDING ACRE YIELDS OF KOREAN LESPEDEZA, POUNDS

Year	7-in. rows	14-in. rows
1943	1,330	1,420
1944	4,730	4,750
1945	4,840	5,120
Average	3,633	3,763

SOURCE: *Jour. Amer. Soc. Agron.*, **38** (1946).

test periods. In dry seasons the results might have been more strongly in favor of wider row plantings and the yields would doubtless have been lower.

Silage Crops. Large-seeded legumes, such as pole beans and soybeans, have been planted with corn with varying results. Plantings usually have been made simultaneously with the corn, and the legumes have given fair growth. In many cases, corn yields were depressed, resulting in dry-matter losses or at best only slight gains. Data taken from studies conducted at Cornell University are given in Table 297. The Kentucky Wonder pole

TABLE 297. GROWING CORN IN COMBINATION WITH POLE BEANS AND SOYBEANS FOR SILAGE (ADAPTED)

Legume	Variation from yield of corn alone (7,718 lb. per acre)				Gain or loss of combination compared with corn alone	
	Corn		Legume			
	Lb. per acre	%	Lb. per acre	%	Lb. per acre	%
Ky. Wonder bean	5,611	72.7	752	8.6	−1,351	−18.7
Wilson soybean	6,688	87.1	1,711	22.1	681	9.2
Peking soybean	6,521	84.8	1,730	22.4	533	7.2

SOURCE: *Jour. Amer. Soc. Agron.*, **27** (1935).

bean depressed the corn yield by 27 per cent and resulted in a net loss per acre of almost 19 per cent. Both varieties of soybeans depressed the corn yield somewhat but resulted in an over-all increase in acre yields of 7 to 9 per cent. This practice of interplanting is more popular in the annual legume region than in the other forage areas of America.

Late-summer Seedings. Companion crops are not used in making late-summer seedings. A grain crop seeded in late summer is too severe competition for the hay seeding. Data on seeding spring oats with alfalfa in Ohio in August are given in Table 298. The spring oats were winter-killed, but they reduced the yield of hay by almost 1½ tons per acre.

TABLE 298. EFFECT OF SEEDING OATS WITH ALFALFA IN AUGUST

Crop	Alfalfa, lb. per acre	
	Sown in oats	Sown alone
First cutting.............	3,370	5,170
Second cutting...........	2,990	3,950
Third cutting............	2,880	2,890
Total.................	9,240	12,010

SOURCE: *Ohio Agr. Expt. Sta. Bul.* 588 (1937).

Late-summer seedings can follow any grain crop, including flax and soy-beans. At this season, grass and legume seed may be sown simultaneously. Early preparation of the seedbed is desirable to destroy most of the weed seeds in the surface soil and to conserve as much moisture as possible. Firming the surface soil with a cultipacker or by other means is most valuable at this season of the year. Late-summer plantings without a companion crop are usually successful if adequate moisture is available to get the seeding off to a good start and if weeds are controlled.

Moisture Relationships. The question of using companion crops in making hay seedings resolves itself into moisture relationships of the hay region being considered. In dry-land farming companion grain crops are usually impractical. In more humid regions, companion crops add to the farm income without materially reducing succeeding hay yields. Under such conditions they appear practical and valuable in the farm program. Even in the humid regions individual farm differences and operator preferences may rule out companion crops in favor of late-summer seedings. Wherever companion crops are used, good varieties should be chosen and effective cultural practices should be applied so that the forage seedings are given every opportunity to develop in a satisfactory manner.

References

1. Getty, R. E.: Experiments with forage crops at the Fort Hays Branch Station, Hays, Kansas, *U.S. Dept. Agr. Tech. Bul.* 410 (1934).

2. Harper, Horace J.: Effect of row spacing on the yield of small grain nurse crops, *Jour. Amer. Soc. Agron.*, **38**:785–794 (1946).
3. Hulbert, H. W.: Sweet clover, *Idaho Agr. Expt. Sta. Bul.* 147 (1927).
4. Oakley, R. A., and H. L. Westover: Forage crops in relation to the agriculture of the semi-arid portion of the northern Great Plains, *U.S. Dept. Agr. Bul.* 1244 (1924).
5. Piper, C. V.: Forage Plants and Their Culture, The Macmillan Company, New York, 1927.
6. Thatcher, L. E., C. J. Willard, and R. D. Lewis: Better methods of seeding meadows, *Ohio Agr. Expt. Sta. Bul.* 588 (1937).
7. Wiggans, R. G.: Pole beans vs. soybeans as a companion crop with corn for silage, *Jour. Amer. Soc. Agron.*, **27**:154–158 (1935).

CHAPTER 32

HAY STANDARDS

The actual value of any hay crop depends upon its nutritional value for feeding livestock. Over the years, certain visible and measurable factors have been found to furnish fairly reliable guides to the actual feeding value of hay. These factors have been adapted as workable standards by which hay can be graded and its money value appraised in the market place.

EVALUATING HAY

The development of hay standards thus has relied on such features as leafiness, color, odor, foreign materials, size of stems, and soundness. The degree or percentage of each of these factors, when combined and evaluated, determines the grade. Hay is also put into categories known as groups and classes, since the kind of hay also influences its value. There are 11 official hay groups[3] as follows: Group I, Alfalfa and Alfalfa Mixed Hay; II, Timothy and Clover Hay; III, Prairie Hay; IV, Johnson and Johnson Mixed Hay; V, Grain, Wild Oat, Vetch, and Grain Mixed Hay; VI, Lespedeza and Lespedeza Mixed Hay; VII, Soybean and Soybean Mixed Hay; VIII, Cowpea and Cowpea Mixed Hay; IX, Peanut and Peanut Mixed Hay; X, Grass Hay; and XI, Mixed Hay.

Classes. One of the most important groups is Alfalfa and Alfalfa Mixed Hay. A few of the class requirements and descriptions for this group are given in Table 299. The first step in grading hay is to determine

TABLE 299. SOME CLASS REQUIREMENTS FOR ALFALFA AND ALFALFA MIXED HAY

Class	*Mixture percentage*
Alfalfa	Alfalfa with not over 5% grasses
Alfalfa Light Timothy Mixed	A mixture of alfalfa and timothy with over 5% but not over 30% timothy
Alfalfa Heavy Timothy Mixed	A mixture of alfalfa and timothy with over 30% alfalfa and over 30% timothy
Alfalfa Clover Mixed	A mixture of alfalfa and clover with over 10% but not over 50% clover and not over 10% grasses
Alfalfa Light Johnson Mixed	A mixture of alfalfa and Johnson grass with over 5% but not over 30% Johnson grass
Alfalfa Heavy Johnson Mixed	A mixture of alfalfa and Johnson grass with over 30% alfalfa and over 30% Johnson grass

SOURCE: *U.S. Dept. Agr.* G–S–304 (1936).

307

its group and class.   After this has been ascertained, grading can be completed.

Grades.   There are four grades of hay for each class.   The first three are numerical—U.S. Nos. 1, 2, and 3; the fourth is called Sample grade—for inferior hay that cannot make a numerical grade.   The grades are used to describe the quality of the hay, and the quality in turn depends in part on

Fig. 75.   Hay grading is highly specialized, requiring the services of experts.   (*New Jersey Agricultural Experiment Station.*)

the way in which the hay was produced.   Special grades are also used to emphasize certain superior or inferior hay characters not covered by the regular grades.   Thus very leafy U.S. No. 1 alfalfa would be labeled U.S. No. 1 Extra Leafy Alfalfa.   Table 300 shows grades which apply to the classes described in Table 299.   Thus U.S. No. 1 alfalfa must be 40 per cent or more by weight leaves, must possess 60 per cent or more of its original color, and may not contain more than 5 per cent foreign materials.

Determining Quality

Grades have been interpreted into quality by Bohstedt with the results given in Table 301.   The carotene and protein contents are highest in grade

TABLE 300. GRADE REQUIREMENTS FOR THE CLASSES OF ALFALFA, ALFALFA LIGHT TIMOTHY MIXED, ALFALFA CLOVER MIXED, AND ALFALFA LIGHT JOHNSON MIXED

U.S. grade No.	Leafiness of alfalfa (% leaves)	Per cent green color	Maximum per cent foreign material
1	40 or more	60 or more	5
2	25 or more	35 or more	10
3	Less than 25	Less than 35	15
Sample grade	Hay which contains more than 15% of foreign material; or which contains more than a trace of injurious foreign material; or which has any objectionable odor; or which is undercured, heating, hot, wet, musty, moldy, caked, badly broken, weathered, frosted, overripe, or very dusty; or which is otherwise of distinctly low quality		

SOURCE: *U.S. Dept. Agr.* G–S–304 (1936).

TABLE 301. HOW QUALITY SHOWS UP IN THE FOUR GRADES OF CLOVER AND TIMOTHY HAY

Grade	Description of grade	Clover			Timothy		
		Carotene, p.p.m.	Protein, %	Fiber, %	Carotene, p.p.m.	Protein, %	Fiber, %
1.......	Excellent	30	15	26	25	10	26
2......	Good	12	12	28	10	7	29
3......	Fair	7	11	30	6	6	30
Sample..	Poor	3	10	35	3	5	35

SOURCE: *Successful Farming*, June, 1946.

1 hay and decrease with the lower ratings. The fiber content, on the other hand, is least in grade 1 hay and increases according to the rating.

Hay standards thus are an attempt to measure the nutritive value of any particular crop. The chemical composition, digestibility and palatability, and the physiological effect on the consuming animal reflect nutritive value. If hay standards correctly interpret quality, then there should be a relationship between leafiness, color, fine stems, aroma, etc., and the protein, vitamin, mineral, and digestible nutrient content, and likewise the palatability. Hay graded U.S. 1 should give better responses when fed to livestock than that receiving a lower grade.

Protein and Feed Value. Early cut hay should be more valuable for feeding than more mature hay because of its greater content of desirable feed elements. That this is true has been established by a number of tests,

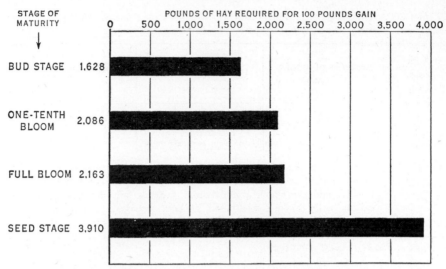

STAGE OF MATURITY ↓

POUNDS OF HAY REQUIRED FOR 100 POUNDS GAIN

BUD STAGE   1,628

ONE-TENTH BLOOM   2,086

FULL BLOOM   2,163

SEED STAGE   3,910

Fig. 76. Gains in weight of steers as affected by the maturity of the alfalfa fed. (*Bureau of Agricultural Economics, U.S. Department of Agriculture.*)

one of which is given in Fig. 76, indicating the increased quantities of hay required to put on 100 pounds of steer gain with increasing maturity of the hay.   Obviously, there were factors in the young alfalfa hay that were in greater quantity or of more value than those found in the older hay. Average analyses of this same alfalfa hay for the various maturity stages are given in Table 302.   The fiber content was lowest at the bud stage and

TABLE 302. Relation of Stage of Maturity of Alfalfa to Chemical Analyses, per Cent

Stage of maturity	Ash	Protein	Fiber	Fat	Nitrogen-free extract
Bud stage..............	10.3	19.6	28.0	2.4	39.6
$\frac{1}{10}$ bloom.............	10.2	18.1	30.1	2.4	39.3
$\frac{1}{2}$ bloom..............	9.6	16.9	32.6	2.6	38.3
Full bloom.............	9.7	15.9	33.3	2.1	39.0
Seeds ripe.............	8.5	14.5	35.3	2.1	39.5

Source: *U.S. Dept. Agr. Misc. Pub.*, 363 (1939).

highest at the seed-ripe stage.   The ash and protein contents were greatest in the young hay and decreased progressively with increasing maturity. A high protein and mineral content is known to be very valuable in feeding livestock and fiber less so.   This along with better palatability and digestibility probably accounts for the superiority of the hay cut at the earliest stage of maturity.

Timothy hay cut at early and later stages was fed to 18 dairy cows and compared for feed value over a 3-month period in Maine. The results of this test, as given in Table 303, show that it cost $1.23 for feed to produce

TABLE 303. A COMPARISON OF EARLY- AND MEDIUM-LATE-CUT TIMOTHY HAY FOR MILK PRODUCTION

Hay type	Milk, lb.	Fat, lb.	Grain fed, lb.	Feed cost per lb. fat	Feed cost per 100 lb. milk
Late cut...............	11,106	565	5,305	$0.24	$1.23
Early cut..............	14,237	769	5,464	0.17	0.94

SOURCE: *Maine Agr. Ext. Serv. Bul.* 220 (1936).

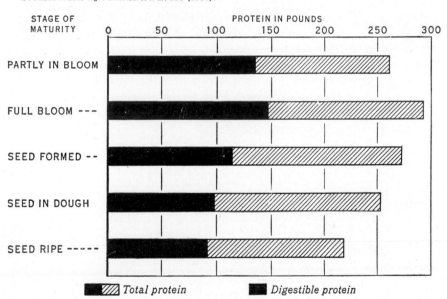

FIG. 77. Total and digestible protein in timothy at different stages of maturity. (*Bureau of Agricultural Economics, U.S. Department of Agriculture.*)

100 pounds of milk with medium-late-cut timothy hay and only $0.94 when early-cut timothy hay was substituted. Butterfat was produced at 24 cents a pound with medium-late hay and for 17 cents a pound with early-cut timothy.

Grass hays follow the same general pattern of nutrient changes with advancing maturity as that shown for alfalfa (Table 302). Using timothy as an example, Fig. 77 shows the general decrease in protein content with increasing age of the crop. Digestible protein is highest in the early and full-bloom stages and decreases rapidly thereafter.

Large-seeded Legumes. The soybean and cowpea present a somewhat different picture than forages such as alfalfa or timothy. Early-cut and late-cut soybean hay were compared (see Table 304) in a dairy feeding trial

TABLE 304. A COMPARISON OF EARLY- AND LATE-CUT SOYBEAN HAY AS FEED FOR DAIRY COWS (ACRE BASIS)

Stage	Hay, tons	Dry matter, tons	Milk produced, lb.	Butterfat produced, lb.
Early cut...............	1.614	1.470	2,058	71.56
Late cut................	1.794	1.608	2,451	92.62

SOURCE: *Jour. Dairy Sci.,* **22** (1939).

in Indiana. The late-cut soybean hay produced 400 pounds more milk per acre and about 20 pounds more butterfat. These results can probably be explained on the basis of more dry matter per acre from that hay cut late and also by a rapid protein increase (see Fig. 78) in the pods with increasing age. This increase more than compensated for the losses that occurred in the leaves and stems. Only the large-seeded legumes respond in this manner. Thus maturity influences quality by a reduction or an increase in protein content, depending on the type of hay.

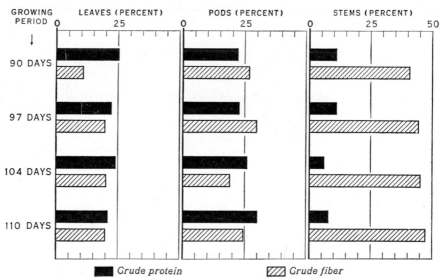

FIG. 78. Late-cut soybean hay is high in protein because of pods and seed. (*Bureau of Agricultural Economics, U.S. Department of Agriculture.*)

Leaves. Leafiness in legume hay rates high in grading because there is a direct relationship between percentage leaves and protein, mineral, and vitamin content as well as digestibility. Analysis for protein in leaves and stems for various hay crops is given in Table 305. In this study leaves are

TABLE 305. PROTEIN IN LEAVES AND STEMS OF DIFFERENT KINDS OF HAY, PER CENT

Kind of hay	Leaves	Stems	Kind of hay	Leaves	Stems
Alfalfa..........	24.0	10.6	Alsike clover....	20.7	9.5
Red clover.......	19.3	8.1	Soybean........	22.0	10.1

SOURCE: *U.S. Dept. Agr. Misc. Pub.* 363 (1939).

shown to be more than twice as rich in protein as the stems. Leaf percentage in hays may vary from 10 per cent in very stemmy hay to almost 70 per cent in very leafy hay, hence the significance of these data. Some additional data on protein content as related to leafiness in alfalfa with

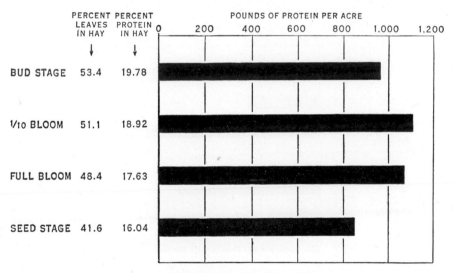

FIG. 79. The more leaves in alfalfa, the more protein. (*Bureau of Agricultural Economics, U.S. Department of Agriculture.*)

advancing maturity are given in Fig. 79. Maximum leaf development is probably attained at the one-tenth bloom stage in this crop. Thereafter, the percentage of leaves decreases and so does the protein content. Conservation of the leaves will mean a higher percentage of protein in cured hay.

TABLE 306.   COMPOSITION OF KOREAN LESPEDEZA LEAVES AND STEMS

Part of plant	Pounds per ton of crop					
	N	Protein	P	K	Ca	Mg
Leaves..................	55.9	349	6.3	19.2	24.9	8.6
Stems..................	23.5	147	3.3	11.0	9.0	4.7

SOURCE: *Ill. Agr. Expt. Sta. Bul.* 518 (1946).

Minerals.   The leaves are also higher than the stems in calcium and phosphorus, the most essential livestock minerals.   In a study (see Table 306) with Korean lespedeza in Illinois, the leaves were found to be twice as rich in phosphorus and three times as high in calcium content as the stems. Thus from a mineral standpoint the leaves are the better source.

Legumes are known to be higher than grasses in mineral content.   Long-time studies on this as carried out at the Illinois Station[7] show that seven legumes averaged 63.9 pounds of minerals per ton of dry hay, whereas the six main grasses averaged only 48.7 pounds of minerals.

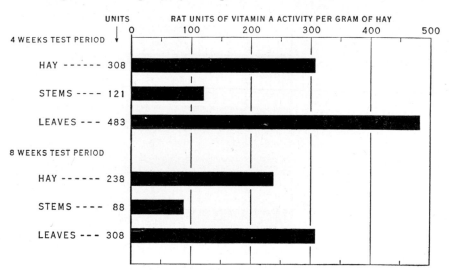

FIG. 80.   Rat units of vitamin A in whole alfalfa hay, stems, and leaves.   (*Bureau of Agricultural Economics, U.S. Department of Agriculture.*)

Green Color.   The most valuable source of vitamin A, as shown in Fig. 80, is also the leaves.   In this test they are two to three times as high as the stems in vitamin A potency.   A direct relationship between color, chlorophyll, and carotene (vitamin A) content is found in hay.   The deeper the green color, the higher the vitamin A potency.   It is well known that hay plants possess a higher concentration of greenness when they are young. In general, too, the legumes are 1½ to 2 times richer than the hay grasses in carotene, probably because of their greater leafiness. As indicated in Table 301 the carotene content of U.S. No. 1 clover hay is about twice as high as grade No. 2, and similar results for timothy are evident.

Green color may be lost by sun bleaching in the field, discoloration due to rain, excessive plant maturity, or heating and deterioration upon storage in the mow or stack. The loss of green color in storage proceeds most rapidly during the summer months and is kept at a minimum during cold weather, as is indicated by data in Table 307. Color is one of the most critical indexes of quality, and thus its importance from a grade standpoint.

TABLE 307. LOSS OF COLOR AS INFLUENCED BY TEMPERATURE AND STORAGE PERIOD

Average outdoor daily temperature during period of storage, °F.	*Loss of carotene per month during period of storage, %*
45 or less (winter months)	3.0
45 to 66 (fall and spring months)	6.5
Above 66 (summer months)	17.8

SOURCE: *U.S. Dept. Agr. Misc. Pub.* 363 (1939).

The significance of good green color in hay from a feeding standpoint is indicated by data on steer-feeding trials as given in Table 308. Steers fed black alfalfa hay were much less efficient in gains made than those fed green alfalfa hay.

Digestibility. Besides the high feeding value of leaves an additional character adding to their superiority as feed over stems is their comparatively high digestion coefficient. Tests by Sotola[8] show that alfalfa leaves were 58 per cent digested compared with only 42 per cent for the stems. This means that the leaves were 1½ times as digestible as the stems.

TABLE 308. STEER-FEEDING EXPERIMENT, 180 DAYS, COMPARING BLACK ALFALFA WITH BROWN AND GREEN ALFALFA HAY

Factors in experiment	Steers fed on shelled corn, oil meal, and		
	Good-color alfalfa hay, lb.	Brown alfalfa hay, lb.	Black alfalfa hay, lb.
Total gain in weight	354	350	202
Feed required to produce 100-lb. gain:			
Shelled corn	376	380	457
Oil meal	25	24	34
Alfalfa hay	398	402	635

SOURCE: *Jour. Agr. Res.*, **18** (1919).

Quality and Palatability

The palatability of any hay crop is important, since this determines to some extent the amount of hay which cattle will consume. Factors influencing palatability include hay class, variety, stage of growth at cutting, and curing and storing techniques used. To test palatability, large offerings of hay were made to cattle in a Wyoming experiment. It was found that greater quantities of good hay were eaten and less refused than in the case of inferior hay (see Table 309). It is apparent that if very large

TABLE 309. INCREASED CONSUMPTION OF GOOD-QUALITY HAY COMPARED WITH INFERIOR HAY

Hay	Average amount hay offered, lb.	Average amount hay refused, %	Average amount hay consumed, lb.
Palatable.............	28.40	18.52	23.16
Unpalatable...........	28.80	41.52	16.84

SOURCE: *Wyo. Agr. Expt. Sta. Bul.* 199 (1933).

TABLE 310. THE INFLUENCE OF STAGE OF BLOOM ON PALATABILITY OF IRRIGATED ALFALFA HAY

Stage of bloom, %	Crude protein, %	Total sugars, %	Leaves, %	Color, %	Grade	Average daily hay consumed, lb.
5	18.3	5.6	30	85	2	32.8
75	15.5	4.3	34	85	2	27.2
100	12.1	3.9	26	70	S*	21.6

SOURCE: *Wyo. Agr. Expt. Sta. Bul.* 199 (1933).
* Sample grade.

quantities of hay are to be consumed by cattle it must be of good quality. An example of a factor affecting quality and therefore palatability is the stage of maturity of the crop at harvest time. The Wyoming Station also studied this (see Table 310), and it was found that cattle consumed more of that hay cut at the 5 per cent bloom stage than when it was cut later. Cattle fed alfalfa cut at the 5 per cent stage consumed more than 10 pounds more hay per day than those animals fed the hay harvested when in full bloom.

Other Factors

Contaminations. Foreign material is present in greater or less degree in many hay lots. Such materials are considered useless for feeding purposes and may even be harmful. Noninjurious materials include weeds, straw, stubble, sedges, and woody or coarse contaminations possessing little feeding value. Sand burs, poisonous plants, and rough-bearded grasses are injurious and detract greatly from the value of the hay. Weedy hay is undesirable, since weeds give the hay a bad appearance, they are unpalatable, low in nutritive value, and are a source of weed seeds which may spread to the buyer's farm. The influence of foreign materials is reflected in the grade ascribed to the hay. In a laboratory study of more than 1,000

TABLE 311. PERCENTAGE OF FOREIGN MATERIAL FOUND IN VARIOUS CLASSES OF MARKET HAY

Classes	Number of samples	Percentage foreign material	Samples falling into grade			
			1	2	3	Sample
Alfalfa and alfalfa mixed............	385	6	69	20	6	5
Timothy and clover .	263	7	76	11	5	8
Prairie..............	213	15	42	19	17	22
Johnson and Johnson mixed............	198	18	37	12	17	34
Lespedeza and lespedeza mixed........	25	15	24	32	12	32
Soybean and soybean mixed............	25	4	88	0	12	..

SOURCE: *U.S. Dept. Agr. Misc. Pub.* 363 (1939).

samples it was found that the presence of larger quantities of foreign materials resulted in general in a lower grade rating. Similarly, the grade is influenced by the condition or soundness of the hay. Good color, leafiness, etc., indicate good condition, but moldiness, discoloration, heating, and any musty or offensive odors contribute to unsoundness. A sweet odor which is lost in overripe or undercured hay adds to the value of hay by increasing its palatability.

Size of Stems. The size and pliability of stems are other important criteria in making good-quality hay. Coarse hard stems are unpalatable and often rejected by livestock. The diameter of the stems can be influenced by planting rate, stage of maturity at harvest, crop variety, and soil fertility. Early-cut hay from fairly thick plantings on fertile soil should give the best type of stems. Soybeans, Johnson grass, and Sudan grass have a tendency to develop coarse stems, and the first cutting of alfalfa each year is usually coarser stemmed than succeeding cuttings.

Quality and Price

Hay grades are interpreted by buyers on a price-per-ton basis. Actual average prices offered for hay at Kansas City, Missouri, are given in Table 312 for 1935 to 1945. The highest quality hay invariably commanded the

TABLE 312. AVERAGE PRICE OF ALFALFA HAY PER TON, BY UNITED STATES GRADES AT KANSAS CITY, MISSOURI, 1935–1945

U.S. grade	Average in dollars per ton		
	1935	1940	1945
No. 1	13.75	15.25	27.55
No. 2 Leafy	12.55	13.70	25.88
No. 2	11.40	11.60	22.13
No. 3	9.30	7.96	16.52

SOURCE: Hay Quotations, Kansas City (1947).

best price, whereas lower grades brought lower prices. This recognition of feeding-value differences on a price basis attests to the value of grades in commercial transactions. Undoubtedly more work needs to be done on hay grading and quality relationships, especially as interpreted in terms of livestock acceptance and performance. Hay grades are not exact interpretations of quality, but they approach the problem in a usable and valuable manner.

References

1. Bohstedt, G.: Hay quality and what it means to you, *Successful Farming*, June, 1946.
2. Gardner, A. K., and Oscar L. Wyman: Quality hay pays good dividends, *Maine Agr. Ext. Serv. Bul.* 220 (1936).
3. Handbook of Official Hay Standards, U.S. Department of Agriculture, Production and Marketing Administration, 1936.
4. Hilton, J. H., J. W. Wilbur, and W. F. Epple: Early, intermediate and late cut soybean hay for milk and butterfat production, *Ind. Agr. Expt. Sta. Bul.* 346 (1931).
5. Huffman, C. F.: Roughage quality and quantity in the dairy ration: a review, *Jour. Dairy Sci.*, **22**:889–980 (1939).
6. Pollock, E. O., and W. H. Hosterman: Hay quality: relation to production and feed value, *U.S. Dept. Agr. Misc. Pub.* 363 (1939).
7. Snider, H. J.: Chemical composition of hay and forage crops, *Ill. Agr. Expt. Sta. Bul.* 518 (1946).
8. Sotola, Jerry: The nutritive value of alfalfa leaves and stems, *Jour. Agr. Res.* **47**: 919–945 (1933).
9. Willard, H. S.: Factors influencing the palatability of hay, *Wyo. Agr. Expt. Sta. Bul.* 199 (1933).
10. Woodward, T. E., W. H. Hosterman, P. V. Cardon, and E. W. McComas: The nutritive value of harvested forage, U.S. Department of Agriculture Yearbook, 1939, pp. 956–991.

CHAPTER 33

QUALITY PRODUCTION

Losses in the nutritive value of hay in haymaking occur generally over the United States. Reduction in feeding value is most severe in the humid section, decreasing in intensity with diminishing rainfall and humidity. Losses thus are greatest in the clover-timothy and annual-legume regions and least in the alfalfa and prairie hay regions. Nutritive losses may vary from about 10 per cent under ideal conditions to more than 50 per cent in severe climates and with inadequate haying methods.

Importance. Since more than 75 million acres are devoted to hay each year, with an output of more than 100 million tons, the problem becomes one of gigantic national significance. An average loss of 20 to 25 per cent of the feeding value of the hay crop means a severe annual setback to agriculture and to consumers as well. This nutrient loss is reflected in the health and well-being of livestock dependent in large part on roughage during the winter months. One of the greatest contributions to the livestock industry would be the development of methods whereby a high-quality roughage could be consistently produced on all livestock farms.

In the previous chapter data have been presented to show the value of hay cut young over old hay, of leafiness, green color, fine stems, and other characteristics. In making quality hay every effort should be made to preserve these characters in the highest state of value. The ordinary processes of growing, timely mowing, curing, and storing the hay need to be managed on the most efficient basis possible. These must, of course, be preceded by the wise choice of crops and the maintenance of soils that have been treated with lime and fertilizer according to the needs of the crop.

FACTORS AFFECTING QUALITY

The factors most important in making high-quality hay are stage of maturity of the crop when harvested, rapid curing, and safe storage. Of these the most difficult to accomplish is rapid drying, especially under field conditions.

Crop Maturity. Early mowing was shown in the previous chapter to result in greater leafiness and a higher protein content. The time of cutting hay crops varies according to regions and latitudes, but the stage of development of the crop at which to cut is usually the same irrespective of geography. Thus, in general, the rules given in Table 313 seem applicable for

319

TABLE 313. STAGE OF MATURITY FOR CUTTING VARIOUS HAY CROPS

Species	*Most favorable time to cut*
Alfalfa, first crop	From $\frac{1}{10}$ to $\frac{1}{4}$ bloom
Alfalfa, second crop	Full bloom
Alfalfa, third crop	About 6 weeks before first heavy frost
Sweetclover	When first blossoms appear
Red and alsike clover	From $\frac{1}{2}$ to $\frac{3}{4}$ bloom
Ladino clover	Full bloom
Soybeans, cowpeas	When pods are well-developed
Sudan grass	After heading but before blooming
Vetch and small grain	When small grain seeds are in milk stage
Small grains	When grain is in milk stage
Timothy	After heading but before blooming
Other perennial grasses	After heading but before blooming

SOURCE: *N.J. Agr. Expt. Sta. Cir.* 440 (1942).

most crops.   Where season permits, the cutting of soybeans and cowpeas seems best at the pod-formed stage, when their protein content is greatest, but annual hay crops must often be cut earlier in the humid regions to take full advantage of the best curing conditions.

Dry-matter Losses.   Field curing is the primary method used in preparing hay for storage.   Until recent years it was the only method available. Thus during unfavorable haying weather severe losses were bound to occur. Losses of dry matter, especially leaves, and of carotene, minerals, and protein occur.   The loss of dry matter has been apportioned as shown in Table 314.   Thus 10 to 30 per cent of the dry matter and 15 to 35 per cent

TABLE 314. DISTRIBUTION OF LOSSES OF DRY MATTER AND OF STARCH EQUIVALENT AS THE RESULT OF FIELD CURING OF HAY, PER CENT

Item	Dry matter	Digestible dry matter	Starch equivalent
Respiration of crop	Up to 10	5–15	5–15
Mechanical injury	5–10	5–10	5–10
Fermentation in the stack	5–10	5–10	5–10
Total	10–30	15–35	15–35

SOURCE: U.S. Department of Agriculture Yearbook, 1939.

of the starch equivalent is lost.   Naturally, such losses vary the country over, depending on curing techniques, methods of harvesting and storing, and crop species.

Studies on the loss of plant constituents of alfalfa in mechanical handling as given in Table 315 show that 30 per cent of the leaves and 10 per cent of the stems were lost, amounting to about 17 per cent of the total dry matter.

TABLE 315. PORTIONS OF THE ALFALFA CROP SAVED OR LOST ON CURING

Proportion saved or lost of	Portion saved						Portion lost					
	Total crop		Leaves		Stems		Total crop		Leaves		Stems	
	Lb.	%	Lb.	%	Lb.	%	Lb.	%	Lb.	%	Lb.	%
Green crop...	1,580	79	770	70	810	90	420	21	330	30	90	10
Dry matter..	478	82.4	154	70	324	90	102	17.6	66	30	36	10

SOURCE: U.S. Department of Agriculture Yearbook, 1939.

It is generally recognized that the leaves are the most difficult part of the crop to save. This loss of leaves is also influenced by the stage of maturity at which any particular crop is harvested. Thus in a Kansas study (see Table 316) it was found that harvesting alfalfa at one-tenth bloom resulted in the lowest loss of leaves, whereas losses were highest in the full-bloom

TABLE 316. PER CENT OF LEAVES LOST IN HARVESTING ALFALFA AT VARIOUS STAGES, 7-YEAR AVERAGE

Stage of growth	Per cent of leaves	Per cent of total crop
$\frac{1}{10}$ bloom..............................	14.5	7.3
Full bloom.............................	20.4	10.1
Seed....................................	22.2	9.3

SOURCE: *Kans. Agr. Expt. Sta. Bul.* 15 (1925).

TABLE 317. TOTAL DRY MATTER LOST WHEN HAY WAS CURED BY VARIOUS METHODS, PER CENT

Method of curing	Aug. 22	Aug. 23	Aug. 25	Ave.
Windrowed immediately when cut......................	7	2	4	4
Windrowed, turned when one-half cured................	8	2	5	5
Swath cured, completely......	9	13	7	10
Swath cured, tedded when one-half cured.............	12	16	13	14
One-half swath cured, then windrowed................	9	5	5	6
Cocked immediately, medium cocks....................	1	1	..	1

SOURCE: *Iowa Agr. Expt. Sta. Res. Bul.* 251 (1939).

and seed stages. As an average about 19 per cent of the leaves were lost, accounting for nearly 10 per cent of the crop.

Various methods of curing tried in Iowa resulted in greater or less loss of dry matter. The data are given in Table 317. Swath curing combined with tedding was most wasteful.

Method of Drying. The method of curing hay has little effect on the chemical composition, vitamins excepted, provided that mechanical losses or those due to leaching or overexposure to the sun do not occur. Data indicating this general conclusion are given in Table 318. Curing with heat, by sun only, or in the shade resulted in equivalent values for the various chemical constituents.

TABLE 318. EFFECT OF METHOD OF DRYING ALFALFA AND RED CLOVER UPON THE CHEMICAL COMPOSITION OF THE HAY, PER CENT

Method of drying	Length of drying period, hr.	Ash	Crude protein	Fiber	Nitrogen-free extract	Fat
Alfalfa:						
In oven 180°F......	6	7.8	13.9	34.4	42.0	1.9
In sun.............	54	7.7	14.0	34.1	42.9	1.2
In shade..........	100	8.6	14.0	34.4	40.8	1.5
Red clover:						
In oven 180°F......	5	6.7	15.9	25.4	50.3	1.8
In sun.............	55	6.7	15.4	26.5	49.7	1.8
In shade..........	79	6.7	14.9	28.2	48.5	1.7

SOURCE: *Minn. Agr. Expt. Sta. Tech. Bul.* 83 (1932).

Effect of Rain. Rain on hay causes leaching of plant nutrients, and sunlight causes loss of carotene content. The effect of rain on the digestible protein and starch equivalent of hay is given in Table 319. Rain increased

TABLE 319. LOSSES OF NUTRIENTS IN HAYMAKING

Factors	Percentage losses	
	Digestible protein	Starch equivalent
Dried indoors, no rain, no mechanical losses.....	14	23
Dried outdoors, no rain, leaf shedding..........	33	39
1–2 showers of rain...........................	28	44
5–6 showers of rain...........................	50	54
Average of all experiments in which it rained.....	40	50

SOURCE: *Jour. Dairy Sci.,* **22** (1939).

the loss over and above that from mechanical means alone by as much as 10 to 15 per cent. Hay that has been rained on may lose up to 50 per cent of the digestible protein content and starch equivalent. It has been found that 20 to 40 per cent of the nutrient value of a hay crop can be removed by soaking the hay in water. The nutrients lost are the most soluble and also the most valuable and easily digested. Moist weather prolongs the respiration period of the plant cells, resulting in increased respiration. Several showers do more damage than a single rain during the curing period.

Additional data[9] on the effect of rain on chemical constituents show that a loss of one-third of the soluble carbohydrates and about one-sixth of the minerals occurred in this study, while the proportion of crude fiber increased by about 50 per cent. In another study by Headden in Colorado[9] the loss of crude protein and soluble carbohydrates from alfalfa hay amounted to one-third of the protein and one-sixth of the nitrogen-free extract. Rain thus is shown to be of great significance in making hay if quality is to be maintained.

Carotene Losses. Overexposure to the sun results in severe losses of carotene. Studies conducted in South Dakota illustrate this point clearly, as shown in Table 320. The greater and longer the exposure to the sun,

TABLE 320. LOSSES IN THE CAROTENE CONTENT OF ALFALFA HAY CURED BY DIFFERENT METHODS

Curing period, days	Milligrams of carotene per pound of dry matter when hay was cured in		
	Swath	Windrow	Cock
0	145	145	145
1	108	91	107
2	40	72	111
3	15	43	109
4	7	41	92
6	1	21	. . .

SOURCE: *S.Dak. Agr. Expt. Sta. Cir.* 53 (1944).

the more severe the carotene loss. Fresh material was 145 times as high in carotene as hay cured in the swath for 6 days. Exposure of hay to sunlight in Mississippi[10] resulted in a loss of nearly one-half of the carotene by exposure for only $1\frac{1}{4}$ hours to bright sunlight in an oven at 80 to 100°C., whereas only 2 per cent was lost under similar conditions but without sunlight. Sunlight thus is shown to destroy carotene in hay crops, and the longer the exposure, the higher the loss.

Vitamin D. On the other hand, hay exposed to sunlight develops vitamin D. Hay cured in the dark or in the hay mow is invariably low in vitamin D, and under such conditions this nutrient must be added to the ration as required by the animals being fed. Vitamin D increases in hay with lengthening exposure to sunlight. It is highest in swath-cured hay, fair in hay cured in the windrow, and low in hay cured in the cock or mow. The vitamin A and D content of hay thus will vary inversely, depending on the method of curing and storage.

Daily Variations in Moisture Content. The time of day at which to harvest the hay crop might well be open to question. Studies in Iowa, given in Table 321, indicated that percentage dry matter or moisture con-

TABLE 321. THE DAILY MOISTURE CONTENT OF ALFALFA GROWING IN THE FIELD IN IOWA

Time of sampling	Moisture content of the alfalfa plant at 2-hr. intervals, %			Ave.
	July 19	Aug. 5	Aug. 21	
8 A.M.	78.2	74.3	74.0	75.5
10 A.M.	77.0	72.6	73.8	74.5
12 M.	76.3	72.2	71.5	73.3
2 P.M.	76.9	72.6	70.2	73.2
4 P.M.	76.4	72.5	71.0	73.3
6 P.M.	76.2	72.6	73.6	74.1
8 P.M.	77.0	73.6	73.4	74.7

SOURCE: *Iowa Agr. Expt. Sta. Res. Bul.* 251 (1939).

tent do not change materially during the daytime. The moisture percentage ranged between 70 and 78, depending on the crop but not the hour of the day. There is no opportunity to capitalize on a time of the day when dry-matter content would be highest.

A rather prevalent belief prevails that hay should not be cut until the dew is off in the morning. Studies, as shown in Table 322, at Cornell University have recently refuted this idea. Hay cut early with the dew on cured just as rapidly as that cut at a later hour. This is important, since labor can be conserved by starting early in the morning and not waiting until the dew is off.

Value of Leaves. The effect of the presence or absence of the leaves on rapidity of curing has been studied at a number of experiment stations. Data from Iowa[6] in which the leaves were removed from the stems show no appreciable effect on the rate of drying. The leafless stems were compared with whole plants. The studies were conducted in the laboratory, on a

TABLE 322. A 2-YEAR COMPARISON OF DRY MATTER IN VARIOUS HAY CROPS TOWARD END OF SWATH-CURING PERIOD WHEN CUTTING OCCURRED BEFORE AND AFTER DEW WAS OFF

Crop	Average per cent dry matter at about 5 P.M.					
	1940 results			1941 results		
	Cut with dew on	Cut with dew off	Difference	Cut with dew on	Cut with dew off	Difference
Alfalfa:						
1st cutting.........	37	35	2	52	49	3
2d cutting.........	45	43	2	49	47	2
Timothy.............	63	61	2	77	79	2
Orchard grass and blue-grasses.............	60	60	0	63	63	0

SOURCE: *Jour. Amer. Soc. Agron.*, **34** (1942).

window ledge and in the sun, but not under field conditions. Studies in Mississippi on curing hay showed a distinct advantage in keeping the leaves on the stems. The rate at which the stomata close on cut alfalfa is given in Table 323. These data indicate rapid but not complete closing of

TABLE 323. PER CENT RATE AT WHICH STOMATA CLOSE IN ALFALFA AFTER CUTTING (CUTTINGS MADE AT 9:30 A.M.)

Hours after cutting	Open	Partly closed	Closed
As cut.............	62.3	36.7	0.0
1½.................	8.0	80.0	12.0
2..................	1.2	60.1	38.7
3½.................	2.6	85.7	11.7
5½.................	3.5	53.9	42.6
6½.................	0.3	41.0	58.7

SOURCE: *Miss. Agr. Expt. Sta. Bul.* 27 (1941).

the stomatal openings on the leaves following cutting. This would lead one to suspect that they were partly effective in emitting moisture. Results of further tests with sweetclover on drying with and without leaves are given in Table 324. These data show a distinct advantage in drying with the leaves on the stem. Similar results were secured with Johnson grass. It was pointed out that the rate of drying is affected by the size and shape of stems, relative weights of leaf and stem, density and behavior

TABLE 324. LOSS OF MOISTURE FROM SWEETCLOVER STEMS AS INFLUENCED BY LEAVES

Condition	Whole plant		Upper 6 in. of plant	
	Moisture in stem, %	Water in stem lost, %	Moisture in stem, %	Water in stem lost, %
Initial moisture.............	70.4	..	85.1	..
Dry 18 hr.:				
Leaves on stem...........	63.0	29	79.0	34
Leaves off stem..........	71.6	0	84.9	2
Dry 70 hr.:				
Leaves on stem...........	41.0	71	61.0	66
Leaves off stem..........	68.0	11	78.0	38

SOURCE: *Miss. Agr. Expt. Sta. Bul.* 27 (1941).

of leaf and stem stomata, moisture content of stem, and rate at which moisture is lost from the leaf.

Field Curing. The time required for bringing the moisture content to 30 per cent in Iowa and Nebraska is given in Table 325. Swath curing

TABLE 325. TIME REQUIRED TO BRING HAY TO 30 PER CENT MOISTURE CONTENT, HOURS

Method	Iowa*	Nebraska†
Swath cured completely..........................	17	27
One-half swath cured then windrowed.............	17	27
One-fourth swath cured then windrowed...........	21	29
Windrowed immediately.........................	23	56
One-half swath cured then medium cocks..........	26	30
One-fourth swath cured then medium cocks........	56	32
Medium cocks made immediately.................	92	104

* *Iowa Agr. Expt. Sta. Res. Bul.* 251 (1939).   † *Jour. Amer. Soc. Agron.,* **19** (1927).

required the least time and haycocks the most. Partial swath curing with subsequent windrowing was just as speedy as swath curing alone. Rate of curing alfalfa hay was also studied in Mississippi. The data show that double windrowing 2 hours after mowing was the fastest method in effecting curing. Eight hours after cutting the moisture content was 18.5 per cent by this method compared with 26 per cent when the hay was cured in the swath without turning.

Hay Crusher. The hay crusher is a relatively new machine used to speed up the curing process. As the hay is mowed it is run through heavy rollers attached to the mower. The stems are crushed and thus exposed to more rapid drying. Early studies conducted in Kansas showed a real advantage for crushing, as shown from the data in Table 326. Crushed alfalfa cut at

TABLE 326. EFFECT OF CRUSHING ALFALFA HAY ON SPEED OF DRYING

Method	Moisture content, %					
	10:30 A.M.	12:00 M.	1:00 P.M.	2:00 P.M.	3:00 P.M.	4:00 P.M.
Normal.......	66	56	47	41	37	35
Crushed......	66	53	39	28	22	17

SOURCE: *Agr. Eng.*, **14** (1933).

10:30 in the morning had reached a moisture content of 25 per cent by 2:30 in the afternoon, or only 4 hours after mowing. Similar results were secured with sweetclover and soybean hay. The effect of crushing Johnson grass, Kudzu, and soybeans was studied in Mississippi.[10] Johnson grass cut

FIG. 81. The hay crusher speeds the curing job. (*John Bean Manufacturing Company*.)

and crushed at 10 o'clock in the morning contained only 25 per cent moisture at 5 P.M., whereas the uncrushed had 37 per cent moisture. Crushing also speeded the drying of Kudzu and soybeans and conserved their carotene content.

Mow Curing. Recent years have seen the introduction of mow curing. This method is most applicable to the humid regions where rain and humid weather make field curing risky. Leaves, carotene, and plant nutrients can best be saved as hay by this method.　It also increases the value of mech-anization on the farm by profitable use of the field chopper on wilted hay. Barn curing was developed cooperatively by the Tennessee Valley Author-ity and the Tennessee Agricultural Experiment Station.　It consists of placing partially dried hay, with a moisture content of 40 to 50 per cent, into the mow, over specially constructed air ducts.　A large blower or fan is used to drive air through these ducts at fairly high rates.　In some cases the air is heated.　Construction and materials are not costly, and this method of curing probably will become increasingly popular.　Figure 82

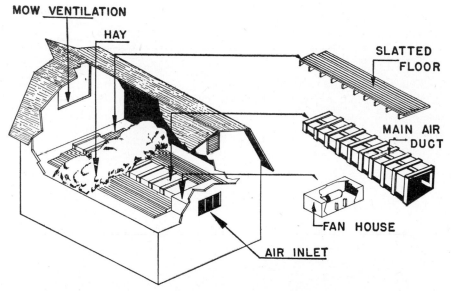

Fɪɢ.　82.　Sketch of hay drier installed in a barn showing hay over part of the system. (*Virginia Polytechnic Institute.*)

shows a diagrammatic sketch of such a design.　Mow curing reduces weather risks and helps make a superior hay.

Tests indicate that barn-cured hay contains three to four times as much carotene as field-cured hay, that it is higher in leaves, and that it has a much better green color.　For example, the carotene content of mow-cured hay in tests at Beltsville, Maryland, was 134 micrograms per gram compared with only 77 for field-cured alfalfa hay as the crop was stored.　Rain further reduced the carotene content to only 40.　At the time of feeding the caro-tene contents were as follows: mow-cured, 50 micrograms; field-cured with rain, 5; and field-cured without rain, 14.　Mow-cured hay usually grades higher than field-cured hay, as may be noted in Table 328.　These data came from 91 samples of hay collected in Tennessee and Virginia and graded by the U.S. Department of Agriculture.　More than half the barn-

TABLE 327. EFFECT OF METHOD OF HARVESTING AND STORING ON CAROTENE CONTENT OF FIRST CUTTING ALFALFA

Condition	Treatment	Carotene, micrograms per gram		
		When cut	As stored	When fed
Rain..............	Mow cured	288	134	50
	Field cured	277	40	5
No rain...........	Field cured	277	77	14

SOURCE: *Agr. Eng.*, 28 (1947).

TABLE 328. EFFECT OF HAY DRIER ON HAY QUALITY AS MEASURED BY GRADES, PER CENT

Method	U.S. No. 1	U.S. No. 2	U.S. No. 3	Sample grade
Barn cured..............	54	34	7	5
Field cured..............	9	26	35	30

SOURCE: *American Blower Company Bul.* 3205 (1945).

cured hay graded U.S. No. 1, and only 5 per cent fell in the sample grade. Only 9 per cent of the field-cured hay made U.S. No. 1 grade, and 30 per cent was given a sample-grade rating. Such data as these explain the results of a feeding trial in Tennessee[19] in which field-cured hay was compared with mow-dried. In a feeding trial lasting for 165 days, heifers fed the mow-cured hay gained on the average 17 pounds more than others fed equal amounts of the same hay cured in the field.

Dehydration. The application of considerable heat in drying hay is often called dehydration. This method is very effective in reducing carotene losses and producing a product high in leaves, minerals, and certain vitamins. Relatively high heat is often used to give speedy drying. More than 680,000 tons of alfalfa hay was cured by this method in 1947, a larger quantity of dry matter than that made into grass silage. The dried product is usually made into meal and used in mixed feeds, especially poultry and hog feeds.

Storage. Losses in feed value occur in storage as well as in the field. Adequately cured hay loses less of its feed value than hay that is undercured. Quality is lost rapidly from hay stored when too moist. This point is brought out in Iowa data given in Table 329. Good green hay was the end product only when moisture content was below 30 per cent. Higher moisture quantities resulted in brown, gray, and moldy hay. Similarly, hay baled in the field at 30 per cent or higher moisture content

TABLE 329. THE MOISTURE CONTENT, HIGHEST TEMPERATURE DEVELOPED, AND THE QUALITY OF HAY RESULTING FROM THE DIFFERENT MOWING TRIALS

Moisture content, %	Highest temperature, °F.	Hay color
58	181	Dark brown, black areas
39	143	Brown and moldy
35	131	Clean brown
32	127	Green
29	102	Good green
25	91	Good green
20	77	Good green

SOURCE: *Iowa Agr. Expt. Sta. Res. Bul.* 251 (1939).

TABLE 330. EFFECT OF PRESSURE ON CAROTENE CONTENT OF HAY AT END OF 130 DAYS' STORAGE

Pressure, lb. per sq. in.	*Loss of carotene, %*
No pressure	27.4
2	10.3
12	7.1
48	6.6

SOURCE: *Agr. Eng.,* **25** (1944).

TABLE 331. EFFECT OF VARYING MOISTURE CONTENT ON THE RATE OF HEAT DEVELOPMENT IN MOISTENED ALFALFA HAY, WITH AND WITHOUT THE ADDITION OF SALT

Added moisture, %	Heat development in the presence of			
	No salt		1% salt	
	Time, days	Maximum temperature, °C.	Time, days	Maximum temperature, °C.
15	4	50.0	9	48.5
20	4	43.5	6	44.0
25	2	45.0	5	44.0
30	2	48.0	4	48.0
35	2	41.0	3	41.0
40	2	47.5	3	44.0

SOURCE: *Jour. Agr. Res.,* **42** (1931).

usually results in an inferior feed. Baling when the moisture is between 20 and 25 per cent seems most advisable.

Depth. Hay properly cured and stored loses carotene during the storage period. Less carotene is lost, however, by deep storage of the hay than by shallow, as shown in Table 330. This information indicates that the deeper the storage of the hay and the greater the pressure, the less the loss of carotene. Deep mows or deep storage methods thus would help preserve the carotene content. Carotene is also lost as a direct function of time of storage (see Table 327). The longer the hay is stored, the less carotene it will contain.

Salting Hay. Salting of hay has been a popular practice. There is a common impression that salting reduces the danger of heating when hay is put into the mow without being adequately cured. Data on the addition of salt to alfalfa hay are given in Table 331. The salt did not decrease heat development significantly in the moistened alfalfa hay. Salting hay probably improves its palatability to livestock, but bacterial fermentation and mold development have not been prevented by the addition of salt nor has it prevented spontaneous combustion.

References

1. Ahlgren, G. H., and C. B. Bender: High quality hay production, *N.J. Agr. Expt. Sta. Cir.* 440 (1942).
2. American Blower Company: Fans, *Bul.* 3205, March, 1945.
3. Bohstedt, G.: Nutritional values of hay and silage as affected by harvesting, processing, and storage, *Agr. Eng.*, **25**:337–340 (1944).
4. J. I. Case Company: How to Produce High Protein Hay, Racine, Wisconsin.
5. Hartwig, H. B.: The effect of dew on the curing of hay, *Jour. Amer. Soc. Agron.*, **34**:482–485 (1942).
6. Henson, Edwin R.: Curing and storage of alfalfa hay, *Iowa Agr. Expt. Sta. Res. Bul.* 251 (1939).
7. Higgins, Floyd L.: Drying of legume hay plants, *Minn. Agr. Expt. Sta. Tech. Bul.* 83 (1932).
8. Hodgson, R. E., J. B. Shepherd, W. H. Hosterman, L. G. Schoenleber, H. M. Tysdal, and R. E. Wagner: Comparative efficiency of ensiling, barn curing, and field curing forage crops, *Agr. Eng.*, **28**: 154–156 (1947).
9. Huffman, C. F.: Roughage quality and quantity in the dairy ration, A review, *Jour. Dairy Sci.*, **22**:889–980 (1939).
10. Jones, T. N., O. A. Leonard, and I. E. Hamblin: Methods of field curing hay, *Miss. Agr. Expt. Sta. Tech. Bul.* 27 (1941).
11. Kiesselbach, T. A., and Arthur Anderson: Curing alfalfa hay, *Jour. Amer. Soc. Agron.*, **19**:116–126 (1927).
12. LeClerc, J. A.: Losses in making hay and silage, U.S. Department of Agriculture Yearbook, 1939, pp. 992–1016.
13. Salisbury, G. W., and F. B. Morrison: Early cut, nitrogen fertilized timothy hay as compared with alfalfa hay for feeding dairy cows, *N.Y. Agr. Expt. Sta. Bul.* 694 (1938).
14. Salmon, S. C., C. O. Swanson, and C. W. McCampbell: Experiments relating to time of cutting alfalfa, *Kans. Agr. Expt. Sta. Tech. Bul.* 15 (1925).
15. Schaller, John A.: A summary of barn hay curing work, *Agr. Eng.*, **22**:292, 295 (1941).
16. Snider, H. J.: Chemical composition of hay and forage crops, *Ill. Agr. Expt. Sta. Bul.* 518 (1946).

17. Stuart, L. S., and Lawrence H. James: The effect of salt on the microbial heating of alfalfa hay, *Jour. Agr. Res.*, **42**:657–664 (1931).

18. Wallis, G. C.: Vitamins D and A in alfalfa hay, *S.Dak. Agr. Expt. Sta. Cir.* 53 (1944).

19. Weaver, J. W., and C. E. Wylie: Drying hay in the barn and testing its feeding value, *Tenn. Agr. Expt. Sta. Bul.* 170 (1939).

20. Zink, Frank J.: The mower-crusher in hay making, *Agr. Eng.*, **14**:71–73 (1933).

CHAPTER 34

SAVING LABOR

Harvesting hay and making silage are time-consuming, expensive farm operations. Many changes in techniques have taken place since the Colonial days when hand harvesting and raking were the standard methods. The horse-drawn dump rake, the three-tined pitchfork, and hand loading of hay from the haycock are expensive tools and methods for making hay today because of their labor demand. Speed and efficiency are required in hay and silage harvesting operations to secure low costs of production together with a high-quality product. These can be attained only by using equipment capable of handling large tonnages at a rapid pace and through adequate and rapid precuring along with early cutting and other tested treatments. Many new haymaking machines, including such innovations as the pickup baler, the field chopper, and modifications of the buck rake, are daily becoming more popular. Only 25 years ago it required about 6 hours of man labor to make a ton of hay; it now takes as little as 1½ hours. In 1947, 75 million acres were harvested for hay in the United States and more than 102 million tons of hay were stored away. The annual task of "making hay" is a tremendous one, involving millions of man-days and costing many millions of dollars.

Steps in Making Hay

The job of making hay consists of cutting the crop, raking it into windrows, baling or bunching, loading, transporting, and storing in mows or haystacks. Each operation requires certain types of machines and man power. Methods of making hay vary from farm to farm and also according to the hay regions. An indication of this can be gained by considering recent findings related to hay handling in America.[1] In 1944, 58 per cent of all hay in the United States was cut by horse-drawn mowers; 42 per cent, with tractors. Horse-drawn rakes windrowed 70 per cent of it, and 73 per cent was put up loose or unbaled. About 62 per cent was stored in barns or sheds, the rest in stacks or sold and delivered before storing.

Cutting. The first step in the haying operation is cutting the green crop. Comparative studies on methods of cutting and the time requirement of each are given in Table 332. The use of a tractor with a 7-foot cutter bar was the most efficient method used in the four states where this study was

TABLE 332. TIME IN MINUTES REQUIRED FOR CUTTING ONE ACRE OF HAY BY VARIOUS METHODS

Method	New York	Maine	Pennsylvania	Vermont	Average
Tractor, 7-ft. bar....	36	37	30	27	33
Tractor, 6-ft. bar....	..	..	30	53	42
Horses, 6-ft. bar.....	66	64	54	40	56
Horses, 5-ft. bar.....	..	..	67	56	62

conducted, requiring only 33 minutes on the average per acre cut. The 6-foot cutter bar and tractor took an average of 42 minutes, whereas the horse-drawn mowers were the most time-consuming. It required almost twice as long to cut an acre of hay with a team of horses and a 5-foot cutter-bar mower as with a tractor cutting a 7-foot swath.

FIG. 83. The side-delivery rake places the hay in windrows. (*International Harvester Company.*)

Raking. Raking the hay into windrows as soon as it is partially cured is the second step, and it may be accomplished by means of tractor- or horse-drawn side-delivery rakes or a dump rake. A comparison of the data collected in the four studies previously mentioned shows that the side-delivery rake and tractor required the least time, whereas the dump rake averaged 5 minutes longer per acre in doing the same amount of work (see Table 333). The difference in time required for raking between the three

TABLE 333. TIME IN MINUTES REQUIRED FOR RAKING ONE ACRE OF HAY BY VARIOUS METHODS

Method	New York	Maine	Pennsylvania	Vermont	Average
Side-delivery, tractor.	34	23	30	20	27
Side-delivery, horses	..	27	33	29	30
Dump............	35	33	28	30	32

methods studied is probably less important than the effective bunching of the hay for good curing and later handling.

Bunching or Baling. Various methods are in use in preparing hay for hauling to the mow or stack for storage. Bunching with a hand fork or baling with one- and three-man balers is in wide use, and field chopping

FIG. 84. The one-man pickup baler is highly efficient. (*International Harvester Company.*)

is used occasionally. Loose hay bunched by hand is sometimes hauled to a stationary baler for packaging. In 1944, 14 per cent of the total hay produced in America was packaged by means of pickup balers and 13 per cent with stationary balers. Only about 2 per cent was stored as chopped hay, whereas 71 per cent was handled as loose hay. The one-man baler is about three times as efficient (see Table 334) as the three-man baler from the standpoint of labor investment. A four-man baler is even more time-consuming and expensive to operate.

Loading, Hauling, Unloading. Loading, hauling the hay, and unloading at the mow or stack are other necessary operations in storage. Mechani-

TABLE 334. TIME IN MAN-MINUTES FOR BALING ONE TON OF HAY BY TWO
METHODS

Method	New York	Maine	Pennsyl-vania	Vermont	Average
One-man..........	36	19	22	23	25
Three-man.........	66	72	72	81	73

cal and hand methods of accomplishing this work are utilized in varying degrees in the different states. In 1944, 45 per cent of all hay in the United States was loaded by hand, 32.6 per cent by means of mechanical methods, and 22.4 per cent hauled by buck rakes. More hay is thus loaded by hand methods than by power in the United States. About 25.5 per cent was unloaded by hand; and forks and slings or other mechanical methods were used to unload 74.5 per cent. Power is more widely used for unloading hay in most of the Northern and Western states, and hand labor in the annual-legume region.

Hay is hauled for storage with trucks, wagons, and horse or tractor power, or by means of power-driven buck rakes. In 1944, 55 per cent of all hay produced was hauled to storage with work animals, 19 per cent on wagons and sleds with tractors, and the rest by motor-driven buck rakes or motor trucks. Tractor power is becoming of increasing significance in the United States in the making of hay. Most hay produced (61.3 per cent) in the United States is stored in mows, 31.7 per cent in 1944 was put in stacks, 6.5 per cent was sold and delivered before storage, and only 0.5 of 1 per cent was made into grass silage. Over 90 per cent of the hay put up in the clover-timothy region goes into haymows. Most of the hay in the humid Pacific Northwest also goes into barns, but the hay in the semiarid and irrigated parts of the West is for the most part stored in outdoor stacks. Chopped hay and grass silage are of minor significance but may increase with added economic pressures, especially in the clover-timothy belt and in the grain hay region of the Pacific Northwest.

Studies in Vermont[2] on loading hay by various methods have given valuable information. Loading baled hay onto a trailer was the most timesaving method, followed by truck with bale loader. Loading loose hay on a truck by hand was least efficient, requiring seven times as long as loading baled hay on a trailer. The buck rake was about twice as time-consuming as the latter method. From the standpoint of labor efficiency, baled hay loaded directly onto a trailer is superior. Baled hay can be handled more readily than loose hay, although the buck rake and the field chopper are relatively fast in handling this kind of hay.

In Ohio studies (see Table 335) on handling and storing the hay the buck

TABLE 335.   COST OF HANDLING AND STORING DRY HAY, WINDROW TO MOW, BY DIF-
FERENT METHODS

Method	Number of men in crew	Tons per hour by crew	Man-hours per ton	Cost per ton, dollars
Auto buck rake................	3.1	1.8	1.7	1.03
Tractor buck rake.............	2.6	1.3	2.0	1.37
Stationary chopper and buck rake	2.3	1.7	1.4	1.52
Wagons and loader.............	3.4	1.1	3.1	1.76
Large field chopper............	3.6	2.9	1.2	1.96
Stationary chopper, wagons, and loader.....................	5.4	1.5	3.6	2.45
Pickup baler..................	3.2	1.2	2.7	2.60

SOURCE: *Ohio Agr. Expt. Sta. Bul.* 636 (1942).

rake, either auto- or tractor-drawn, proved to be the cheapest method. The three-man pickup baler was the most expensive method, averaging $2.60 per ton of hay stored.   In Vermont[2] hauling baled hay with a tractor and wagon or truck was very efficient as a timesaver, but hauling loose or chopped hay with the truck was also satisfactory.   Hauling by wagon and horses required extra time, and the buck rake was least efficient, probably because of the long hauling distance.

Further studies in Ohio on the buck rake (see Table 336) indicate a relationship between distance of haul and efficiency.   Close hauls were the most economical, with increasing costs as distances became greater.   Thus

TABLE 336.   RELATION OF DISTANCE TO FIELD TO EFFICIENCY AND COST OF HANDLING
HAY WITH AUTO AND TRACTOR BUCK RAKES

Type of buck rake and distance to field, rods	Average distance to field, rods	Men in crew	Tons of hay per hour	Man-hours per ton	Cost per ton, dollars
Auto buck rake:					
20–59................	35	3.2	2.0	1.6	0.97
60–99................	75	3.2	1.9	1.7	1.03
100–139..............	118	3.1	1.7	1.8	1.08
140 and over..........	173	2.9	1.6	1.8	1.15
Tractor buck rake:.......					
20–59................	38	2.6	1.4	1.8	1.24
60–99................	71	2.8	1.4	2.0	1.33
100–139..............	117	2.4	1.1	2.2	1.48
140 and over..........	180	2.0	0.9	2.2	1.62

SOURCE: *Ohio Agr. Expt. Sta. Bul.* 636 (1942).

with the auto buck rake when the hauling distance was 35 rods, 2 tons of hay per hour could be handled, but when the distance was increased to 140 rods or more only 1.6 tons per hour was possible. Auto buck rakes were more efficient than tractor buck rakes.

Studies on unloading hay at the mow by various methods are given in Table 337. Unloading baled hay by hand required the least time, and

TABLE 337. AVERAGE TIME COST OF UNLOADING ONE TON OF HAY INTO BARN BY VARIOUS METHODS

	Average time cost, min.			
Job method	Loose hay	Baled hay	Bucked hay	Chopped hay
With hand fork...............	17	..	..	..
With slings...................	30	19	42	..
With grapple fork.............	30	35	59	..
With bale elevator.............	..	31	..	..
Into stationary chopper.........	49	..	60	..
Into blower...................	..	..	..	18
By hand......................	..	12	..	..

SOURCE: *Vt. Agr. Expt. Sta. Bul.* 351 (1946).

feeding bucked hay into a stationary chopper was most time-consuming. The use of slings, grapple forks, and bale elevators saved labor but was more time-consuming than unloading by hand. In Ohio studies[7] on storing hay brought to the barn with buck rakes, slings proved faster and more economical than grapple forks in mowing away hay. Again in this study the auto buck rake was more efficient than the tractor buck rake.

Interestingly enough the most speedy methods in handling hay often require the highest investment in machinery. The smallest investment in machinery is found where hand methods are employed together with horses for power. The field chopper and one-man baler are by far the most expensive investments, but they rate high in saving labor and increasing farm efficiency. Another item affecting the cost of making hay is the average acre yield.[8] High yields normally reduce the cost per ton provided that increased difficulties of mowing and curing do not offset this advantage.

MAKING CORN SILAGE

The making of corn silage is one of the biggest autumn jobs on most dairy farms. The corn is normally cut green in the field with a corn binder, loaded onto wagons or trucks, and hauled to a stationary ensilage cutter where it is chopped and blown into the silo. The job has often been done by groups of farmers combining efforts in helping one another. Crews of 8 to 15 men are required, indicating a considerable expenditure of labor and effort. Large farms with adequate labor do their own silo filling and need not exchange work with neighbors.

Fig. 85. A field chopper and wagon for harvesting corn silage. (*Farm Implement News.*)

Recently, corn binders have been equipped with attached elevators carrying the corn bundles onto wagons drawn alongside. Quite often, however, this is not speedy enough, especially where work is exchanged among neighbors, and the green corn must be cut in advance of silo filling.

Studies made at Purdue University indicate the approximate man-hours per ton of silage made by different methods. In Table 338 data showing

TABLE 338. LABOR USED IN HARVESTING SILAGE WITH CORN BINDER AND STATIONARY SILO FILLER

Labor	Man-hours		
	Per acre	Per ton	%
Cutting..................	0.8	0.08	3.7
Loading..................	11.7	1.11	53.7
Hauling and unloading......	7.0	0.66	32.1
Feeding..................	2.3	0.22	10.5
Total..................	21.8	2.07	100.0

SOURCE: *Agr. Eng.*, **24** (1943).

labor distribution by the conventional method of making silage may be found. Ten men were used to furnish labor in this study, and the length of haul was 0.4 mile. The data given do not include two men in the silo distributing the silage. This study shows 21.8 hours per acre of corn harvested or 2.07 hours per ton put into the silo. More than 50 per cent of the total time consumed was spent in loading the corn bundles onto trailers in the field and 32 per cent in hauling from the field and unloading at the ensilage cutter.

In another study given in Table 339 a field harvester was used. Field loading was thus eliminated and the efficiency of the job increased so that

TABLE 339. LABOR USED IN HARVESTING SILAGE USING A FIELD SILAGE HARVESTER

Labor	Man-hours		
	Per acre	Per ton	%
Harvesting..................	1.7	0.13	11
Hauling...................	5.1	0.39	33
Unloading.................	8.5	0.65	56
Total..................	15.3	1.17	100

SOURCE: *Agr. Eng.,* **24** (1943).

only 1.17 man-hours per ton of silage made was required. A study of labor distribution indicates that unloading took 56 per cent of the time and was the weakest point in this method. Nine men were used, not including two in the silo.

Following through on the above findings the Purdue investigators tried an automatic winch and other modifications for unloading. By this

TABLE 340. LABOR USED HARVESTING SILAGE, WITH HARVESTER, AUTOMATIC WINCH FOR UNLOADING, MODIFIED EQUIPMENT AND TECHNIQUE

Labor	Man-hours		
	Per acre	Per ton	%
Harvesting..................	0.8	0.09	20
Hauling...................	2.4	0.27	60
Unloading.................	0.8	0.09	20
Total..................	4.0	0.45	100

SOURCE: *Agr. Eng.,* **24** (1943).

method harvesting and unloading the chopped green material became secondary to the job of hauling from the field to the silo (see Table 340). Only 4 hours were spent per acre of corn harvested and 0.45 man-hour per ton was required. This was a 500 per cent increase in efficiency over the corn binder and stationary silo filler. Only five men were needed for the field work, and the length of haul was 0.8 of a mile.

Fig. 86. Unloading corn silage with automatic equipment. (*Farm Implement News.*)

An examination of the data given in this chapter indicates that no one method is best for all farms or forage-making regions. Such factors as hay and corn acreage, topography, cost of custom work, cost of labor and machinery, form of hay desired for feeding, and the time element will determine the value of each method and machine. The data presented indicate a heavy saving of labor by the effective use of the baler, buck rake, tractor, and field chopper. While these machines are costly, there will nevertheless probably be an increasing trend toward mechanization of the hay- and silage-making process because of the great laborsaving advantage.

References

1. Brodell, A. P., T. O. Engebretson, and Charles G. Carpenter: Harvesting the hay crop, F.M. 57, Bureau of Agricultural Economics, U.S. Department of Agriculture, 1946.
2. Carter, Robert M.: Hay harvesting, *Vt. Agr. Expt. Sta. Bul.* 351 (1946).

3. Davidson, J. B., C. K. Shedd, and E. V. Collins: Labor duty in the harvesting of ensilage, *Agr. Eng.*, **24:**293–294 (1943).
4. Dow, George E.: Labor efficiency in harvesting hay, *Maine Agr. Expt. Sta. Bul.* 453 (1947).
5. Keepper, W. E., and L. B. Adkinson: Costs and labor used in harvesting hay by various methods, 204 Pennsylvania farms, 1945, *Pa. Agr. Expt. Sta. Paper* 1324 (April, 1946).
6. Lamborn, E. W., and L. B. Adkinson: Costs and labor used to harvest hay by different methods in New York, 1945, Cornell University, Ithaca, New York, Agr. Econ. 569, 1946.
7. Morison, F. L.: A study of the newer hay harvesting methods on Ohio farms, *Ohio Agr. Expt. Sta. Bul.* 636 (1942).
8. Selby, H. E.: Cost and efficiency in producing hay in the Willamette Valley, *Oreg. Agr. Expt. Sta. Bul.* 248 (1929).

CHAPTER 35

GROWING SILAGE CROPS

Good silage is an especially important source of winter feed in those regions where corn, sorgos, or sunflowers can be grown well and hay is difficult to cure. Silage provides succulent and nutritious feed at a reasonable cost and is an excellent supplement for hay. It is used primarily in feeding dairy cattle and to a lesser extent for beef cattle, horses, and sheep. In the humid regions there is a growing tendency to ensile hay crops (see Chap. 36) in order to save the maximum quantity of nutrients.

CORN (*Zea mays*)

Corn is the principal silage crop in America. Between 5 and 6 million acres are grown annually for this purpose. Making corn into silage enables the farmer to utilize 50 per cent more of the feeding value of the crop than he can when the crop is used for grain. Many factors influence the value of corn for silage. Quantity and quality of material are significant in all instances, and these are related to the ratio of ears to stalks and leaves and to total dry matter produced. The practices which make for high yields of grain are also most valuable in producing silage corn. The use of adequate lime and fertilizer, the best varieties, and good cultural practices are involved.

SELECTION OF VARIETIES

A first consideration is the selection of adapted varieties. Factors involved are total yield, ratio of ears to stalks, relative maturity, standability, and adaptation. The wide variation in proportions of dry matter of ears to stems and leaves is shown in Table 341. In this study the Illinois hybrids 710, 355, and 147 had the highest proportion of ears and should thus produce a high quality of silage, other factors being equal. The Yellow Dent, with less than 25 per cent of the total weight in the ears, was decidedly inferior. Differences in dry-matter content and total ear production are known to vary with the stage of development of each hybrid. These differences for two varieties are evident from a Michigan study.[15] When harvested on Sept. 1 the Michigan variety 1218 had a higher proportion of ears to stover than the Indiana variety. On Sept. 12, however, the Indiana variety had developed to make it an equivalent silage variety.

TABLE 341. PER CENT DRY-MATTER CONTENT OF EAR, STALK, AND LEAF AT HARVEST FOR SILAGE. CONTRIBUTION OF EACH PART TO DRY MATTER OF ENTIRE CROP

Entry	Per cent of dry matter of crop in		
	Ears	Stalks	Leaves
Illinois 710............	44.1	29.5	26.4
Illinois 355............	43.8	24.8	31.4
Illinois 147............	43.7	26.1	30.2
Illinois 546............	39.1	27.6	33.3
Funk 220.............	38.8	29.2	32.0
Illinois 156............	35.8	27.4	36.8
Yellow Dent...........	24.2	35.0	40.8

SOURCE: *Ill. Agr. Expt. Sta. Bul.* 494 (1942).

If a corn variety will mature sufficiently to give good quality, then greatest yields can be obtained from late-maturing varieties, as indicated by data in Table 342. The late-maturing group of varieties in the Connecticut

TABLE 342. YIELDS PER ACRE OF SILAGE CORN OF DIFFERENT MATURITY RATINGS

	Connecticut*				Michigan†	
Group	Stage of maturity	Green weight, tons	Dry matter, lb.	Variety	Maturity rating, days	Ave. grain yield, bu.
Early.........	Hard dough	12.4	6,491	Minn. 402...	123	53.5
Medium......	Soft dough	16.5	7,218	Wis. 350.....	129	64.0
Late.........	Kernels			Mich. 1218...	131	64.3
	forming	20.3	8,064	Wis. 606.....	135	68.5
				Mich. 561....	139	71.4
				Ind. 416.....	143	74.2

* *Conn. (Storrs) Agr. Expt. Sta. Bul.* 121 (1924).
† *Mich. Agr. Expt. Sta. Quart. Bul.* 22 (1940).

study produced 20.3 tons of green matter per acre compared with only 12.4 tons for the early group. In Michigan the early-maturing Minnesota 402 yielded nearly 20 bushels less grain per acre than Indiana 416, a variety that matures about 20 days later.

CULTURAL PRACTICES

Corn is not a poor soil crop but will do best on fertile well-drained sandy loam, loam, and silt loam soils. The crop should be grown in rotation with other crops, following one or more years of sod, preferably clover or alfalfa.

When grown on sloping land, contour planting will produce higher yields, due to the more effective use of rainfall. The plowing down of a heavy sod in preparation for corn not only tends to make the best use of rainfall, but also adds to the organic matter in the soil, improves the soil tilth, and thus increases yields. The use of contour strips in which corn alternates with small grains and sod will reduce erosion to a negligible factor on all but the most erodible soils.

Fig. 87. Corn is the major silage crop grown in the United States.

Lime and Fertilizer. Where lime is needed to correct acidity, enough should be used to raise the pH value to 6.0 or above. In order to produce high yields, corn should be well fertilized. It will respond strongly to an application of 10 to 15 tons of farm manure per acre or one-half that amount of poultry manure applied to the land prior to plowing. When manure is used, a complete fertilizer mixture applied at moderate rates will further stimulate yields. If corn follows a cultivated crop without manure application, the fertilizer is often increased sufficiently to produce the desired yield. About 150 pounds of fertilizer is applied in the row at planting time; the balance is broadcast on top and worked into the soil before planting.

Planting Time. The time of planting corn for maximum production varies with the season and locality. Corn should be planted as soon as the ground is warm and danger of severe frosts has passed. General planting dates in the United States are given in Table 343. Thus in the South planting begins in the middle of March and in the North not before early May. Date of planting tests conducted by many experiment stations bear

TABLE 343. APPROXIMATE DATES FOR PLANTING CORN BASED ON LATITUDES

Region	Beginning	General	Ending	Planting period, days
Gulf states..............	Mar. 15	Apr. 5	May 10	55
Central latitudes.......	Apr. 15	May 1	May 25	40
Northern states........	May 10	May 20	June 1	20

SOURCE: U.S. Department of Agriculture Yearbook, 1910.

out these dates. In Arkansas,[10] Apr. 15 proved to be best at the latitude of Fayetteville and May 15 to June 1 at Scott. In Nebraska[9] corn planted in late April was equally productive with that seeded in May or early June.

Seeding Rate. The rate of seeding corn also affects yields. The best seeding rate, however, is dependent on local rainfall, soil structure, moisture-holding capacity and fertility level, the corn hybrid variety, and probably other factors. Data on planting rate from Nebraska and Mississippi may be found in Table 344. A total of 10,668 plants per acre gave the highest

TABLE 344. RELATION OF RATE OF PLANTING CORN TO AVERAGE YIELDS PER ACRE

Plants per hill	Nebraska*		Mississippi†	
	Plants per acre	Average yield, bu.	Plants per acre	Average yield, bu.
1	3,556	37.3	3,605	61.2
2	7,112	46.5	7,210	76.4
3	10,668	49.5	10,815	81.5
4	14,224	46.8	14,420	84.0

* *Nebr. Agr. Expt. Sta. Bul.* 293 (1935).   † *Miss. Service Sheet* 373 (1944).

acre yield in Nebraska, and in Mississippi 14,420 plants per acre gave the best returns. In the Mississippi test added fertility permitted growing the extra plants per acre with the resulting high yields. In Tennessee[11] the number of plants per acre was considered more significant than distance between rows or number of plants per hill. Silage corn is usually spaced closer in the row than corn grown for grain.

Stage of Maturity. The best-quality silage is made from corn in the dented or glazed stage of maturity. Data from Ohio as given in Table 345 show the most protein, carbohydrates, and fats at this stage of development. Between the silk and early dent stages the protein content increased from 357 to 439 pounds per acre, carbohydrates almost doubled, and fats in-

TABLE 345. COMPOSITION OF 10 TONS OF CORN AT DIFFERENT STAGES OF MATURITY,
POUNDS

Stage of maturity	Dry matter	Crude protein	Crude fiber	Nitrogen-free extract	Fat
Silks drying............	3,743	357	986	2,136	40
In the milk.............	4,642	409	1,023	2,891	71
Early dent.............	6,282	439	1,180	4,205	156

SOURCE: *Ohio State Univ. Crop Talk* 6 (1924).

creased four times. A similar study with silage corn harvested at the early milk, soft-dough, and ripe stages was made in Connecticut.[19] The ripe corn contained a higher percentage of protein, ash, carbohydrates, and fats than did that harvested earlier. Corn usually contains about 50 per cent moisture in the ears and 70 to 75 in the stalks and leaves at the glazing stage. Feeding and preservation experiments show that this moisture content produces the best silage.

Tests with corn harvested when the ears contained 50 per cent and 40 per cent moisture show comparative bushel yields when dried to 15.5 per cent moisture (see Table 346). The corn with 50 per cent moisture content was still in the soft-dough or very early dent stage. Increases in grain were most rapid in the medium- and late-maturing hybrids and slowest in the early one. This would indicate that the most productive silage varieties will be those which normally reach the early-dent stage at silo-filling time. Earlier varieties will result in reduced yields, and later ones will lower the quality of the silage.

TABLE 346. GAIN IN YIELD OF AN EARLY, A MEDIUM, AND A LATE HYBRID AS THE
GRAIN MATURED FROM 50 TO 40 PER CENT MOISTURE CONTENT

Hybrid	Yield, bu.			Days required	Gain per day in acre yield, bu.
	50% moisture content	40% moisture content	Increase		
Minn. 402 (early)........	46.5	51.6	5.1	12	0.43
Mich. 1218 (medium).....	51.5	63.2	11.7	14	0.84
Mich. 561 (late)........	60.2	72.2	12.0	16	0.75

SOURCE: *Mich. Agr. Expt. Sta. Quart. Bul.* 22 (1940).

Digestibility of corn is about 6 per cent higher after glazing than before, according to Ohio tests.[8] This gives added incentive to defer silage making until corn has reached the glazing stage. On the other hand, frosted corn dries out quickly and must be ensiled within a short time following frosting. Freezing reduces the carotene content somewhat, drying out follows, and this results in some loss of leaves.

Loss of feed constituents on ensiling also indicates the value of good maturity prior to ensiling. Data on stage of harvesting[21] show that the smallest loss of nutrients during fermentation occurred when the corn was in the 80 per cent dough stage and the rest in the milk stage. Harvesting earlier increased the percentage of nutrient losses.

SORGOS (*Sorghum vulgare*)

The sorghums are preferred to corn in the drier sections of America. They are probably the most certain forage and silage crops for the dry-land plains area of southwestern United States.

ADAPTATION

The sorghums are considered resistant to drought and heat and respond quickly to an available moisture supply. Comparative yield tests over a 10-year period in Colorado are given in Table 347. Black amber sorgo

TABLE 347. COMPARATIVE AVERAGE YIELDS OF FORAGE CROPS GROWN IN COLORADO

Crop	Relative yield, %	Crop	Relative yield, %
Black amber sorgo...	100	Barley............	45
Foxtail millet	71	Corn	39
Proso millet	53	Spring rye..........	34
Sudan grass.........	50	Field peas.........	28

SOURCE: *Colo. Agr. Expt. Sta. Bul.* 355–A (1938).

easily outyielded any other crop tried here, whereas corn produced less than half the yield of amber sorgo. The importance of moisture in relation to sorghum yields in this area is evident from a Colorado[17] study. Higher yields of sorghum forage were obtained from planting on fallow ground where moisture had been conserved compared to stubble. Black amber, Leoti red, and Freemont were superior to other varieties tried.

PLANTING

Sorghum, like corn, requires a warm soil for planting. Date of planting trials indicate that it may be planted about the same time as corn or 1 to 2 weeks later. Rate of seeding sorgo indicates that highest forage yields are obtained with close planting, provided that enough moisture is available. Spacing plants 2 inches apart in 42-inch rows in Nebraska (see Table 348)

TABLE 348. THE EFFECT OF DIFFERENT SPACINGS BETWEEN PLANTS, IN ROWS 42 INCHES APART ON THE YIELD AND DEVELOPMENT OF ATLAS SORGHUM IN NEBRASKA

Spacing, in.	Stalks headed, %	Stalk diameter, in.	Plant height, in.	Grain per plant, lb.	Forage yield per acre, tons
2	30	0.72	53.3	0.020	3.41
4	37	0.74	53.7	0.023	3.08
6	40	0.75	54.0	0.030	3.06
8	55	0.84	56.7	0.051	2.93
12	72	0.96	57.0	0.084	2.55
18	69	0.95	58.0	0.076	2.16

SOURCE: *Nebr. Agr. Expt. Sta. Bul.* 329 (1940).

gave a yield of 3.41 tons of forage per acre, whereas wider spacing reduced forage yields. Grain production per plant increased with wider spacings along with plant height and stalk diameter. Row spacings are so dependent on moisture supplies, soil fertility, and sorghum variety that all must be considered in arriving at a satisfactory planting rate.

HARVESTING

Sorghum is best harvested for silage when the seed is in the hard-dough stage. Yields are usually highest at this stage, as shown in Table 349, and

TABLE 349. RELATIVE YIELDS OF BLACK AMBER SORGO HARVESTED AT VARIOUS STAGES OF MATURITY

Stage	Relative yields	Stage	Relative yields
First heads appearing.	100	Seed soft dough......	129
Well headed.........	117	Seed ripe..........	138

SOURCE: *Nebr. Agr. Expt. Sta. Bul.* 329 (1940).

sugar content supposedly has reached a maximum. Silage made from immature sorghum often becomes too acid during the fermentation process. If the crop is injured by frost or drought before maturity, however, ensiling should follow immediately. Sorghum silage has a somewhat lower feeding value than corn silage, since many of the seeds escape digestion.

SUNFLOWERS *(Helianthus annuus)*

The northern parts of the United States or high altitudes are most suited to growing sunflowers. In the high altitudes of the Western states, temperatures during the growing season are low, and corn and sorghum do not grow readily. Since sunflowers are more resistant to cold weather and to mild frosts than corn or sorghum, they are useful for such areas.

PLANTING

The principal variety of sunflower grown in the United States for silage is the Mammoth Russian. Data from a time of seeding test[2] as conducted at Bozeman, Montana, show that Apr. 29 plantings gave higher yields than those made on May 29 or June 10. Tests at other stations indicate that sunflowers may be seeded about the same time as corn or a little earlier.

Sunflowers are usually seeded in rows with a corn planter or a grain drill. Best results have come from drilling rows 24 to 30 inches apart, using 6 to 8 pounds of seed per acre. The crop is cultivated and harvested in the same manner as corn.

YIELDS AND COMPOSITION

Comparative yields of sunflowers and corn are available from Washington, New York, Wisconsin, and other states. In the trials reported in Table 350 the sunflower produced larger tonnages per acre than corn. In

TABLE 350. COMPARISON OF YIELDS PER ACRE OF CORN AND SUNFLOWERS, TONS

Crop	2-year ave. Washington,* green weight	6-year ave. New York,† dry matter	9-year ave. Wisconsin,‡ green weight
Sunflowers...........	11.6	3.73	11.0
Corn................	6.0	3.09	6.8

* *Wash. Agr. Expt. Sta. Bul.* 162 (1921).
† *Cornell Agr. Expt. Sta. Bul.* 456 (1926).   ‡ *Wisc. Agr. Ext. Cir.* 220 (1928).

a summary of corn and sunflower yields in America, Vinall[18] showed that sunflowers yielded 46 per cent more than corn on unirrigated land and on irrigated land 92 per cent more than corn. Most of these tests were run in the northern part of the United States. In spite of this good record by sunflowers they are becoming less popular as silage in America. This may be due to the recent development of superior short-season corn hybrids that are also cold-resistant.

An analysis[18] of sunflower silage shows that it contains almost as much crude protein as corn but less carbohydrates. It is considered somewhat less valuable for silage than corn. Feeding trials indicate that sunflower silage is of good quality when properly made.

HARVESTING

Early cutting of sunflowers may result in the production of a wet silage On the other hand if the crop stands too long, the bottom leaves dry up and fall off and the stems become hard and woody, resulting in low-quality un-palatable silage. The leaves are extremely high in protein and ash content (see Table 351), and their loss is very undesirable. Data on changes

TABLE 351. PER CENT COMPOSITION OF THE DRY MATTER OF GREEN AND DEAD SUNFLOWER LEAVES

Leaves	Ash	Crude protein	Crude fiber	Nitrogen-free extract	Crude fat
Fresh green leaves........	18.1	17.3	12.3	47.1	5.4
Dead leaves.............	17.9	15.6	17.4	44.0	5.1

SOURCE: *Ill. Agr. Expt. Sta. Bul.* 268 (1925).

in plant composition with increasing maturity are given in Table 352. These data do not indicate the best time to harvest for silage, but it is usually considered to be the dough stage. Sunflowers can be harvested in a manner similar to corn, and they are as readily preserved.

TABLE 352. AVERAGE ANALYSES OF SUNFLOWERS AT DIFFERENT STAGES (GREEN BASIS), PER CENT

Stage analyzed	Ash	Protein	Fat	Fiber
Bud stage............	1.53	1.41	0.55	5.48
Full blossom.........	1.59	1.21	0.50	3.90
Petal dropping.......	1.78	1.12	0.66	5.56
Dough stage.........	1.69	1.10	1.06	4.96

SOURCE: *W.Va. Agr. Expt. Sta. Cir.* 82 (1920).

About 40 million tons of silage are made each year in the United States. Nearly 95 per cent of the silage is made from corn and sorghums, the rest from pea vines, sunflowers, and green forage crops. Silage is palatable, succulent, and relished by all types of livestock, especially dairy cattle. It has a fair quantity of carotene but is often low in protein and minerals, and therefore it should be fed with legume hay, not in place of it.

References

1. Anthony, Ernest L., and H. O. Henderson: Sunflowers vs. corn for silage, *W.Va. Agr. Expt. Sta. Cir.* 82 (1920).
2. Atkinson, Alfred, *et al.*: Growing and feeding sunflowers in Montana, *Mont. Agr. Expt. Sta. Bul.* 131 (1919).
3. Champlin, Manley, and George Winright: Corn culture in South Dakota, *S.Dak. Agr. Expt. Sta. Bul.* 181 (1918).

4. Cushing, R. L., T. A. Kiesselbach, and O. J. Webster: Sorghum production in Nebraska, *Nebr. Agr. Expt. Sta. Bul.* 329 (1940).

5. Gaines, W. L., and W. B. Nevens: The sunflower as a silage crop, *Ill. Agr. Expt. Sta. Bul.* 268 (1925).

6. Gull, P. W., and John Pitner: The response of four corn varieties to variable stands with four nitrogen levels, *Miss. Agr. Expt. Sta. Serv. Sheet* 373 (1944).

7. Holden, E. D., and E. J. Delwiche: Sunflowers for silage, *Wis. Agr. Ext. Serv. Cir.* 220 (1928).

8. Jones, Earl: Growing silage corn, Ohio State University, Crop Talk 6, 1924.

9. Kiesselbach, T. A., Arthur Anderson, and W. E. Lyness: Cultural practices in corn production, *Nebr. Agr. Expt. Sta. Bul.* 293 (1935).

10. McClelland, C. K.: Effect of different dates of planting corn on yields, *Ark. Agr. Expt. Sta. Bul.* 22 (1927).

11. Mooers, C. A.: Planting rates and spacing of corn, *Tenn. Agr. Expt. Sta. Bul.* 124 (1921).

12. Nevens, W. B.: Types and varieties of corn for silage, *Ill. Agr. Expt. Sta. Bul.* 391 (1933).

13. Nevens, W. B., and G. H. Dungan: Yields of corn hybrids harvested for silage, *Ill. Agr. Expt. Sta. Bul.* 494 (1942).

14. Osborn, L. W.: Experiments with varying stands and distribution of corn, *Ark. Agr. Expt. Sta. Bul.* 200 (1925).

15. Rather, H. C., and A. R. Marston: A study of corn maturity, *Mich. Quart. Bul.* 22: 278-288 (1940).

16. Schafer, E. G., and R. O. Westley: Sunflower production for silage, *Wash. Agr. Expt. Sta. Bul.* 162 (1921).

17. Tucker, R. H.: Sorghums, *Colo. Agr. Expt. Sta. Bul.* 355-A (1938).

18. Vinall, H. N.: The sunflower as a silage crop, *U.S. Dept. Agr. Bul.* 1045 (1922).

19. White, G. C., *et al.*: A comparison of early, medium and late maturing varieties of silage corn for milk production, *Conn. (Storrs) Agr. Expt. Sta. Bul.* 121 (1924).

20. Wiggans, R. G.: Sunflowers as compared with corn as a silage crop for New York, *Cornell Agr. Expt. Sta. Bul.* 456 (1926).

21. Wright, P. A., and R. H. Shaw: A laboratory study to determine the best time to ensile corn, sunflowers, and Sudan grass, *Jour. Agr. Res.*, **32**:321-333 (1926).

CHAPTER 36

MAKING GRASS SILAGE

Silage made from green forage crops is usually called "grass silage." Any crop which produces satisfactory hay can be made into good silage. Thus extra pasturage, first-crop hay, or cereals cut green are often used for this purpose. Although in 1945 less than 1 per cent of all silage made came from the forage crops, the popularity of grass silage is on the increase. Making grass silage is of particular value in humid sections of America such as the clover-timothy belt, the annual legume region, and the Pacific Northwest coastal area. In such regions frequent rains and high humidity make it difficult to produce high-quality hay. Nutrient losses in making hay have ranged from 20 to 30 per cent of the total value of the crop—sometimes more. By making grass silage this loss can often be reduced to as little as 10 or 15 per cent.

EARLY STUDIES

Grass silage was first made successfully in America by the Kansas Agricultural Experiment Station when that institution ensiled alfalfa in 1917 and preserved it adequately. It was discovered at that time that the use of soluble carbohydrates ensured adequate preservation. This finding resulted from a study of the various silages by these investigators, data for which are shown in Table 353. Alfalfa, it can be noted, contained the smallest amount of soluble carbohydrates (nitrogen-free extract), whereas the sorghums and corn were relatively high. Recognition of this variable led to trials[11] in which materials high in carbohydrates were used

TABLE 353. PER CENT COMPOSITION OF SILAGE MADE FROM ALFALFA, CORN, AND SORGHUM

Silage	Moisture	Ash	Crude protein	Crude fiber	Nitrogen-free extract	Ether extract
Alfalfa............	67	4.17	5.5	9.8	12.2	1.11
Corn..............	74	1.78	3.0	5.9	14.3	0.80
Kafir sorghum......	67	2.16	2.9	7.4	20.0	0.96
Sweet sorghum......	69	1.91	2.5	6.8	18.6	0.93

SOURCE: *Kans. Agr. Expt. Sta. Bul.* 217 (1917).

for preservation purposes.   In these subsequent tests alfalfa was ensiled
alone, with sprouted corn, and with blackstrap molasses, both materials
being good sources of carbohydrates.   Use of germinated corn and molasses
gave excellent keeping qualities, superior to alfalfa ensiled alone.   The
Kansas investigators also showed at this early date that partial wilting
before ensiling aided the keeping qualities.   From 1917 to 1935 no work
of consequence on grass silage in America was reported.   At the end of
this period new findings on the significance of the carbohydrate-protein
ratio made by Prof. C. B. Bender at the New Jersey Experiment Station
reawakened interest.

Another method of preserving grass silage is by the addition of acids.
Beet leaves were ensiled successfully in Europe as long ago as 1885 by adding dilute hydrochloric acid.   The A.I.V. method was discovered in Finland
and reported by Virtanen in 1925.   This method consists of adding equal
quantities of dilute sulfuric and hydrochloric acids to green fodder being
ensiled.   More recently, phosphoric acid has been used, both alone and in
combination with other acids.

EFFICIENT PRESERVATION

It is generally conceded that making hay crops into silage is an effective
method of reducing nutrient losses, since making silage instead of hay eliminates the hazards of field curing.

Compared with Hay.   In a comparison of preserving methods with mixed
alfalfa and timothy the results given in Table 354 were found in Vermont.

TABLE 354.   PER CENT NUTRIENT LOSSES OCCURRING IN ALFALFA AND TIMOTHY
PRESERVED AS HAY AND AS SILAGE

Feed constituent	Field-dried	Artificial drying	Molasses silage
Dry matter................	15.8	5.0	8.2
Ash......................	21.5	9.9	6.8
Crude protein.............	22.8	16.7	8.0
Crude fiber...............	11.8	1.0*	0.6
Nitrogen-free extract.......	13.8	3.0	13.9
Ether extract..............	28.4	4.5	15.6*

SOURCE: *Vt. Agr. Expt. Sta. Bul.* 434 (1938).
* Gain.

The smallest losses of nutritive value occurred in the making of grass silage
and through artificial hay drying, the two methods being comparable from
this standpoint.   Field-cured hay showed losses two to three times the
magnitude of those from mow curing or silage.

Silage Treatments. The most efficient method of preserving grass silage cannot be stated with certainty. A study[13] of nutrient losses and of palatability of silages made by several methods gave variable results. The largest loss of dry matter occurred in the molasses silage; the least, in that preserved by partial drying. Ensiling as partially dried material or with molasses preservative proved to be superior from a palatability standpoint to other methods tested, but otherwise had no real advantage. In a study of preserving methods reported in Table 355 the molasses pre-

TABLE 355. PERCENTAGE LOSS OF FEED CONSTITUENTS IN SILAGE MADE FROM YOUNG GRASS (DRY-MATTER BASIS)

Constituent	No preservative	A.I.V.	Molasses
Dry matter..........	24.1	18.1	12.5
Ether extract........	53.2*	28.6*	35.3*
Fiber...............	24.0	23.0	5.8
Protein	28.2	11.4	8.2

SOURCE: *Jour. Dairy Sci.* 22 (1939).
* Gain.

servative was superior to ensiling without a preservative or by the A.I.V. method. The wilting or partial drying technique was not tried. It appears reasonable to conclude, however, that the addition of a preservative reduces dry matter and protein losses in making grass silage.

CONTROLLING FERMENTATION

The purpose of adding soluble carbohydrates is to supply materials readily transformed by bacteria into lactic and acetic acids. As the acidity increases in the silage, the bacterial activity decreases and finally stops, thus giving good preservation. It is necessary that the silage contain enough carbohydrates to carry the process to completion. Thus, if they are not supplied in sufficient quantity by the crop itself, they must be added to it. The direct addition of acids to ensiled green materials, although not generally recommended, accomplishes the same results without the need for fermentation.

Carbohydrate Content of Crops. Since soluble carbohydrates help preserve grass silage it is of interest to examine the sugar content of various crops that can be used for silage. As shown in Table 356 early-cut alfalfa contains only 4.3 per cent soluble carbohydrates whereas field corn contained 20.3 per cent. The grasses contain two or more times as much sugar as the legumes. Obviously, the lower the soluble carbohydrate content of the crop, the more molasses or other preserving materials that must be

TABLE 356. PERCENTAGE OF WATER-SOLUBLE CARBOHYDRATES IN VARIOUS PLANTS

Crop	Stage	Sugars (dry basis)
Alfalfa	Early bloom	4.3
Clover, red	Begin to seed	9.9
Clover, sweet	Early bloom	6.2
Corn, field	Milk	20.3
Corn, sweet	Roasting ear	28.6
Cowpea	Early bloom	6.6
Oats	Heading	9.9
Soybean	Pods mature	5.2
Sudan grass	Seed milk	13.4
Wheat	Setting seed	12.9

SOURCE: *Jour. Dairy Sci.* 20 (1937).

added for good keeping. On the other hand, the presence of carbohydrates equivalent to that in field corn eliminates the need for added materials.

Materials and Rates. Preservative materials to be added when inadequate amounts of carbohydrates are supplied by the crops to be ensiled should be cheap, readily available, and easy to use. It is also desirable that they contribute to the feeding value of the silage. Those materials most widely used, together with accepted rates, are listed in Table 357.

TABLE 357. QUANTITY OF PRESERVATIVE NEEDED PER TON OF GREEN FORAGE ENSILED, POUNDS

Crop	Molasses	Phosphoric acid (75%)	Ground grain	Corn-and-cob meal	Whey, dried
Soybeans	100	30	200	250	60
Alfalfa and clovers	60	20	150	200	40
Legume-grass mixtures	40	15	125	150	30
Grasses and cereals	30	10	75	100	20

SOURCE: *Wis. Agr. Ext. Serv. Cir.* 299 (1940).
12 lb. of molasses equals 1 gal., 13.2 lb. phosphoric acid equals 1 gal.

Legumes require more preservative per ton than legume-grass mixtures or grasses alone because of their lower carbohydrate and higher protein content. The carbohydrates are widely used, but phosphoric acid silage is seldom made now because of its questionable feeding value.

The Wilting Method. Another method that has proved successful in making grass silage is known as the "wilting method." Crops ensiled when they contain just the right proportion of dry matter will keep well.

TABLE 358. DRY-MATTER CONTENT OF VARIOUS SILAGE CROPS READY FOR HARVESTING

Crop	Stage	Dry matter, %
Alfalfa.....................	Begin to bloom	26
Corn......................	Milk	22
Corn (sweet)...............	Roasting ear	19
Oats......................	Heading	24
Orchard grass..............	Blooming	30
Peas......................	Full bloom	17
Red clover.................	Before bloom	25
Soybeans..................	Pods mature	29
Sudan grass................	Seed milk	30
Sweetclover................	Full bloom	25

SOURCE: *Jour. Dairy Sci.*, **20** (1937).

Variation in dry-matter content of the many different crops at their favored stages for cutting is shown in Table 358. Thus dry matter ranges from 17.3 per cent in peas to 30 per cent in Sudan and orchard grass. The dry-matter content of well-preserved grass silage usually ranges from 25 to 30 per cent. Moisture contents under or over these amounts result in lower quality silage. Losses from silo drainage can be reduced by partial wilting prior to ensiling, but unless carefully done there is danger of spoilage. The Kentucky Station recommends wilting for short periods, as given in Table 359. Thus all crops if cut in the morning can be ensiled the same

TABLE 359. APPROXIMATE TIME REQUIRED FOR ADEQUATE WILTING OF SILAGE CROPS

Crop	Stage of maturity	Dry-matter content at cutting, %	Sun wilting before ensiling, hr.
Alfalfa......................	¼ bloom	22–27	3
Bluegrass....................	Before bloom	25–30	2
Cereals......................	Early milk	22–27	3
Korean lespedeza.............	½ to full bloom	30–35	1
Red clover...................	½ to full bloom	23–28	3
Soybeans....................	Pods ½ filled	23–28	4
Sweetclover.................	½ to full bloom	20–25	4
Timothy.....................	Before bloom	25–30	2

SOURCE: *Ky. Agr. Ext. Serv. Cir.* 361 (1941).

day without a preservative by preliminary wilting. It is only fair to state, however, that the wilting method seems less certain for the average operator than where preservatives are added.

Crop Mixtures. Since carbohydrates will help preserve grass silage, it would seem possible to make good silage by mixing high carbohydrate crops with those of low content. Actually this practice has been successful, and mixing corn and soybeans, sorghum and soybeans, and other crops at the silage cutter is widely practiced. Corn and soybeans or other legumes are best mixed in the ratio of 1 to 1 or at most 1 to 2. The corn and legume should be run through the silage cutter simultaneously to prevent layering in the silo. Mixtures of sorghum and soybeans or corn and soybeans are sometimes grown together and can be ensiled without extra mixing efforts.

MAKING THE SILAGE

Growing grass silage crops and handling them in such a manner as to produce an economical and high-quality product is the ultimate aim of every producer. Critical considerations are acre yields, harvesting techniques, preservatives, and costs.

Acre Yields. The quality and quantity of silage from a given crop are of primary consideration to any producer. Yields and nutritive value of grass hay crops are usually less than legumes. Corn is normally a superior silage producer throughout much of the region where it is adapted. Results of comparative yield tests conducted in Illinois are given in Table 360.

TABLE 360. YIELDS AND NUTRIENT CONTENT OF HAY AND SILAGE FROM SOME ILLINOIS CROPS

Crop	Yield per acre, tons		Digestible protein per acre, lb.		Total digestible nutrients per acre, lb.	
	Hay	Silage	Hay	Silage	Hay	Silage
Corn......................	....	8.6	...	220	.....	3,220
Sorghum, sweet............	....	9.5	...	150	.....	2,870
Alfalfa...................	2.14	7.7	450	470	2,150	2,040
Soybeans.................	1.34	4.8	300	280	1,360	1,300
Clover, red..............	1.13	4.1	160	200	1,170	1,160
Clover, sweet............	1.12	4.0	240	250	1,120	1,120
Grains cut green..........	0.84	3.0	70	124	810	830
Cowpeas.................	0.94	3.4	240	140	930	670

SOURCE: *Ill. Agr. Ext. Serv. Cir.* 605 (1946).

Corn was superior to other crops in the production of total digestible nutrients per acre but inferior to alfalfa, soybeans, and sweetclover in protein produced. In areas less favorable to corn, such as the Northeastern states, the hay crops should give the superior yields of both protein and total digestible nutrients.

Methods of Harvesting. Hay crops used for silage are cut, raked, and loaded much as cured hay. A windrower attached to a horse- or tractor-drawn mower saves raking and eliminates this extra operation. Danger of picking up stones is also reduced compared with raking.

Fig. 88. Unloading chopped grass at the silo. (*International Harvester Company.*)

The common cylinder-rake bar loaders, if well built, will pick up one-swath windrows unless the crop is exceptionally heavy. Heavy-duty loaders, designed for green crops, are more satisfactory and will handle dry hay equally well. The loader elevates the crop to a wagon or truck. From 1 to 1½ tons can be put on per load, and this is then hauled to the silage cutter and fed in by hand.

More recently forage harvesters which cut, chop, and elevate green material into attached wagons have been used. These machines cut small swaths 3½ to 4 feet wide and can be operated with any two-plow tractor. From 6 to 10 tons of forage or more can be harvested per hour. A great saving in labor and an increase in efficiency result.

Ensiling. Any flywheel type of silage cutter will cut and elevate green hay crops. Machines with 14-inch throats or wider do the job faster and more economically than smaller machines. The silage cutter should be set to chop at ¼ to ½ inch, since longer cut silage does not pack well and shorter cutting reduces the speed of filling the silo. If a field chopper has been used in harvesting, only a blower elevator is needed to complete the job at the silo.

Adding the Preservatives. The preservative is added as the green crop is chopped or blown into the silo. Most silage cutters are equipped with a molasses pump attachment that automatically regulates the rate of flow. Gravity and air-pressure systems are also used. Phosphoric acid can be applied in the same way as molasses. Adding ground corn meal or grain can be accomplished by means of a hopper mounted on or alongside the cutter. The hopper feeds the ground grain into the cutter through adjustable openings. Without such equipment, ground grain can be poured on top of the feed table at fairly regular intervals.

Seepage. Seepage is of considerable importance in making grass silage. Some operators putting in green succulent material erroneously add extra water to it, or additional water is added through dilution of molasses to encourage free flow of this material. Excessive drainage from the base of the silo results, and the liquid may collect in low spots in the barnyard. The problem can be met in a number of ways. Molasses should not be diluted with water if not absolutely necessary, and the driest green material should be placed at the bottom of the silo. Some wilting of very succulent crops before ensiling is considered necessary. Ground grain or small quantities of cured hay or straw can be added to absorb excess moisture. Another method is to provide drainage in the bottom of the silo so that excess liquid can get away.

Cost of Producing. Grass silage has a reputation of being cheaper to produce than corn silage. The costs vary with the crop, but with alfalfa this belief seems correct, as borne out by data in Table 361. This study showed a cost of $4.98 to make 1 ton of corn silage in New Jersey but only $3.09 for a ton of alfalfa silage. Soybeans proved to be the most expensive

TABLE 361. AVERAGE COST OF PRODUCING CROPS FOR ENSILING ON NEW JERSEY FARMS

Crop	Alfalfa	Mixed forage	Soybeans	Corn silage
Yield per acre, tons............	5.2	4.2	5.5	8.0
Cost up to harvest:				
Per acre..................	$8.38	$11.89	$22.64	$28.12
Per ton..................	1.59	2.80	4.10	3.51
Cost of harvesting:				
Per acre..................	7.88	9.07	12.75	11.80
Per ton..................	1.50	2.14	2.31	1.47
Total cost per acre..........	16.26	20.96	35.39	39.92
Total cost per ton..........	3.09	4.94	6.41	4.98

SOURCE: *N.J. Agr. Expt. Sta. Bul.* 684 (1940).

of the crops tested to make into silage. The smaller yields per acre from other crops usually operate in favor of the corn silage. In many areas it is doubtful if crops other than alfalfa can compete with corn successfully.

Value in Feeding

Grass silage is relished by all classes of livestock. It can be used to supplement poor hay or inadequate pasture and in normal feeding practice readily replaces corn silage.

Feeding Studies. Feeding trials in the United States in which grass silage and hay made from identical fields have been compared indicate superiority for the silage. It usually contains fifteen to twenty times more carotene and 10 to 20 per cent more protein than the hay. Dairy cattle respond by producing milk with vitamin-A-rich butterfat to a greater degree than if fed the hay alone. Grass silage on the other hand is low in vitamin D commonly found in good sun-cured hay. It has also been found that less loss of plant nutrients occurs in feeding grass silage than corresponding hay. Cattle often reject one-tenth to one-fourth of the hay placed in front of them but consume practically all the silage provided that it is finely chopped and of good odor and taste.

Composition. The composition of silage from various crops, especially as it compares with corn, is of interest. In general, silage from grasses, legumes, and small grains is higher than corn in all constituents except the carbohydrates. Legume silage is especially superior to corn in protein, minerals, and carotene content.

Feeding Rates. Grass silage is usually fed to dairy cattle at the rate of 3 pounds per 100 pounds of live weight along with 1 to 1½ pounds of dry

TABLE 362. THE COMPOSITION OF VARIOUS GRASS SILAGE CROPS

Kind of crop	Per cent in the fresh material					Carotene in fresh silage, units per lb.
	Protein	Fat	Fiber	Carbo-hydrates	Minerals	
Mixed grass.......	3.02	1.01	10.0	11.4	2.6	28,180
Mixed grasses and legumes.........	3.48	0.94	9.8	11.3	2.5	27,770
Timothy..........	2.87	1.06	10.8	11.2	2.1	37,920
Legume...........	4.24	1.07	8.8	11.0	2.9	27,530
Small grain........	2.60	0.94	10.4	11.5	2.5	24,030
Oats–peas.........	2.92	0.95	10.0	11.7	2.4	17,210
Potato–alfalfa.....	4.15	0.48	6.7	15.0	1.7	600
Potato–oat hay....	2.41	0.35	6.3	17.3	1.7	670
Corn.............	2.34	0.77	8.4	14.9	1.6	15,480

SOURCE: *Mass. Agr. Expt. Sta. Bul.* 425 (1945).

hay. Dairy cows have been known to consume more than 100 pounds of silage per day, but this is considered excessive. Beef cows and heifers use 30 to 40 pounds daily and steers, about 30 pounds. Barn-fed breeding ewes can use 8 to 12 pounds per day and lambs, 2 to 4 pounds each. Mature hogs can consume 3 to 6 pounds daily and horses, $2\frac{1}{2}$ to 3 pounds of good-quality silage for each pound of hay replaced.

GENERAL CONSIDERATIONS

There is much to be said for wider use of hay crops for silage purposes. Similarly certain weaknesses are apparent and the subject should be considered critically for proper evaluation.

Advantages. Greater use of the silo and silo-filling equipment is secured throughout the year by making grass silage. Silage made in the spring can be used for summer feed if needed, and then the silo can be refilled in the late summer or fall. Surplus pasture can be ensiled, thus reducing waste. Weedy hay crops preserved as silage have greater feeding value than when they are cured for hay.

Less storage space is required for silage than for hay. Loose hay needs about $3\frac{1}{2}$ times—and baled or chopped hay 2 times—as much storage space as an equivalent quantity of dry matter in silage. Grass silage in the silo contains about 14 pounds of dry matter per cubic foot, loose hay in the mow 4 pounds, and chopped or baled hay about 8 pounds per cubic foot. Silos are cheaper to construct than strong barns; but on the other hand some hay will be needed for feeding, so that storage must be provided for it. The fire hazard from spontaneous combustion, careless smokers, or faulty electrical wiring is reduced.

Grass silage can often be produced at a 15 to 25 per cent lower cost than row-crop silage, since certain grasses and legumes are perennials and need not be seeded each year. Greater erosion control and soil improvement are effected by growing hay crops than with cultivated row crops. In addition legume silage is 2 to $2\frac{1}{2}$ times as rich in protein as corn silage.

Disadvantages. The production of grass silage also has some very real drawbacks. More labor is usually required to make grass silage than in making hay or corn silage. More tons of green material must be handled to secure corresponding yields of dry matter. This adds to the cost of harvesting and storing.

Stronger silos are required for grass silage than for corn, because the higher moisture content makes for increased pressures. Ordinary silos usually must be reinforced before being used for this purpose. Grass silage is hard on concrete, and inside silo coatings are often needed to reduce corrosion.

There is greater risk of spoilage in making grass silage than corn silage.

If grass is ensiled when it is too wet, it will produce a strong putrid silage. If ensiled too dry, excessive heating will follow, causing charring and loss of nutrients. A direct outlay of cash is often called for in purchasing molasses or other preservatives, and this may amount to $50 or $100 per silo. This initial outlay can be offset through greater feeding value, since the use of preservatives adds to the value of the silage.

The total feeding value of an acre of hay crop harvested for silage is usually less than that from an acre of corn. This is especially true in meadows 3 or more years old. Furthermore, grass silage has only 80 or 90 per cent the feeding value of corn silage because it contains less dry matter and the dry matter has a lower feeding value.

Increasing Popularity. The production and development of grass silage have taken place largely since 1917. It is too early to predict the national influence which this process will have on American agriculture, but it seems destined to play an important role, especially in the humid regions of America where high-quality haymaking is most difficult. It should also stimulate the production of better pasture and hay crops and thus assist in increased productivity of livestock and their products even during periods of drought and pasture shortages.

References

1. Archibald, J. G., and C. H. Parsons : Grass silage, *Mass. Agr. Expt. Sta. Bul.* 425 (1945).
2. Bender, C. B., and D. K. Bosshardt: Grass silage: A critical review of the literature, *Jour. Dairy Sci.*, **22:**637–651 (1939).
3. Besley, H. E., C. Eby, and W. R. Humphries: Development of machinery for harvesting and storing grass silage, *N.J. Agr. Expt. Sta. Bul.* 689 (1941).
4. Bohstedt, G., W. H. Peterson, and F. W. Duffcc: Grass silage, *Wis. Agr. Ext. Cir.* 299 (1940).
5. Camburn, O. M., H. B. Ellenberger, J. A. Newlander, and C. H. Jones: Legume and grass silage, *Vt. Agr. Expt. Sta. Bul.* 434 (1938).
6. Carncross, John W., Allen G. Waller, and Emil Rauchenstein: A survey of practices and costs of producing grass silage on 50 New Jersey farms, *N.J. Agr. Expt. Sta. Bul.* 684 (1940).
7. Garrigus, W. P.: Grass silage, *Ky. Agr. Ext. Cir.* 361 (1941).
8. Nevens, W. B., K. E. Harshbarger, and K. A. Kendall: Grass and legume silages for dairy cattle, *Ill. Agr. Ext. Cir.* 605 (1946).
9. Perkins, A. E., *et al.:* Making silage from hay crops, *Ohio Agr. Expt. Sta. Bimo. Bul.* **23:**3–12 (1938).
10. Reed, O. E., and J. B. Fitch: Alfalfa silage, *Kans. Agr. Expt. Sta. Bul.* 217 (1917).
11. Swanson, C. O., and E. L. Tague: Chemical studies in making grass silage, *Jour. Agr. Res.*, **10:**275–292 (1917).
12. Wilson, J. K., and H. J. Webb: Water soluble carbohydrates in forage crops and their relation to the production of silage, *Jour. Dairy Sci.*, **20:**247–263 (1937).
13. Woodward, T. E., and J. B. Shepherd: Methods of making silage from grasses and legumes, *U.S. Dept. Agr. Tech. Bul.* 611 (1938).

CHAPTER 37

GRASSLAND FARMING

Grass farming in America began in early colonial times. It was characterized by lack of management, soil exploitation, and low carrying capacity per acre of land. There was a long-continued decline both in productivity and in nutritive value of the forage. There were no improved crop varieties and little practical liming or fertilizing. Even the farm manure was applied almost entirely to corn and other cultivated crops. Grasslands were often considered capable of caring for themselves. Pastures fared worse than the hay crops, being relegated often to the hilly and many times to the rocky and wooded areas where good grass yields could seldom be obtained.

During the latter part of the nineteenth century Europe turned toward the development of a scientific grassland program. Depletion of her soils by erosion and excessive cultivation was severe, and the need for change was indicated. In the years preceding the First World War, Europe developed its grasslands to produce good crops of hay and pasture capable of supporting an animal unit on 1 or 2 acres. The program was based on the recognition of grass as a "crop" and treating it as such. The development of cheap nitrogen sources, the use of phosphate fertilizer and later potash, doubled and trebled forage productivity in northern Europe, and the close-growing grass crops gave a high degree of erosion control.

Development in America. In the period following the First World War American agriculture awoke to the potentials of grass. Demonstration of the value of complete and of mineral fertilizer to hay and pasture crops produced some notable results. Associated with the recognition of the need to fertilize these crops was the introduction of superior species and the development of better varieties. Alfalfa spread eastward rapidly after 1900. Ladino appeared on the scene in 1930. Bromegrass, reed canary, and orchard grass were found valuable for certain localities. The timothy acreage decreased, and the legumes increased. Thus there was a general improvement in the type of crops being grown.

Factors that brought about this change in attitude toward the grass crops were mostly economic. The period of land expansion ended, exploitation of our basic soil fertility had run its course, especially in the humid areas, and agriculture was becoming more conscious of labor as a factor in efficiency and in the cost of producing farm products. The basic economy of pastures was recognized through such surveys as were conducted in New

York,[17] showing that it cost four times as much to feed a milking cow in the barn as it did on pasture. The daily milk return from such an animal was indicated at about 10 per cent less than the actual cost of barn feeding. There is no wonder that dairy farmers attempted to lengthen the pasture season as much as possible.

In 1936 the U.S. Department of Agriculture collected crop production costs in 16 of the Northeastern and Middle Western states. The data, shown in Table 363, gave extra impetus to the production of hay and pasture in

TABLE 363. YIELDS AND COSTS OF TOTAL DIGESTIBLE NUTRIENTS PRODUCED PER ACRE WITH VARIOUS CROPS

Crop	T.D.N. produced per acre, lb.	Cost of producing 100 lb. of T.D.N., dollars	Relative rank
Oats...................	932	2.02	100
Wheat.................	1,146	1.88	93
Barley.................	1,217	1.70	84
Corn silage............	2,320	1.54	76
Corn grain............	1,778	1.38	68
Timothy hay...........	1,257	1.21	60
Clover and timothy......	1,347	1.15	57
Soybeans..............	1,725	1.06	52
Red clover hay.........	1,622	0.97	48
Alfalfa hay............	2,522	0.83	41
Pasture...............	.....	0.64	32

SOURCE: U.S. Department of Agriculture Clip Sheet 949 (1936).

every livestock program. The grain crops, being relatively expensive to produce compared with forage, were reevaluated by many livestock producers. Increased consumption of good forage per dairy unit was advocated and was later proved economically sound, as shown in Table 364. Average results for 10 herds fed plenty of roughage and 10 herds fed little roughage are presented. The high-roughage herds, receiving 72 per cent of their T.D.N. from roughage, produced milk for $2.11 a hundredweight compared with $2.57 for the herds receiving only 53 per cent of their T.D.N. from roughage. Extra roughage of good quality in the dairy ration appears to be very practical.

Grasses Now Considered as Crops. Grasses and legumes, whether grown for hay, pasture, or silage, are now generally recognized as "crops," and some applied treatment is accorded them. Applications of fertilizer at time of seeding down, top-dressing, and the use of superior mixtures are now practiced in many parts of America. This elevation of pasture and hay species to a crop basis is fundamental to the development of a sound grass-

TABLE 364. COSTS OF FEEDING COWS PLENTY OF ROUGHAGE AND LITTLE ROUGHAGE

Source of feed	Average per cow					
	10 herds fed plenty of roughage			10 herds fed little roughage		
	Pounds of T.D.N.	Price of 100 lb. T.D.N.	Total cost	Pounds of T.D.N.	Price of 100 lb. T.D.N.	Total cost
Concentrates.......	1,688	$4.23	$ 71.40	2,829	$4.23	$119.67
Hay..............	1,172	3.35	39.26	1,183	3.35	39.63
Silage............	1,543	2.07	31.94	1,276	2.07	26.41
Pasture...........	1,537	1.14	17.52	766	1.14	8.73
Total...........	5,940	$2.70	$160.12	6,054	$3.21	$194.44

	High-roughage group	Low-roughage group
Cost of T.D.N. per 100 lb. of milk.............	$2.11	$2.57
Feed cost per pound of butterfat..............	0.55	0.67
Percentage of T.D.N. from roughage...........	72	53
Pounds of milk produced per pound of concentrates...................................	3.4	2.0

SOURCE: *N.J. Agr. Expt. Sta. Cir.* 505 (1947).

land system of farming. Pastures still lag, and the quicker pastures are brought into the general rotation scheme, the faster the grassland program will progress. Along with the choice of superior grasses and legumes, together with fertilizing, must go good crop management. Early cutting for high-quality hay or silage and the use of methods for maintaining the quality are essential. Rotation grazing and the production of grass silage strengthen the program.

GRASSLAND FARMING DEFINED

Grassland agriculture has not been defined adequately. The term "grass" in this case means either grasses or legumes grown for forage purposes. Thus fields of alfalfa, red clover, timothy, bluegrass, or soybeans are all included. Grassland farming on the other hand has several meanings.

In the broadest use of the term, any farm that produces a major portion of its hay, pasture, and silage is considered to be on a grassland system. Many farms in the livestock-producing regions of America could easily qualify as grassland farms by lengthening their rotations to include more forage.

Some definitions are more specific. Thus rotation whereby corn is raised one year in six or eight and a sod crop occupies the land the major portion of the time is considered grassland farming. Under this long rotation scheme grass plays by far the major role, and corn is used as a clean cultivated crop followed by a small-grain crop in which the grass is reestablished.

Fig. 89. Windrows on a grassland farm in New York. (*Cornell Agricultural Experiment Station.*)

The most restrictive conception of grassland farming rules out all cultivated crops. Hay and pasture crops are utilized to the limit of the farm capacity. When the forage fields run out, they are reestablished by plowing and planting to a small grain in which the grass is seeded. The cereal crop is pastured, used for hay, or made into grass silage. All concentrates needed to supply balanced rations for livestock are purchased, but full use of good-quality hay and silage together with superior pastures results in the minimum need for concentrate feeds. True grass farming is probably more common in the New England states than in any other section.

General Considerations

Grass farming may be considered practical wherever soil and climatic conditions and the livestock enterprise are satisfactory. A combination of roughage-consuming livestock and high forage production is possible over large areas of America. Primary reliance on grass, however, is found in areas where grain production is difficult and often impractical. Thus the New England and Great Lakes states, the annual-legume region, and the Pacific Northwest are primarily interested in grass. The prairie and intermountain states are also interested in grass culture, along with the production of wheat and sorghums for grain.

Livestock-feeding Implications. A number of fundamental livestock-feeding implications are immediately evident in this system of farming. Grass and its products must be utilized to the limit to be profitable. Dairymen say that 70 per cent of the total milk production from dairy cows can be made from good roughage. Superior pastures together with high-quality hay are essential. Beef cattle are normally fattened with grain, but range fattening on alfalfa and prairie hay is practiced to a limited extent. In the Shenandoah Valley and other Eastern areas cattle are fattened on pasture and shipped direct to market. The sheep-fattening industry is similar in many respects to beef production. Good grain supplies are essential for hogs and poultry, which can use only a limited amount of hay, grass silage, and pasture. The Southern states are capable of supplying grazing the entire year.

Quality Roughage Essential. High-quality roughage production must be kept in mind at all times so that it can be utilized to the limit in feeding. Early cutting, adequate fertilizing, and maintenance of the legume stand are essential. Hay must be cured with maximum speed and efficiency. Such speed in curing means low vitamin-D content of the hay crops and may call for supplemental feeding of this material. The pro-vitamin-A content is greater, however, and compensates for loss of vitamin D. The production of silage from grass is necessary in an intensive system of grass farming. Since most if not all of the farm is in grass there is no alternative. The knowledge, experience, and know-how required are greater than when corn silage with its easy keeping qualities is produced.

In humid regions, good hay can be produced consistently only through artificial drying. Hay containing 40 to 50 per cent moisture is placed on top of lateral flues in the mow and dried to 30 per cent or less. A higher quality product usually results, but extra labor is required to move green material of medium moisture content as well as extra expense in building the necessary flues and operating a forced draft.

Suitable Crops. All the hay and pasture crops commonly used in America have a place in grassland culture. Obviously the perennial crops will play the major role, and other crops will fill in the gaps and substitute as the needs arise. Persistent and productive legumes are fundamental. The species meeting the high requirements here are alfalfa, ladino clover, and the lespedezas, which reseed naturally. Alfalfa is the most generally adapted hay legume. Ladino is superior for pasture purposes and useful for hay. Unless these legumes can be grown and maintained, a completely satisfactory grassland program is impossible. Unfortunately, many of our soils are unadapted to alfalfa or conditions are not such that it can be maintained for any long period of time except in the Western states.

Legume-grass mixtures are widely utilized.   Thus alfalfa–bromegrass, ladino–orchard grass, Bermuda grass–lespedeza, soybeans–Sudan grass, and many other mixtures are common.   Irrespective of the mixture, management must be so designed as to maintain the legume.   The grasses

Fig. 90.   Chopping hay with a forage chopper and blowing it directly into the mow. (*New Hampshire Agricultural Experiment Station.*)

usually are not problematic but maintain stands under adequate fertility almost indefinitely.   When it becomes necessary to plow up a semiper-manent crop and to reseed, such annuals as corn, small grains, Sudan grass, sorghums, cowpeas, and soybeans may be grown for one or more years.

Advantages and Disadvantages

One of the most precarious points in an all-grass program is the essential nature of grain for feeding.   Concentrates must be purchased at consist-ently rational prices, which means a ready supply at a favorable milk, beef, or mutton feed ratio.   Experience through the years indicates that when animal products have a strong market grain products are in a similar posi-tion.   Reliance on other regions for the concentrate supply may from time to time catch the grass farmer short, making it necessary for him to make expensive local adjustments.   A sound roughage program resulting in a high-quality product will reduce the need for high protein feeds which are usually most expensive. High carbohydrate feeds are usually in more ready supply than the proteins.

Erosion Control. The plowing up of much of our sod land and its intensive cultivation has resulted in severe national erosion problems. Dust storms in the prairie states and sheet and gully erosion in the more humid regions have been common. Putting this land back into sod crops will afford maximum protection against the hazards of nature. Worn-out and eroded fields have been brought back to a profitable state of productivity by way of the grassland system. The recent use of strip cropping and contour farming has helped to reduce the need for close-growing crops in erosion control but has not eliminated it.

Soil Improvement. Full use of available fertility and moisture is afforded by close-growing crops. The dense root masses fully occupy the soil, reducing leaching and surface runoff of applied fertilizers or of rainfall. The organic-matter content slowly improves through accumulation and subsequent decay of grass roots. Occasional plowing and planting to a cultivated crop permits maximum utilization of the organic matter.

Sod crops make for ease in distributing lime, mixed fertilizer, and manure. Such materials can be applied as top-dressing on firm surfaces at nearly any season of the year, although fall and spring are preferred. Manure is returned to sod crops instead of all too frequently going on cultivated crops to the entire exclusion of hay and pasture fields.

Declining Hay Yields. It is generally true that crop yields of forage are highest in the humid sections in the first and second year following seeding. From then on there is a continuing reduction in productivity. This is

TABLE 365. RELATION BETWEEN LENGTH OF HAY ROTATION AND YIELD OF HAY ON 328 FARMS

Years in Hay	Hay yield per acre, tons
0–3	1.57
4–5	1.50
6	1.34
7+	1.26

SOURCE: *N.H. Agr. Expt. Sta. Bul.* 273 (1933).

partially due to the loss of legume stand but also to decreasing fertility due to inadequate attention. The stand soon deteriorates to a point where plowing and reseeding become essential. At the moment this appears to be a major obstacle in any complete form of grassland development. Rundown pasture areas can often be improved by renovating without plowing. Thus some results obtained by improving a thin bentgrass sod in Rhode Island normally yielding ½ to 1 ton per acre are given in Table 366. This method has not been successful in improving meadows, because of different

TABLE 366. YIELDS FROM RENOVATED BENTGRASS PASTURES IN RHODE ISLAND

Mixture planted, lb. per acre	Total green wt. per acre, lb.	Composition calculated from dry weights, lb.			Hay equivalent per acre, lb.
		Grass	Legumes	Weeds	
Brome 8, alfalfa 8, ladino 1...................	14,031	1,656	5,963	6,482	3,109
Orchard 4, alfalfa 8, ladino 1...................	13,770	3,718	5,563	3,787	3,349

SOURCE: *R.I. Agr. Expt. Sta. Contrib.* 683 (1946).

management practices. Where pastures can be plowed, this seems to be the best procedure, but renovation deserves consideration in the grassland system if it can be practiced successfully.

Inflexibility of Grassland Farming. A straight grassland program is less flexible than a diversified-crop enterprise. Machinery and labor are geared to the grassland system, and experience and machines for producing the grain crops are usually lacking. Swinging the hay and pasture crops into cultivated crops or cereal grains would require considerable cash outlay for equipment and the development of know-how again for such crops. Another serious problem is the lack of straw for bedding. Since grain crops are omitted, the straw or other form of bedding must be purchased, and this represents an additional cash outlay. The use of low-quality hay for bedding instead of feed is sometimes suggested.

Lower Overhead Costs. From a rotation standpoint the grassland program reduces the overhead required in seedbed preparation and planting. The seedbed may be prepared several times only in every 6 to 10 years instead of two or three times in every 3 to 5 years. This marks a real saving to the producer and is also time-conserving. Unfortunately, long-time forage stands do not permit regular and systematic incorporations of lime and fertilizer into the soil but must rely on top-dressings, which often are not as satisfactory.

Efficiency in Labor Utilization. The concentration of labor on a few crops makes for a high degree of efficiency in handling them. Speed and quality production are more probable here than under diversification. Opportunity for good distribution of farm labor exists in the more specialized types of farming, although peaks and troughs must be expected. Growing grasses and legumes eliminates interference and competition from other farm crops for labor. All efforts can be concentrated on the growing of hay, pasture, and grass silage. Since these crops do not mature too rapidly, an early start at harvesting gives a good spread to the work and promotes full labor utilization. Grass silage production can be spread over a good part of the growing season, and the spreading of lime, fertilizer, and manure can take up any slack periods when they will not detract from the haying or silo-filling processes.

Fig. 91. A hay-unloading operation in New Hampshire. (*New Hampshire Agricultural Experiment Station.*)

Machinery Requirements. Certain advantages and disadvantages result in the machinery requirements of the grassland farm. Machinery for making the seedbed, seeding, growing, and harvesting the grass crops is still needed. Equipment for planting, growing, and harvesting corn and for harvesting the cereal crops can be omitted. Fewer machines favor specialization, thus increasing labor efficiency. On the other hand, lack of machinery for growing the grain crops will prevent quick change-over of the farm program when concentrate prices become unfavorable.

The regular machinery used in making hay should be part of the equipment. Plows, disks, harrows, and other implements for seedbed preparation are called for. Fertilizer spreader and grass-seed planting equipment are needed. In addition, sturdy equipment is needed in making grass silage. This calls for strong or reinforced loaders, wagons or trucks, a silage cutter, and one or more tractors. Molasses or ground grain for preservative must be purchased unless the wilting technique is used. A common complaint in making grass silage is the heavy work involved in moving grass materials which are not only heavy in themselves but often bind together and are difficult to pull apart. A field harvester chopper will take much of the drudgery out of the ensiling operation, but it is another machine and a fairly expensive one.

Fig. 92. The field chopper is very efficient in reducing the labor involved in making grass silage. (*Allis Chalmers Manufacturing Company.*)

Disease and Insect Control. During the last several decades the corn borer menace has reached a serious status in the economic production of corn. The Hessian fly has attacked wheat and other of the small grains in epidemic proportions. Rust and smut have been important factors causing yield reductions of the small grains. Swinging over to the all-out growing of grasses and legumes would eliminate these hazards. On the other hand insect pests such as the potato leaf hopper and the clover weevil do severe damage to the alfalfa and clover crops. The wilt and leaf spot diseases are already widespread. Increase in grass-legume culture will almost certainly result in increased disease and insect problems which must be faced and controlled.

Weed Control. Weeds normally come into hay and pasture fields as they thin out due to lowered fertility and loss of the legume. This results in reduced yields and lowered quality. Maintenance of a high level of fertility may reduce this problem to minor significance, but it cannot be overlooked under present practices. Weeds can be ensiled and maximum feeding value secured thereby. In hay or pasture fields composed mostly of grass, it is also possible to destroy broad-leaved weeds with the 2,4-D weed killer. Where legumes are present, this procedure would probably prove impractical since there is danger of destroying the legumes. As the field deteriorates it reaches a point where it becomes necessary to plow and reseed.

Livestock Adjustments. Livestock adjustments can be made where grassland agriculture is practiced. The dairy herd especially can be expanded in size to the limit of the roughage supply. Larger herds make for greater efficiency, other factors being equal. Roughage consumption capacity can be increased by feeding young stock all they will consume at all times and by breeding for large roughage capacity.

Economic Data Lacking. The true economics of a complete grassland farming program have not been completely determined. The place of corn and other grain crops probably should be minor but to what degree is still uncertain. Individual farmer preferences, variable climates and soils, local markets, and the spread of risks through diversification merit consideration. Data are generally available to assist in developing the philosophy of grass farming but are lacking to prove or disprove its total merits.

References

1. Abeel, M. F.: Roughage production in New Hampshire, *N.H. Agr. Expt. Sta. Bul.* 273 (1933).
2. Beaumont, H. B.: Grassland farming in New England. Better Crops with Plant Food, Reprint Z–9–41, American Potash Institute, Washington, D.C.
3. Bender, C. B.: Feeding grass silage, *N.J. Agr. Expt. Sta. Bul.* 695 (1942).
4. Besley, Harry E.: Grassland farming, *Agr. Eng.*, **20**:459–461 (1939).
5. Besley, Harry E., Claude Eby, and Walter R. Humphries: Development of machinery for harvesting and storing grass silage, *N.J. Agr. Expt. Sta. Bul.* 689 (1941).
6. Cardon, P. V.: Toward a grassland agriculture, *Jour. Amer. Soc. Agron.*, **31**: 225–231 (1939).
7. Carncross, John W., and Joseph F. Hauck: Roughage makes milk profits, *N.J. Agr. Expt. Sta. Cir.* 505 (1947).
8. Colby, W. G.: Pasture culture in Massachusetts, *Mass. Agr. Expt. Sta. Bul.* 380 (1941).
9. Etheridge, W. C., C. A. Helm, and E. Marion Brown: An all-year pasture system for Missouri, *Mo. Agr. Expt. Sta. Cir.* 186 (1935).
10. Fink, D. S.: Grassland experiments, *Maine Agr. Expt. Sta. Bul.* 415 (1942).
11. Grau, Fred V.: Ladino clover for triple-purpose pastures, *Pa. Agr. Ext. Cir.* 261 (1944).

12. Green Fields Are Gold, Joint Committee on Grassland Farming, Norwich, New York.

13. Grizzard, A. L.: Grass is a crop, treat it as such, Reprint NN–9, American Potash Institute, Washington, D.C.

14. Lipman, J. G.: The fertilization and management of grasslands, *Jour. Amer. Soc. Agron.*, **21**:19–28 (1929).

15. Lowery, J. C., and W. W. Cotney: All-year pasture system for Alabama, *Ala. Agr. Ext. Serv. Cir.* 287 (1944).

16. Lowry, S. J., and L. M. Caldwell: Grass farming for depleted soils, *Ky. Agr. Expt. Sta. Cir.* 52 (1942).

17. Misner, E. G.: Costs and returns for milk production in summer and winter, *Farm Econ.* (Cornell University), **43**:648 (1927).

18. Moreland, Wallace S.: A Practical Guide to Successful Farming, Chap. 20, "Grassland Farming," Halcyon House, Garden City, New York, 1943.

19. Prince, Ford S.: Further shifts in grassland farming, Reprint C–1–41, American Potash Institute, Washington, D.C.

20. Rhode Island Agricultural Experiment Station: Fifty-eighth annual report, *R.I. Agr. Expt. Sta. Contrib.* 683 (1946).

21. Schultz, T. W.: Economic effects of more roughage output in the corn belt, *Jour. Amer. Soc. Agron.*, **33**:414–419 (1941).

22. U.S. Department of Agriculture: Improving pastures and grasslands for the northern states, *U.S. Dept. Agr. Misc. Pub.* 590 (1946).

23. Wilcox, Walter W.: Livestock production in Iowa as related to hay and pasture, *Iowa Agr. Expt. Sta. Bul.* 361 (1937).

24. Woodward, T. E., and J. B. Shepherd: *U.S. Dept. Agr. Clip Sheet* 949 (1936).

CHAPTER 38

INSECTS GOOD AND BAD

Insects play a significant part in the production of the harvested forages. Their role is favorable in pollination and seed set but also often injurious, reducing yields and quality and causing distress and anxiety the world over. Thousands of insects can be found in farm fields, and the numbers alone lead to confusion, misunderstanding, and lack of appreciation. Countless hordes of insects are said to inhabit each acre of hay, and the struggle for existence and survival which goes on continually in the close green canopy of nature taxes the imagination.

HELPFUL INSECTS

The beneficial insects are essentially of three kinds. First and foremost are the Hymenoptera (pollinators), especially the honeybee (*Apis*) and bumblebee (*Bombus*). This group renders such a service to agriculture that its role is of major importance. The second group of helpful insects includes the predators that feed on the destructive insects. Among these are spiders, damsel bugs, wasps, mites, and many others. A third source of assistance comes from the parasites that attack harmful pests. Among these are the *Tiphia* which infest and destroy white grubs of the Japanese beetle. The *Fryinids* attack aphids and many other similar insects and thus help to maintain the "balance of nature." In addition to insect predators, such vertebrates as birds, frogs, snakes, and others consume vast quantities of insects.

Value in Pollination. Many legumes require cross-pollination together with flower tripping to produce seed. It is the bees that render this essential service in their unending search for nectar and pollen during the growing season. Bees can detect variations in sugar concentration in the nectar, and also they select pollen sources. It is these factors which determine bee visits—not the color or odor of the flower parts. Seldom does the seed grower realize the important role of bees, but without them legumes would fail to set seed and agriculture would suffer a major setback. Most of the grasses are wind-pollinated, and bees play only a minor role with these species.

Effect on Seed Yields. Low seed yields of the legume crops are often attributable to lack of pollinating bees. The pollinating job is tremendous —a single acre of red clover may contain 300 million individual florets and

alsike, up to 400 million.   Each of these flowers must be visited by a pollinating insect for seed to set.   In Ohio it has been estimated that with maximum insect population a yield of 20 bushels of alsike or 12 bushels of red
clover seed per acre is possible.   Average yields of these seeds in Ohio,
however, are 1.6 bushels per acre for alsike and only 1 bushel for red clover,
indicating the general shortage of adequate pollinators.

The importance of pollinating insects was studied for a number of the
clovers in Ohio, and a portion of the data is given in Table 367.   The small

TABLE 367.   AVERAGE NUMBER OF SEEDS PER HEAD OF ALSIKE CLOVER AS INFLUENCED
BY MODE OF POLLINATION

Ohio County	Mode of pollination		Insect (caged)	Field
	Self	Wind		
Logan.............	5.5	...	121	65
Marion.............	...	3.4	120	29
Wyandot..........	0.4	...	125	33
Allen.............	...	...	...	85
Miami.............	..	...	...	90

SOURCE: "ABC and XYZ of Bee Culture," A. I. Root Company, 1945.

seed set without the aid of bees is particularly striking, indicating essentially
that self- or wind-pollination is almost ineffectual.   The addition of bees
to caged areas increased seed set two to three times over natural field conditions, thus showing the importance of these insects.

Relative Importance of Type of Bee.   In a Utah study on tripping alfalfa
flowers a number of bee species were found to be important.   These were
honeybees (*Apis mellifera*), the alkali bee (*Nomia melanderi*), and several
species of the leaf-cutting bee (*Megachile perihirta*), (*M. mendica*), (*M. co-
quilletti*), and (*M. onobrychidis*).   Of these the honeybees were said to be
the most important because of their wider distribution and greater abundance.   They are, however, recognized as less efficient in tripping alfalfa
flowers than several other bee species.   In the study reported in Table 368,
bumblebees were most efficient trippers, doing 17 blossoms per minute, and
the honeybees were least efficient, averaging only 7 flowers per minute.
Another 3-year study on clover in Ohio indicated that 82 per cent of the
red clover was pollinated by honeybees, 15 per cent by bumblebees, and
3 per cent by other insects.   Thus honeybees, because of their great
numbers, appear to be the most important of the hymenoptera in the pollination of legumes.

Abundance of Bees.   The direct relationship between bee colonies and
alfalfa seed production in Utah is evident from data given in Table 369.

TABLE 368. COMPARATIVE TRIPPING RATES OF THE PRINCIPAL ALFALFA POLLINATORS

Species	Number of bees observed	Number of blossoms tripped	
		Total	Per minute
Bumblebees.........	7	478	17
Megachile:			
Large............	31	1,350	15
Medium..........	53	1,048	9
Nomia..............	58	1,209	10
Honeybees..........	36	1,508	7

SOURCE: *Jour. Amer. Soc. Agron.*, **38** (1946).

TABLE 369. RELATION BETWEEN HONEYBEE COLONIES MOVED INTERSTATE TO UTAH ALFALFA FIELDS AND ALFALFA SEED PRODUCTION

Year	Colonies moved to Utah, thousands	Seed produced, thousand lb.
1928	14.2	3,200
1929	10.9	2,100
1930	1.1	750
1931	2.8	800
1932	4.0	165
1933	2.7	198
1934	10.0	3,564
1935	9.7	3,564
1936	10.8	3,168

SOURCE: *Jour. Amer. Soc. Agron.*, **28** (1946).

During years when many bee colonies were moved into Utah from California there was normally high seed production, and when colonies were not moved into the state, alfalfa seed was greatly restricted. The most effective way of increasing legume-seed production, other factors being equal, is by placing bee colonies throughout the seed field. Plenty of bees, good seed-setting weather, and control of injurious insects and pests insure high legume-seed yields.

HARMFUL INSECTS

There are a great number of insects which attack the legume and grass forage crops. Injury is caused in a number of ways such as (1) sucking the plant juices; (2) consumption of leaves and floral parts; (3) destruction of roots and rhizomes; (4) boring into stems, roots, and seeds; and (5) transmitting disease organisms.

Insects Attacking Legumes. Those insects which restrict themselves primarily to the legumes are listed in Table 370. Thus all parts of forage

TABLE 370. INSECTS THAT ATTACK THE FORAGE LEGUMES AND METHODS OF CONTROL

Common name	Part of plant attacked	Control
Alfalfa caterpillar...............	Leaves and buds	Irrigation and cultural methods
Alfalfa-stem nematode...........	Stems, buds, and sprouts	Rotations
Alfalfa webworm................	Leaves	Clean culture and poison
Clover- and alfalfa-seed chalcis...	Seeds	Cultural methods
Clover-flower midge.............	Flowers and seed	Early mowing
Clover-leaf weevil...............	Leaves	Rotations
Clover-root borer...............	Roots	Rotations
Clover-root curculio.............	Roots	Rotations
Green clover worm..............	Leaves and stems	Mowing
Leaf hopper....................	Leaves and stems	Mowing treatments
Lygus bug.....................	Flower buds	Dusting

legumes are attacked by one or another of the insects listed above. Some attack the leaves, others the flowers and seed, and still others the roots. Crop rotations, clean cultivation, mowing treatments, destruction of plant residues and weeds, poison baits, and selected insecticides are helpful in reducing the insect numbers.

A serious problem in the West in producing alfalfa seed is the lygus bug. There are three species of this pest, and they injure the seed crop in varying degrees, as shown in Table 371. Thus, in this California test, *Lygus hesperus* was more severe than the other species.

TABLE 371. MEAN PERCENTAGES OF POD-SET AND OF BROWN SEED OF ALFALFA INFESTED BY *Lygus* SPP. IN EXPERIMENTAL CAGES

Species in cage	Mean per cent of	
	Pod-set	Brown seed
Lygus hesperus............	20.1	39.4
Lygus oblineatus..........	23.0	30.2
Lygus elisus..............	23.3	20.9
Check (uninfested)........	28.4	7.3

SOURCE: *Jour. Econ. Ent.*, **37** (1944).

Good control of *Lygus* in alfalfa fields with resultant seed increases has been secured by dusting with DDT. Thus applications of 10 per cent DDT dust doubled and trebled alfalfa seed yields in Utah. Applied up to the

TABLE 372. MEAN NUMBER OF *Lygus* PER PLOT AND YIELDS OF SEED IN POUNDS PER ACRE IN RELATION TO FREQUENCIES OF APPLICATION OF INSECTICIDES

Insecticidal treatment	Weekly		Semiweekly		Means	
	Lygus	Seed, lb.	*Lygus*	Seed, lb.	*Lygus*	Seed, lb.
Sulfur-pyrocide......	156	119	171	131	163	125
Sabadilla, 10%......	159	200	115	275	137	237
DDT, 3%.........	117	209	97	276	107	242
DDT, 10%........	99	302	65	363	82	332

SOURCE: *Jour. Amer. Soc. Agron.*, **38** (1946).

early bud stage it gave good control of *Lygus* without reducing or injuring the bee population. Seed increases with alfalfa and red clover were obtained in Michigan[7] by dusting with DDT, benzene hexachloride, or chlordane for insect pest control.

Insects Attacking Grasses. There are also a large number of insects which limit their attacks to the grasses. A few of these are listed in Table 373.

TABLE 373. SOME INSECTS INJURIOUS TO GRASSES AND CONTROL METHODS OFTEN PRACTICED

Common name	Plant part attacked	Control
Billbugs..........................	Stems and leaves	Clean cultivation
Chinch bug.......................	Stems and leaves	Cultural treatments. Barriers
Common white grub...............	Roots	Cultural treatments
Fall army worm...................	Plant tops	Rotations
Grass mite.......................	Leaves and stems	
Grass thrip......................	Stems	Early mowing
Japanese beetle grubs.............	Roots	Rotations
Meadow plant bug.................	Stems and leaves	Cultural methods

In general, these pests are controlled by their natural enemies. In some areas and in certain seasons, they build up to epidemic proportions, and then artificial control measures must be taken to combat them.

Insects of Grasses and Legumes. Some insect groups attack both grasses and legumes. A few of the more significant ones are listed in Table 374.

TABLE 374. SOME INSECTS ATTACKING BOTH GRASSES AND LEGUMES AND THEIR CONTROL

Common name	Plant part attacked	Control
Aphids..........................	Plant tops	Crop rotation
Grasshoppers.....................	Plant tops	Cultural methods. Poisoned baits
Leaf hoppers.....................	Plant tops	Crop rotations. Mowing
Spittle bugs.....................	Stems and leaves	Cultural treatments

Of these the grasshoppers often reach epidemic proportions, especially in the western Plains area. There are many species of grasshoppers, leaf hoppers, and aphids, and the various species are often specific for either grasses or legumes, sometimes preferring certain species of these plants to others (see Table 375).

TABLE 375. INJURY CAUSED BY GRASSHOPPERS FEEDING ON FOLIAGE OF SEEDLING GRASSES

Grass Species	Habit of growth	Number of selections	Range of damage,* %	Average damage, %
A. cristatum...............	Spring	68	30–100	82
A. inerme.................	Spring	41	20–95	74
A. repens.................	Winter	3	70–90	83
A. spicatum...............	Spring	21	40–90	69
B. inermis................	Winter	40	5–50	19
D. glomerata..............	Winter	17	50–95	80
Festuca elatior.............	Winter	5	75–90	87
Phalaris arundinacea........	Winter	15	0–40	8
Poa ampla................	Spring	10	50–90	76

SOURCE: *Jour. Amer. Soc. Agron.*, **31** (1939).
* Damage represents an estimate on amount of leaves destroyed by grasshoppers.

The difference observed among the seedling grasses in resistance to attacks by grasshoppers ranged from as little as 8 per cent damage for reed canary grass to 87 per cent for tall fescue. This suggests that certain grass species may be more easily established than others in areas where grasshoppers are numerous enough to do considerable damage without completely destroying the plants.

The preceding tables have been introduced primarily to show the great complexity of the insect problem. Fortunately, nature maintains a series of checks and counterbalances in the form of parasites and predators, thus keeping the harmful insect population within bounds. From time to time, however, severe outbreaks of certain insects occur, and then special control measures (such as dusting with insecticides or spreading poison bait) appear warranted.

The insect most familiar to most of us is the grasshopper. It does its work aboveground, cutting off and consuming stems and leaves of grasses and legumes. Thrips attack the plants on the underside of the leaf sheaths. Thus their destructiveness goes unobserved except for the whitening of the grass inflorescences, a condition often called "silver top." The spittle bugs, leaf hoppers, and plant lice suck juices from the leaves and stems of susceptible plants, reducing the growth and nutritive value. The sod worms, cutworms, and army worms attack the plants near the ground surface, devouring and destroying them as they progress. Japanese beetle grubs, June beetle grubs, and wireworms, working below ground, feed on the sod roots, weakening and eventually destroying the plants.

INJURY TO CROPS

Harmful insects injure the harvested forages in a number of ways. They reduce yields, increase the cost of production, and lower the quality of the product. Reduction in carotene content may be noted from data in Table 376. Alfalfa attacked by leaf hoppers gave only 50 per cent as much carotene upon analysis as alfalfa from treated plots free of the leaf hopper attacks.

TABLE 376. EFFECT OF LEAF HOPPER YELLOWING UPON THE CAROTENE CONTENT OF SECOND CUTTING GRIMM ALFALFA

Plant material	Condition	Moisture, %	Carotene, milligrams
Green alfalfa...........	Fresh	72.83	262
	Dried	9.10	50
Yellowed alfalfa........	Fresh	72.33	105
	Dried	9.60	28

SOURCE: *Phytopath.*, **26** (1936).

CONTROL MEASURES

Since meadow and hay crops involve large acreages, control practices using chemicals have been too costly. New insecticides may offer a solution for the control of forage insects if the cost and the quantity required per acre are small, provided that they are not toxic to livestock. Fortunately, normal rotation practices have proved one of the most effective control measures. Early spring or fall plowing seems preferred for interrupting the life cycle of most insect pests, resulting in their starvation or death by exposure.

In some areas permanent meadows are occasionally burnt over to destroy the eggs and young of certain insects. Grasshopper catchers are sometimes employed in the prairie and intermountain states. Large numbers of these pests together with leaf hoppers are caught with such mechanical devices. Spreading of various types of poison bait is still another technique employed, especially against the grasshopper pests. Lights are useful for trapping certain meadow insects, the moths being attracted by the light and captured in the trap. Perhaps the most important control measure is nature's own, whereby predators and parasites feed on and destroy vast numbers of insects annually.

There is no doubt that insects play a very significant role in the production of our forage crops. Bees are essential for seed production, and the type of bee and its distribution influences the degree of seed set. Destructive insects occur generally over the United States, some attacking the seeds and flowers, others consuming the leaves or destroying the roots and rhizomes. Control measures through crop rotation and other farm practices, together with the "balance of nature" maintained by insect predators and parasites, prevent severe epidemics except as they occur occasionally.

References

1. Creel, C. W., and L. P. Rockwood: The control of the clover-flower midge, *U.S. Dept. Agr. Farmers' Bul.* 971 (1918).
2. Flint, W. P., and W. H. Larrimer: The chinch bug and how to fight it, *U.S. Dept. Agr. Farmers' Bul.* 1498 (1934).
3. Herman, W., and R. Eslick: Susceptibility of seedling grasses to damage by grasshoppers, *Jour. Amer. Soc. Agron.*, **31**:333–337 (1939).
4. Johnson, Howard W.: Effect of leafhopper yellowing upon the carotene content of alfalfa, *Phytopath.*, **26**:1061–1063 (1936).
5. Osborn, Herbert: Meadow and Pasture Insects, The Educator's Press, Columbus, Ohio, 1939.
6. Parks, T. H.: Some insects injurious to red clover, *Ohio Agr. Ext. Bul.* 10, vol. 16 (1920–1921).
7. Pederson, C. E.: Insecticides increase legume seed, *Mich. Agr. Expt. Sta. Quart. Bul.* **30**:298–308 (1948).
8. Root, A. L., and E. R. Root: The ABC and XYZ of Bee Culture, A. I. Root Company, Medina, Ohio, 1945.
9. Sorenson, C. J., and John W. Carlson: Insecticidal control of Lygus bugs in alfalfa seed production, *Jour. Amer. Soc. Agron.*, **38**:495–501 (1946).
10. Stitt, L. L.: Difference in damage by three species of lygus to alfalfa seed production, *Jour. Econ. Ent.*, **37**: 709–710 (1944).
11. Urbahns, Theodore D.: The chalcis-fly in alfalfa seed, *U.S. Dept. Agr. Farmers' Bul.* 636 (1914).
12. Vansell, George H., and Frank E. Todd: Alfalfa tripping by insects, *Jour. Amer. Soc. Agron.*, **38**:470–488 (1946).

CHAPTER 39

SOME IMPORTANT DISEASES

Many diseases attack the forage crops, but only a few of these have been fully investigated. Since there is no adequate yardstick for measuring losses, the economic importance of forage diseases is not always fully appreciated. Many students are familiar with such diseases as alfalfa wilt and corn smut, but only because they are very common and widespread. The general indifference to forage-crop diseases can well be attributed to the position of these crops in American agriculture. In general, they are relegated to a secondary position because of inadequate appreciation of their value in our livestock economy. It seems certain that as the forage crops gain their just recognition more attention will be given to the diseases and their control.

Plant diseases increase in severity generally with intensive culture of any particular crop. This is certainly true of the forages. It is well illustrated by the increase in alfalfa wilt in recent years throughout the eastern United States, an area which had been relatively free of this disease. With an increasingly intensive system of grassland agriculture, more severe outbreaks of grass and legume diseases can be expected unless steps are taken at an early date to forestall them. Diseases are usually more severe in the more humid regions than in areas of low rainfall and humidity.

NATURE OF INJURY

Diseases may reduce the yield, lower the quality of the forage, and shorten the life of the crop. Such drastic effects result from diseases causing stunting, yellowing, wilting, leaf spots, blights, rotting, and other damage. For example, a severe infection of alfalfa leaf spot (*Pseudopeziza medicaginis*) will cause alfalfa to drop its lower leaves. When red clover is attacked by crown rot (*Sclerotinia trifoliorum*), the plant wilts and eventually is completely destroyed. All parts of the forage plant—leaves, stems, roots, and flowers—are subject to attack by one or more disease-producing organisms.

SOME CROP EXAMPLES

Disease-producing organisms are usually specific for a particular crop, and less frequently does the same pathogen affect several crop species. Some forage crops are attacked by more, or more destructive, diseases than others. In this respect alfalfa and the clovers together with Sudan grass and the other sorghums appear to be particularly susceptible, whereas the perennial grasses are the least affected.

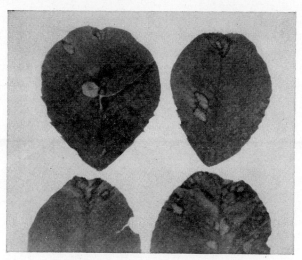

Fig. 93. Leaflets of ladino clover showing white papery-type lesions of leaf spot caused by *Ascochyta* sp. (*U.S. Regional Pasture Laboratory.*)

Alfalfa. A large number of diseases attack alfalfa, contributing in large measure to the costs of production and the hazards of securing and maintaining good stands. Some of the more important diseases are listed in Table 377 together with the plant organs attacked. Every part of the alfalfa plant, except the seed, is susceptible to attack by one or more of these

TABLE 377. DISEASES AFFECTING THE ALFALFA CROP AND ORGAN ATTACKED

Disease	Cause	Plant organ attacked
Bacterial stem blight	*Pseudomonas medicaginis*	Stems and leaves
Bacterial wilt	*Corynebacterium insidiosum*	Vascular tissue
Black stem	*Phoma* sp. and *Ascochyta imperfecta*	Stems and leaves
Cercospora leaf spot	*Cercospora zebrina*	Leaves and stems
Crown wart	*Urophlyctis alfalfae*	Crown
Downy mildew	*Peronospora trifoliorum*	Stems and leaves
Leaf spot	*Pseudopeziza medicaginis*	Leaves and stems
Root rots	*Fusarium* sp., *Cylindrocarpon* sp.	Roots
Rust	*Uromyces striatus*	Leaves and stems

diseases. Alfalfa wilt is considered most severe, although black stem, the leaf diseases, and root rot (*Fusarium* spp.) are increasingly common. Attacks vary with the weather, stage of growth and age of the alfalfa plants, and with the variety planted.

Red Clover. Red clover seems to have just as many diseases as alfalfa. This is indicated by the partial list given in Table 378. Of these the Southern and Northern anthracnose, together with powdery mildew, are probably most significant, but Sclerotinia crown and root rot is causing increasing difficulties. No part or organ of red clover except the seed is

TABLE 378. DISEASES THAT AFFECT THE RED CLOVER CROP AND ORGAN ATTACKED

Disease	Cause	Plant organ attacked
Bacterial leaf spot..................	*Pseudomonas syringae*	Leaves
Black stem disease...................	*Phoma trifolii*	Stems and leaves
Crown rot..........................	*Sclerotinia trifoliorum*	Crown and roots
Fusarium root rot..................	*Fusarium* sp.	Roots
Northern anthracnose...............	*Kabatiella caulivora*	Tops
Powdery mildew.....................	*Erysiphe polygoni*	Leaves
Pseudoplea leaf spot................	*Pseudoplea trifolii*	Leaves
Rusts..............................	*Uromyces trifolii*	Leaves and stems
Sooty blotch.......................	*Cymadothea trifolii*	Leaves
Southern anthracnose...............	*Colletotrichum trifolii*	Tops
Stemphylium leaf spot..............	*Stemphylium sarcinae- forme*	Leaves

TABLE 379. DISEASES ATTACKING THE SORGHUM CROPS AND ORGANS ATTACKED

Disease	Cause	Plant organ attacked
Anthracnose...................	*Colletotrichum graminicolum*	Leaves
Bacterial spot..................	*Pseudomonas syringae*	Leaves
Bacterial streak................	*Xanthomonas holcicola*	Leaves
Bacterial stripe................	*Pseudomonas andropogoni*	Leaves
Damping off....................	*Fusarium* spp., *Pythium* spp., *Helminthosporium* spp.	Seedlings
Kernel smut...................	*Sphacelotheca* sp.	Heads
Leaf blight....................	*Helminthosporium turcicum*	Leaves
Pythium root rot..............	*Pythium* spp.	Roots
Rust..........................	*Puccinia purpurea*	Leaves
Stalk rots....................	*Rhizoctonia solani*, *Spicaria elegans*, others	Stalks
Zonate leaf spot..............	*Gloeocercospora sorghi*	Leaves

immune to disease.   The severity of the diseases varies according to age of the crop, climatic conditions, and variety.   It can be noted that some of the same diseases that attack red clover also affect the alfalfa plant.

Sorghums.   The sorghums are as severely injured as red clover and alfalfa by bacterial and fungus diseases.   Since these crops are annuals, losses may not appear as serious to the casual observer.   This is not the case, since many of the sorghum diseases develop rapidly, causing severe losses.   The long list of diseases attacking the sorghums (Table 379), again, is not complete, but it illustrates the immensity of the problem facing pathologists and plant breeders alike.

Others.   The diseases of soybeans have been studied primarily for their effects on grain yields.   A few diseases attacking soybeans and other forage crops are listed in Table 380.   Diseases that attack timothy, bromegrass, reed canary, and other crops are also known, but no effort is made here to include all these.

TABLE 380.   PLANT DISEASES FOUND IN ADDITIONAL FORAGE CROPS

Crop	Disease	Cause	Plant organ attacked
Meadow fescue....	Net blotch	*Helminthosporium dictyoides*	Leaves
Meadow fescue....	Crown rust	*Puccinia coronata*	Leaves
Orchard grass......	Leaf spot	*Stagonospora subseriata*	Leaves
Soybeans..........	Anthracnose	*Glomerella glycines*	Leaves and stems
Soybeans..........	Blight	*Pseudomonas glycinea*	Leaves
Soybeans..........	Brown spot	*Septoria glycines*	Leaves
Sweetclover.......	Black stem	*Ascochyta* spp.	Stems
Sweetclover.......	Downy mildew	*Peronospora trifoliorum*	Leaves and stems
Sweetclover.......	Root rots	*Fusarium* spp., *Phytophthora* spp.	Roots

THE VIRUS PROBLEM

Besides the bacterial and fungus diseases of the forages there are many virus diseases which attack especially the legumes.   The most common are the mosaics.   They are difficult to identify, and very little is known concerning their effects on yield.   Mosaics of alfalfa, ladino and red clover, of field peas and soybeans, have been identified.   They are characterized by mottling and puckering of the leaf, resulting in an abnormal appearance. The virus diseases are often transmissible from one species of host plant to another.   Data from studies showing the reaction of some of the legume plants to various viruses are given in Table 381.   In this study the white clover virus infected beans, peas, and sweetclover but did not attack soybeans.   Bean virus 1 on the other hand attacked the bean but was not transmissible to the other three hosts.   Differences in susceptibility or

TABLE 381. SUMMARIZED SCHEME FOR THE DIFFERENTIATION OF CERTAIN VIRUSES AFFECTING LEGUME PLANTS

Virus	*Phaseolus vulgaris*	*Pisum sativum*	*Melilotus officinalis*	*Glycine max*
Bean virus 1	***	—	—	—
Bean virus 2	***	**	**	*
Pea virus 1	—	**	—	**
Pea virus 2	—	***	***	—
White clover virus 1	***	***	***	—
Soybean virus 1	—	—	—	***
Broadbean local-lesion virus	—	**	2	***

SOURCE: *Jour. Agr. Res.*, **51** (1936).
*** Severe infection. ** Moderate infection. * Slight infection. — No infection. 2 No data.

resistance to viruses also exist among crop varieties. The use of varieties resistant to viruses is an important means of control.

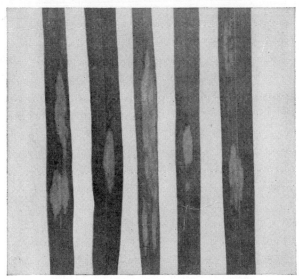

FIG. 94. Leaves of orchard grass showing size and shape of lesions caused by *Rhynchosporium orthosporum*. (*U.S. Regional Pasture Laboratory.*)

EXTENT OF DAMAGE

Estimates of economic losses from forage-plant diseases run into many millions of dollars annually. However, specific data showing reduction in yield and quality are, for the most part, lacking, because of the difficulty in obtaining such records. It is acknowledged by research workers and practical growers that leaf lesions, loss of green color and leaves, reduction of stand, and other such factors are of major importance in forage production. The loss of stand caused by alfalfa wilt alone results in crop survival for only 3 or 4 years instead of 7 or 8 as might be expected. It is estimated that 5 to 10 per cent of the value of our hay and silage crops is lost to diseases each year.

Control Measures Inadequate

Few control measures have been advocated other than the timely mowing and crop rotation practiced normally on most farms. Early mowing is suggested to control certain diseases (for example, black stem of alfalfa) when they appear in epidemic proportions. Similarly short rotations in which alfalfa is not grown for at least 2 years are helpful in controlling the wilt disease. Seed treatments using mercury dusts hold some promise for controlling certain seed-borne grass diseases. There is also evidence available[5] showing that these treatments may be used with good results on legume seeds. However, they should not be used with seed inoculants.

From the standpoint of economy and long-time satisfactory results the breeding of plant varieties resistant to the various diseases appears to be the most practical solution. Considerable progress along this line has already been made. A few examples of varieties now in common use are the southern anthracnose-resistant red clovers, Cumberland and more recently Kenland; the wilt-resistant alfalfa varieties, Ranger and Buffalo; and the leaf-spot resistant Tift Sudan grass. Enough information is available to show that this method of disease control is highly effective. Disease resistance should rank high among the objectives of all future plant-breeding programs.

References

1. Brown, J. G., and R. B. Streets: Diseases of field crops in Arizona, *Ariz. Agr. Expt. Sta. Bul.* 148 (1934).
2. Dickson, James G.: Outline of Diseases of Cereal and Forage Crop Plants of the Northern Part of the United States, Burgess Publishing Co., Minneapolis, 1940.
3. Leuke, R. W., John H. Martin, and C. L. Lefebvre: Sorghum diseases and their control, *U.S. Dept. Agr. Farmers' Bul.* 1959 (1944).
4. Pierce, W. H.: The identification of certain viruses affecting leguminous plants, *Jour. Agr. Res.*, **51**:1017–1039 (1935).
5. U.S. Department of Agriculture: Improving pastures and grasslands for the Northeastern United States, *U.S. Dept. Agr. Misc. Pub.* 590 (1946).

CHAPTER 40

PLANT–BREEDING CONTRIBUTIONS

A number of factors have combined to retard the improvement of forage crops through breeding. Among these factors are the small size of the flower and flower parts, variations in self-fertility and self-sterility, genetic barriers within genera, the frequent occurrences of polyploidy, and our incomplete knowledge of the cytology of many of these plants. Another obstacle is created by the fact that many of our forage species are introduced and, therefore, growing in a region other than that of their primary adaptation. Further, perennial legumes must be adapted to extreme variations in environmental factors. This interferes with their normal reproduction processes and survival and further handicaps the plant breeder.

Nearly all the important hay and silage crops belong to the legume and grass families. It might be assumed that, since only two plant families are involved, breeding techniques could be fairly uniform within each family. This is not the case, since each species requires special techniques for breeding and also often for testing. The records of accomplishment in the production of hybrid corn are well known, but less in evidence are results from breeding work with the hay grasses and legumes; nevertheless, some progress has been made.

INHERENT VARIABILITY

All the forage species vary in plant characters, and these variations form the basis for developing improved varieties and strains. Characters such as disease resistance, drought endurance, productiveness, cold resistance, carotene content, superior seedling vigor, and many others are readily found. In addition, plants may be found which are tall or short, leafy or nonleafy, hairy or pubescent, early- or late-maturing. These and the many other variations are the starting point for the plant breeder whose ultimate objective is to achieve the most favorable possible combination of characters in a widely adapted variety.

GENERAL TECHNIQUES

Breeding work with the forage crops may involve selection, selfing, crossing, polycrossing, the development of hybrids and synthetics, maternal-line selections, artificial inoculation, tests of hardiness, productivity, and many other techniques. The methods employed will vary with the species, its mode of reproduction, and the ultimate goal of the plant breeder. Early work with the hay crops consisted primarily of making selections of outstanding maternal-line plants, increasing the seed supply from these, and testing the progeny. Later work has continued selection with the addition of such techniques as inbreeding, crossing, and close breeding to develop synthetic or hybrid varieties. These more refined techniques have recently produced such outstanding varieties as Atlantic, Buffalo, and Ranger alfalfa and Kenland red clover.

Fig. 95. Vegetable-parchment bags are used to ensure self-pollination of panicles of orchard grass. (*U.S. Regional Pasture Laboratory.*)

Some Accomplishments

Alfalfa. The common alfalfa introduced into California in 1850 was not adapted to Northern winters. In 1857, Wendelin Grimm brought alfalfa seed from Germany and planted this through several successive generations, saving seed each year. This alfalfa, now known as Grimm, proved to be winter hardy in the northern climates and has been in great demand throughout the Northeast. This is an illustration of the introduction of superior germ plasm that resulted in a good variety without the aid of direct plant breeding. Grimm has since been used by breeders as a source of good plants.

Many other alfalfa varieties have been developed since Grimm was recognized in 1905. The Cossack variety was selected for winter hardiness and productiveness from Siberian seed by N. E. Hanson of South Dakota and introduced in 1907. Baltic was selected out of the Grimm variety by Wheeler in South Dakota and released in 1908. Hardigan and Meeker

Baltic, released in 1920, were selections out of Baltic. Ladak was introduced in 1910, being a selection out of *Medicago falcata* which was brought over earlier from India. It was described as a good yielder, resistant to cold and drought, and later was found to resist bacterial wilt. All these varieties and several others were for the most part developed through simple selection by men observant enough to recognize the desirable traits of certain individual plants in larger plant populations.

FIG. 96. Reaction of alfalfa to bacterial wilt in a controlled test. *Left*, a resistant selection; *right*, susceptible Grimm has succumbed to the disease. (*Nebraska Agricultural Experiment Station.*)

Bacterial Wilt. As alfalfa became more generally grown in the humid sections new problems appeared in its culture. Although winter-hardy alfalfa varieties were available for the Northern states, stands became increasingly difficult to maintain. The cause of the difficulty was finally determined in 1927 to be bacterial wilt, a disease which has become severe in recent years. The Grimm, Common, Hardigan, and Ontario variegated varieties were very susceptible. Ladak and Hardistan have a degree of resistance to the disease but were not satisfactory from the standpoint of yield and leaf spot resistance.

Recognizing this new problem in growing alfalfa, breeders have engaged in extensive programs to develop resistant varieties. New varieties possessing resistance to wilt and having other desirable characters are Buffalo and Ranger. Buffalo was developed by the Kansas Experiment Station and Ranger at Nebraska, both in cooperation with the U.S. Department of Agriculture. Atlantic alfalfa, bred by the New Jersey Station, has not been equal to Buffalo or Ranger in wilt resistance, but it is a very vigorous variety and under Eastern conditions has maintained good stands longer than most standard varieties. This would indicate that it is possible for the plant breeder to develop varieties adapted to Eastern conditions.

The Buffalo variety originated from Kansas Common after a series of selections and years of close breeding in isolated plots. Ranger is a synthetic from Cossack, Turkistan, and Ladak varieties. These were previously selfed for varying numbers of generations, outcrossed to wilt-resistant lines, increased individually, and then composited. Atlantic is also a synthetic variety possessing a broad genetic base that includes Hairy Peruvian and other strains. In yield tests in many states, Buffalo and Ranger compare favorably to older varieties in new stands and have outyielded them in older stands. Atlantic gives the greatest productivity in the first few years. The Ranger and Buffalo varieties will do much to lengthen the life of alfalfa in wilt-infested soils. Ranger is more susceptible than Buffalo to leaf spot diseases in the humid Eastern climate. Atlantic will make its contribution in the eastern United States, especially in short rotations.

Red Clover. In the years following the First World War, difficulty was encountered in maintaining good stands of red clover. This was traced to the use of foreign seed of unadapted stocks imported in large quantities during this period. The American form of red clover had developed a hairiness of leaves and stems not common to the European types. This is clear evidence of evolutionary forces at work and indicates how the plant breeder can reinforce and accelerate the development of desirable plant characters. The hairy form was found to be more resistant to leaf hopper attacks and thus has persisted while the smoother types have been destroyed in this country. European seed was also inferior in disease resistance, and the plants lacked persistence.

Plant breeders working with red clover have sought increased yields, persistence, and resistance to anthracnose and mildew diseases. The Tennessee Station developed a variety with some resistance to anthracnose at an early date. Later, in 1928, the U.S. Department of Agriculture, cooperating with several of the experiment stations, determined that three regions of adaptation existed in the Eastern states—southern, central, and northern. In the southern region, the need is for strains which are resistant to southern anthracnose and other diseases and capable of withstanding high summer temperatures and winter fluctuations in temperature. The central region requires disease-resistant, winter-hardy varieties, and the northern region requires winter-hardy varieties with long periods of dormancy.

As a result of collaboration by plant breeders from the U.S. Department of Agriculture and the state experiment stations, two varieties, Cumberland and Midland, were produced and released about 1940. These varieties were developed by searching for old farm strains and making selections of superior individuals. Local strains so developed proved superior in the respective states, and broader use of these strains was brought about by compositing seed lots from each. The Cumberland is a blend of three disease-resistant strains—one each from Tennessee, Kentucky, and Virginia—and is adapted to the southern clover region. Midland is a composite of four strains—one each from Iowa, Illinois, Indiana, and Ohio. Besides being a good yielder in its region of adaptation, Cumberland is partly resistant to the southern anthracnose disease and has proved quite persistent in the southern region, where it often maintains a good stand into the third year. Midland has performed equally well in the central region, where it is partially resistant to northern anthracnose and is a superior yielder. Kenland red clover was recently produced by maternal-line selection from plants artificially inoculated with southern anthracnose and crown rot diseases. It appears to be very resistant to southern anthracnose, has some resistance to crown rot, and produces a superior second cutting of hay. It seems to act as a short-lived perennial.

Timothy. A few improved varieties of timothy have been produced· In southern Indiana an early-maturing variety known as Shelby has been generally accepted. The Huron variety, released by the Ohio Experiment Station, is a late-maturing type resulting from local selection. It produces hay later in the season than commercial timothy and grows longer into the summer period in pasture mixtures. Other selections made in Ohio include Marietta and Lorain. Marietta matures about a week earlier than ordinary timothy and so is ready to cut for hay at the same time as alfalfa and red clover. Lorain is said to be well adapted to northern Ohio, being 10 days later in maturing than ordinary timothy and about 16 days later than Marietta.

Bromegrass. Bromegrass is an important hay and pasture species in the Middle West, and it is rapidly becoming so in the East. Only a limited amount of breeding work has been done with this species, but some of the selections are now recognized and considered superior to others in certain sections of the country.

The Parkland and Superior varieties of bromegrass were selected in Canada. Superior is a high-producing hay and pasture variety. Parkland is a noncreeping strain possessing reduced rhizomes which supposedly reduces the danger of developing the sod-bound condition associated with ordinary bromegrass. It is also less tenacious and more readily destroyed in plowing and rotation with cultivated crops.

Perhaps the most work on strain comparisons with this species has been conducted in Nebraska, Michigan, Wisconsin, Iowa, and New Jersey. Workers at these stations recognized differences in vigor and apparent value of bromegrass selections for their regions and made comparative tests accordingly. They grouped the strains into Northern and Southern types. Their data indicate greater seedling vigor for the Southern types and also more tolerance of heat and drought. The Southern types were also superior forage producers and thus are considered best adapted for planting in the central and southern region of bromegrass adaptation. The Lincoln, Fisher, and Achenbach strains are generally recognized as Southern type. All the named strains of bromegrass are the result of natural selection in old fields identified by plant breeders or interested farmers.

Bermuda Grass. In the southeastern region of America an intensive search for a good permanent hay grass has been going on for some time. Bermuda grass is considered primarily a pasture grass, but in 1929 a strain of Bermuda grass was found that had both stolons and rhizomes and was a vigorous grower. It was increased by stolons and became known as Tift Bermuda. In 1937 two tall strains of Bermuda were brought over from Africa and grown adjacent to Tift and Common. Natural crossing was effected by this method and enough seed obtained to plant 5,000 seedling plants in 1938. These were carefully studied, and a hybrid having Tift as the seed parent was selected as being superior in size and vigor to Tift and Common Bermuda. It proved somewhat resistant to leaf spot, produces almost no seed, and is as cold-tolerant as Common Bermuda. Further studies indicated it to be a good hay producer. It possesses a habit of erect growth, resists lodging to a greater extent than Tift, and is more productive, yielding about 75 per cent more dry matter per acre than Tift. Quality of the hay was good, and it was shown to be a good partner to grow with crimson clover. It was named Coastal Bermuda in 1941. Its ability to grow well on both acid and alkaline soils has since been recognized.

Sudan Grass. Sudan grass is a desirable hay and pasture species to grow in midsummer. Unfortunately, in the humid sections this crop is very susceptible to a number of leaf spot diseases which greatly lower its productiveness and hay quality. Plant breeders recognized this difficulty and set out to correct it. Work conducted by Burton in Georgia has been most productive to date.

Burton collected selected seed lots from the Midwest and Southwest, grew the seed in plots, and looked for superior plants. Since none of the samples were satisfactory, crosses were made with certain sorghums, among them Leoti. An examination of 35,000 first-generation plants from this original cross showed six disease-resistant coarse-stemmed progeny. The coarse stem was undesirable for Sudan grass; so these six resistant plants were backcrossed to superior Sudan selections. From these back-crosses enough seed was obtained to grow 30,000 second-generation plants. Only one plant from this population had the disease resistance of Leoti and the good characters of Sudan grass. Seed of this plant was increased and the new strain called "Tift."

In breeding Tift Sudan two weaknesses became apparent. Its tendency to stay green and vegetative makes it an inferior seed-producing variety. In Texas, where seed is produced commercially, it is rated at 75 per cent as good as Common Sudan. It also is higher in prussic acid content and, therefore, in some sections of the country may be more dangerous to graze than the Common. For hay this danger is of no consequence since the prussic acid content decreases rapidly as the crop matures.

Seed of the new strain was sent to a number of experiment station workers and widely tested by them in 1942. The results of these tests[2] show that Tift Sudan was considered superior in yield and disease resistance at most stations. Once an adequate seed supply is established, this variety prob-ably will be rather generally accepted.

Sorgos. Sorghums for forage and grain are playing an increasingly important role in the Southwest, due to the development of many superior varieties. The first improved strain of sorgo was developed in Indiana in 1857 and called Early Amber. In 1867 a Minnesota farmer made selec-tions from this strain and produced the Minnesota Amber. Selections from Minnesota Amber for earliness and drought resistance resulted in Dakota Amber, released in 1915. Other strains of the Black Amber type have been produced and released. Red Amber sorgo was found in a seed mixture of the Orange sorgo variety returned to the United States from Australia in 1903.

Orange sorgo, believed to have been introduced by Leonard Wray, has been widely grown in Kansas. The U.S. Department of Agriculture first grew it in 1881. Kansas Orange was long the most popular variety for forage in Oklahoma, New Mexico, and Texas, but is too late in maturing for Kansas. Early Sumac was then selected out from Sumac and released in 1922. This variety proved suitable for western Kansas. Both the Sumac varieties, unfortunately, possess reddish-brown seed with a very undesirable bitter flavor. Leoti sorgo was found on a Kansas farm by a U.S. Department of Agriculture worker in 1920. It is sweet, early, and resistant to red spot disease but susceptible to smut.

Atlas Sorgo. The most valuable contribution in sorgo breeding to date is the development of the Atlas variety. It is the result of a cross between Sourless sorgo and Blackhull Kafir, selection being made in the second generation and continued until tall plants with sweet juicy stems and palat-able nonbitter white seeds were produced. The new variety was resistant to lodging, as shown in Kansas studies.[11] In these tests it lodged only 2 per cent, compared with 14 per cent for Early Sumac sorgo. The high-test weight of Atlas sorgo indicates good quality of grain, and actually it might be considered a dual-purpose crop, since it yields well in both forage and grain. Forage yields obtained at Hays, Kansas, over a period of 8 years are given in Table 382. In these tests it outyielded field corn by 2 tons of

TABLE 382. AVERAGE YIELDS OF CURED FORAGE FROM SORGHUM VARIETIES
GROWN AT HAYS, KANSAS

Variety	Tons per acre
Early Sumac	3.45
Leoti Red	3.85
Standard Sumac	4.30
Atlas	4.37
Corn	2.32

SOURCE: *Kans. Agr. Expt. Sta. Bul.* 266 (1934).

dry matter per acre. This explains the popularity of sorgo in the semiarid regions of the Southwest. Atlas was distributed in 1928 and has become the most popular sorgo variety in eastern Kansas, Missouri, and eastern Nebraska. Because of its good grain-producing qualities it is more valuable for silage than other varieties. The grain alone is more readily digested by livestock and more palatable than that from a variety such as Kansas Orange.

Silage Corn. Many new varieties of silage corn have been developed since 1930 by the technique of producing hybrids. This involves inbreeding, selection of segregates, and hybridization followed by testing of the hybrids. There must be a continuous sifting of these varieties to determine those best suited for silage purposes. Characters are sought in the hybrids just as in the old open-pollinated varieties which make them superior for silage. Such characters include high grain production to give good quality and superior forage yields. Lodging and disease resistance are significant for ease of harvesting and quality of product.

Performance trials with corn varieties are conducted by many of the experiment stations. Results of such a test conducted in Wisconsin are given in Table 383. The hybrids tested were shown to be much superior to the Murdock check variety in both grain and forage produced. Comparative performance ratings in which grain quality and resistance to lodging and disease were considered showed some hybrids superior to others and all hybrids in this test superior to the Murdock check. The production of hybrid corn is the most outstanding example of progress in plant breeding.

MORE WORK NEEDED

Other examples could be cited of contributions in the field of forage crops through plant breeding. Most of the progress here, however, has been through the selection of superior plants with their subsequent increase and release. Progress in breeding the forage crops has lagged behind the grain, fiber, and oil crops because of difficulties in technique and less economic pressure.

TABLE 383. AVERAGE RESULTS OF PERFORMANCE TRIALS FOR CERTAIN CORN HYBRIDS

Variety or hybrid no.	Relative maturity, days	No. of trials	Performance rating, %	Increased yield of grain over check variety, %	Silage yield, tons per acre
Murdock...	115–120	25	78.3	....	12.7
615	115	22	100.7	18.7	15.5
625	115	25	100.1	16.4	16.0
640	115	8	102.3	25.4	14.5
645	115	22	101.3	19.3	13.4
676	120	19	103.4	27.3	15.9
675	120	21	95.4	19.0	16.7
680	120	20	101.8	29.4	16.2
690	120	8	104.8	36.3	15.1
696	120	20	104.2	32.4	16.6

SOURCE: *Wis. Agr. Ext. Spec. Cir.* (1941).

Introduction of outstanding forage plants from abroad is always a possibility. The present breeding techniques may be further perfected, and the development of superior methods for inducing polyploidy artificially probably will be found. The pleasing possibility exists of greater use of interspecific and intergeneric crossing. All these factors indicate that breeding for superior forage crops holds great promise.

References

1. Burton, Glenn W.: Coastal Bermuda grass, *Ga. Coastal Plain Expt. Sta. Cir.* 10 (1943).
2. Burton, Glenn W.: Tift Sudan, *Ga. Coastal Plain Expt. Sta. Cir.* 11 (1943).
3. Evans, Morgan W.: Varieties of timothy suited to Ohio, *Ohio Agr. Expt. Sta. Bimo. Bul.* **31**: 136–141 (1946).
4. Grandfield, C. O.: Buffalo alfalfa, *Kans. Agr. Expt. Sta. Cir.* 226 (1945).
5. Hollowell, E. A.: The swing to red clover, *Successful Farming*, **41**: 16, 28, 71 (1943).
6. Martin, John H.: Sorghum improvement, U.S. Department of Agriculture Yearbook, 1936, pp. 523–560.
7. Neal, N. P.: Wisconsin corn hybrids, *Wis. Col. Agr. Spec. Cir.*, March, 1941.
8. Newell, L. C., and F. D. Keim: Field performance of brome grass strains from different regional seed sources, *Jour. Amer. Soc. Agron.*, **35**:420–434 (1943).
9. Nevens, W. B., and G. H. Duncan: Yields of corn hybrids harvested for silage: and methods to determine best time to harvest, *Ill. Agr. Expt. Sta. Bul.* 494 (1942).

10. Pieters, A. J., and E. A. Hollowell: Clover improvement, U.S. Department of Agriculture Yearbook, 1937, pp. 1190–1214.
11. Swanson, A. F., and H. H. Laude: Varieties of sorghum in Kansas, *Kans. Agr. Expt. Sta. Bul.* 266 (1934).
12. Tysdal, H. M., and H. L. Westover: Alfalfa improvement, U.S. Department of Agriculture Yearbook, 1937, pp. 1122–1153.
13. Vinall, H. N., and M. A. Hein: Breeding miscellaneous grasses, U.S. Department of Agriculture Yearbook, 1937, pp. 1032–1102.

CHAPTER 41

SEED PRODUCTION

The production of adequate quantities of adapted, variety-pure seed is fundamental for a progressive national forage-crop program. Growing, harvesting, and processing the small seeds of grasses and legumes requires special knowledge and techniques. Certain regions of America because of favorable climatic conditions or for economic reasons are better adapted to growing the seed than other sections are. Thus there are seed-producing and seed-consuming areas in the United States. The only large area in the United States which makes a specialty of growing forage seeds is the Western states.

About 500 million pounds of hay and pasture seeds are used each year by American farmers in making new plantings. To supply this great volume of seed requires thousands of acres devoted to seed production and many growers, processors, and seedsmen. Each is dependent on the other for a satisfactory product capable of giving superior performance. Production of seed of improved varieties is receiving increased attention, and a recognized objective is the handling of such seed in the trade channels so that identity is maintained. Interestingly enough, less than 1 per cent of all forage-crop seeds sown are from certified seed of improved varieties.

Centers of Production

Alfalfa. Alfalfa seed is raised primarily in the Plains and Western states. The five leading states together with their acreages and average yields are shown in Table 384, along with data for the United States as a whole. Kansas, Oklahoma, and Arizona produce the largest quantities of alfalfa seed. Production of alfalfa seed and average acre yields declined from 1930 to 1945 owing to harmful insects, plant diseases, and decreases in the numbers of pollinating insects. In more recent years yields have increased, aided by a more general use of pollinators and also of insecticides for the control of destructive insects.

Red and Alsike Clover. Red clover is produced in the greatest volume in the Middle Western states, as shown in Table 385. Thus Illinois, Missouri, and Iowa are among the five major producers of this seed. Idaho and Oregon ship large tonnages eastward. Total red clover seed production has averaged almost 1½ million bushels annually for the 12-year period 1936 to 1948. Seed of alsike clover is produced in largest quantities north-

400

TABLE 384. PRODUCTION OF ALFALFA SEED IN THE UNITED STATES

State	Acreage harvested, thousands		Yield per acre, bu.		Production, thousand bu.	
	Average 1936–1945	1947	Average 1936–1945	1947	Average 1936–1945	1947
Kansas............	111.3	239	1.35	1.30	143.5	311
Oklahoma.........	77.7	120	1.84	2.00	139.8	240
Arizona...........	33.2	61	3.44	3.30	108.6	201
California.........	19.3	33	3.15	4.20	59.9	139
Nebraska..........	74.7	108	1.26	1.10	92.4	119
United States.......	801.1	1,021	1.49	1.66	1,179.0	1,699

SOURCE: U.S. Department of Agriculture, Crop Reporting Board, Annual Summary 1947.

TABLE 385. PRODUCTION OF RED AND ALSIKE CLOVER SEED IN THE UNITED STATES

State	Red clover production, thousand bu.		State	Alsike clover production, thousand bu.	
	Average 1936–1945	1947		Average 1936–1945	1947
Illinois..........	219.5	181	Oregon.........	80.4	93
Missouri.........	103.2	155	Minnesota.......	62.6	88
Iowa............	148.9	111	Wisconsin.......	34.6	50
Wisconsin.......	124.5	108	Idaho..........	29.5	48
Idaho..........	150.5	106	California.......	9.1	25
United States....	1,435.3	1,195	United States....	320.4	366

SOURCE: U.S. Department of Agriculture, Crop Reporting Board, Annual Summary 1947.

ward of the red clover centers. Oregon was the major producer in 1947, with more than 93,000 bushels produced. Minnesota, Wisconsin, and Idaho were other important sources of this seed.

Lespedeza. Lespedeza seed is raised mostly in the Southeast, or the same general region where the crop is used for forage. Thus North Carolina, Missouri, and Kentucky are major growers. Most of this seed is consumed in the region where it is produced.

Timothy. Iowa is the major producer and consumer of timothy seed. In 1947, Iowa produced 955 thousand bushels, Ohio 234, Missouri 159, Minnesota 100, and Illinois 90 thousand bushels of timothy seed. Over 413 thousand acres were harvested for seed in the United States, and the

TABLE 386. PRODUCTION OF LESPEDEZA SEED IN THE UNITED STATES

State	Acreage harvested, thousands		Yield per acre, lb.		Production, million lb.	
	Average 1936–1945	1947	Average 1936–1945	1947	Average 1936–1945	1947
North Carolina	143.2	160	196	210	28.5	34
Missouri......	206.7	181	186	175	41.4	32
Kentucky....	76.8	77	218	280	17.4	22
Tennessee....	112.6	70	214	240	24.8	17
Georgia......	26.4	65	189	180	5.4	12
United States.	745.7	756	197	204	151.2	154

SOURCE: U.S. Department of Agriculture, Crop Reporting Board, Annual Summary 1947.

average acre yield was almost 4 bushels. Timothy-seed production has been gradually declining as other grasses have gained in favor in the United States.

Redtop. Nearly all the redtop seed is produced in Illinois and Missouri. In 1947 almost 11 million pounds was produced in Illinois and about 5 million in Missouri. This grass is used extensively for pasture and turf as well as hay.

Sudan Grass. Colorado and California combined produced more than one-third of all the Sudan grass seed raised in the United States in 1947.

TABLE 387. PRODUCTION OF SUDAN GRASS SEED IN THE UNITED STATES

State	Acreage harvested, thousands		Yield per acre, lb.		Production, million lb.	
	Average 1936–1945	1947	Average 1936–1945	1947	Average 1936–1945	1947
Colorado.....	14.0	12	291	370	4.4	4
California....	5.7	6	757	735	4.3	4
Texas........	66.0	8	354	375	22.8	3
Kansas.......	11.6	7	265	290	3.2	2
Oregon.......	1.6	4	595	525	1.0	2
United States.	144.8	55	335	378	50.3	21

SOURCE: U.S. Department of Agriculture, Crop Reporting Board, Annual Summary 1947.

Texas normally produces the bulk of this seed, and Kansas and Oregon are also important sources. The average yield for 1947 was 378 pounds per acre, but California averaged 735 pounds and Oregon 525.

Fig. 97. A field of sweet Sudan grass cut for seed. (*Texas Agricultural Experiment Station.*)

CULTURAL METHODS

Cultural methods of seed production vary with the producing region and the crop involved. Often in the case of legumes the second crop is used for seed instead of hay. Row, drilled, or broadcast seedings and fertilizer applications are regional problems as is insect control. Bees are needed for cross-pollinating legume plants and to ensure tripping the flowers. Wild bees or honeybee colonies are effective, and at least one hive per acre of legumes for seed is often suggested.

Seeding. Seed is usually grown from fields sown and managed, except for harvesting, in much the same way as hay crops. In some instances, however, such crops as bromegrass and orchard grass are sown in rows because yields of seed are often higher than with broadcast plantings. A comparison of row and broadcast plantings of bromegrass treated with various amounts of ammonium sulfate was made in Michigan (see Table 388). The cultivated rows yielded twice as much as the broadcast plots, and the addition of 200 pounds of ammonium sulfate proved most practical for increasing seed yields. The effect of fertilizer and bromegrass variety was studied in Nebraska[16] with results from fertilizer being similar to those given above. These investigators also found that certain bromegrass varieties yielded more seed than others.

Where seed production is the primary aim in seeding alfalfa, cultural practices assume increasing importance. Thus in Utah certain studies (see Table 389) on seeding rates under dry-land conditions were made, using rates of 2, 4, and 9 pounds per acre. The highest seed yields were secured at the 2-pound seeding rate with reductions of 17 per cent at 4 pounds and 29 per cent at 9 pounds. Row plantings were also tried under

TABLE 388. EFFECT OF CULTURAL TREATMENTS UPON THE SEED YIELD OF SMOOTH BROMEGRASS

Treatment	Seed yield, lb. per acre	
	28-in. rows (cultivated)	Broadcast
Alfalfa-bromegrass mixture.........	...	303
Bromegrass:		
No treatment..................	363	155
200 lb. ammonium sulfate in early spring......................	558	248
400 lb. ammonium sulfate in early spring......................	590	321
800 lb. ammonium sulfate in early spring......................	609	319

SOURCE: *Mich. Agr. Expt. Sta. Cir. Bul.* 192 (1944).

TABLE 389. ACRE YIELDS OF SEED OF ALFALFA SOWN FOR SEED PRODUCTION AND A SUMMARY OF AVERAGE ACRE YIELDS

Acre seeding rate	Acre yield, lb.	Relative yield
2	189.4	100
4	156.6	83
9	134.4	71

SOURCE: *Utah Agr. Expt. Sta. Tech. Bul.* 226 (1931).

the dry-land conditions of Utah. Rows 21 up to 49 inches apart proved superior in yields of seed to drilled plantings at the 2-pound-per-acre rate. When grown in hills a spacing of 21 by 28 inches resulted in the highest yield. The hill plantings also produced more seed than the regular row plantings. Wide spacings thus appear to be particularly valuable in semi-arid regions, whereas closer plantings are undoubtedly more productive as moisture supplies increase.

Burning. Burning off dead top growth of certain grasses early in the spring is also an effective means of increasing seed yields. Bahia and Bermuda grass seed yields were increased several fold by this treatment in trials in Georgia (see Table 390). In another study[3] burning followed by certain fertilizer treatments greatly increased seed yields of Bahia grass in the range of 2½ to over 10 times according to the treatment tried.

Irrigation. The effect of irrigation on seed production of alfalfa has been studied. Results in Utah[4] indicate that no irrigation was as satisfactory as any irrigation scheme tried, but the soil water table was high on the plots

TABLE 390. THE EFFECT OF BURNING UPON SEED YIELDS OF SEVERAL SOUTHERN GRASSES

Species	Pounds of seed produced per acre in			
	1942		1943	
	Burned	Not Burned	Burned	Not Burned
Common Bahia grass........	221	126	101	13
Common Bermuda grass.....	46	16	29	3
Bermuda grass.............	47	1	5	0.5
Ribbed Paspalum...........	34	35	41	46

SOURCE: *Jour. Amer. Soc. Agron.*, **26** (1944).

where tests were conducted. A study made in Kansas[7] on alfalfa under greenhouse conditions showed that a continuous supply of high moisture was beneficial to seed produced per plant. Equally satisfactory were low moisture supplies from the start of the seed-crop growth until the prebud stage followed by high moisture during the flowering and ripening period. Low moisture supplies throughout the growth and seed production periods definitely limited seeds set per plant. High food reserves and adequate soil moisture favored increased seed production.

SEED YIELDS

Seed yields vary with the crop grown, the skill of the grower, and climatic and soil environments. Possible yields are given in Table 391. Whether or not it is profitable to harvest any given crop for seed depends on the current prices and prospective acre yields.

TABLE 391. COMMON SEED YIELDS OF VARIOUS CROPS ON AN ACRE BASIS

Crop	Acre yield, lb.	Crop	Acre yield, lb.
Alfalfa.................	60–360	Orchard grass..........	150–600
Alsike clover............	30–360	Red clover.............	30–360
Bromegrass.............	100–800	Redtop................	50–100
Ladino.................	30–120	Sweetclover............	60–300
Lespedeza..............	100–400	Timothy...............	100–250

Varieties vary in their seed-producing ability, as shown by Utah studies[4] on alfalfa. In these studies Argentine produced the most seed per acre and Turkistan the least, being only 27 per cent of the Utah Common.

Varieties differ in seed-producing capacity, and this must be considered as an economic factor by all prospective seed growers. It would appear also that growing seed of varieties adapted to the consuming centers is even more significant.

Fig. 98. Harvesting sweetclover for seed. (*U.S. Department of Agriculture and the Nebraska Agricultural Experiment Station.*)

Stage to Harvest Seed

Alfalfa. The crop of alfalfa that develops during the hottest and driest part of the season is said to be the best one to save for seed production. In the extreme north and also under dry-land conditions this is often the first crop. In most of the country, however, it is the second crop, and south of Kansas it may be the third. Alfalfa seed may be harvested when two-thirds to three-fourths of the pods have turned brown.

Other Legumes. It is usually the second crop of medium red clover that is used for seed. The influence of stage of cutting the first crop on subsequent seed production is given in Table 392. Cutting in the early bloom stage was superior to all other stages, but waiting until three-fourths bloom did not reduce yields greatly. Earlier or later cutting resulted in decreased seed production. In this same study mammoth clover produced its highest yields when not clipped at all. Even early clipping treatments reduced the yields, and clipping in the bud stage or later resulted in no seed produced. Mammoth clover gives only one good cutting a year, and this accounts for its response to cutting for seed production. Similarly studies with alsike clover showed no clipping to be superior to clipping when the

TABLE 392. THE INFLUENCE OF CUTTING UPON THE SEED YIELD OF MEDIUM
RED CLOVER

Time of cutting	Stage of growth	Bushels of seed per acre, 4-year ave.
Not clipped........	....	1.9
May 23...........	10 in. high	2.1
June 1...........	14 in. early bud	2.7
June 8...........	18 in. early bloom	3.0
June 15..........	20 in. ¾ bloom	2.6
June 23..........	20 in. ¼ brown	1.1
July 1...........	20 in. ¾ brown	0.9

SOURCE: *Jour. Amer. Soc. Agron.*, **34** (1942).

crop was 7 inches tall. Cutting at later stages resulted in complete seed failure.

Other Crops. Seed of legumes and grasses should be well matured before harvesting. A study of reed canary grass showed that the best stage for harvest was when the seed hulls were entirely gray or brown (see Table 393). Earlier harvesting resulted in lighter seed and in seed of lowered germination.

TABLE 393. MATURITY, WEIGHTS PER 1,000 SEEDS, AND GERMINATION
PERCENTAGES OF REED CANARY GRASS SEED

Color of hulls	Seeds of the various grades of color present, %	Weight per 1,000 seeds, grams	Relative weight per 1,000 seeds, %	Germination 16 days, %
Entirely gray or brown..	48.5	0.865	100.0	91.0
Down to 75% gray or brown..............	23.5	0.775	89.8	83.5
Down to 50% gray or brown..............	13.2	0.691	79.9	83.0
Down to trace gray or brown..............	8.2	0.574	66.4	72.5
Entirely green.........	4.1	0.452	52.3	51.5
Trace of green.........	2.5	0.358	41.4	36.5

SOURCE: *Minn. Agr. Expt. Sta. Bul.* 263 (1930).

HARVESTING, THRESHING, AND CURING

When seeds are adequately matured, they should be harvested, threshed, and cured promptly. Legume crops are often cut and windrowed immediately, and they are then allowed to complete the curing process. A minimum of handling is essential to avoid loss from shattering. A few legumes, such as Austrian peas and Hungarian vetch, can be combined directly without the necessity of cutting and windrowing.

After the curing process is completed, seeds may be threshed directly from the windrow by means of a combine with pickup attachment. Other methods include the use of clover hullers, threshers, or stationary combines. Where stationary threshing is practiced, the straw can often be rethreshed

Fig. 99.   Harvesting hairy vetch seed in the Pacific Northwest.   (*J. I. Case Co.*)

profitably. Sweetclover presents a special problem because it ripens unevenly and the seed shatters readily. The Ohio Station has developed an economical attachment for the corn binder[17] to use in harvesting broadcast plantings. The bundles are cured in the field and then hauled to a stationary thresher. Sweetclover is sometimes combined direct as it stands in the field, even though this often results in loss of some of the seed.

Seed of the hay grasses may be combined direct in the field if thoroughly ripe, or cut with a binder, cured in the field, and then threshed at a stationary thresher or combine. Extra care is required in threshing to avoid seed injury from cracking or excess air blasts which may blow the seed out with the straw. Cleaning followed by storage in a dry, cool atmosphere is essential for a high-quality product.

Maintaining Genetic Purity

The forage grasses and legumes have what is described in the seed trade as indistinguishable seeds from a varietal standpoint. Since this is the case, special precautions must be taken to maintain genetic identity and purity. The International Crop Improvement Association and the various state associations have made rules and regulations for producing certified seed of recognized varieties. These groups are engaged in promoting better seed with assurance of variety and origin to the purchaser. Factors such as weed and disease control, high germination, cleaning, and grading are also important in this program.

Classes of Seed. Three classes of seed are recognized, namely, foundation, registered, and certified. These classes must meet the minimum standards set by the International Crop Improvement Association. Foundation seed is the source of all certified seed, either directly or through registered seed. It is normally maintained by the originating agricultural experiment station and should be genetically pure. Registered seed is produced from foundation or other registered seed in such a manner as to maintain genetic identity and purity. The certified seed can be produced from either registered or foundation stocks and must also be handled in such a manner as to maintain its identity and pass the purity requirements.

Certification. Certifying agencies set up their own qualifications for seed growers. In general, the farm and available machinery must be suitable and the grower must be capable, dependable, and cooperative. Isolation is required for many crops, depending on the mode of reproduction of the crop. The crop must be established from one of the three classes of seed already given. Field inspection by qualified representatives followed by seed germination and purity tests is made prior to tagging and sealing the seed. The field inspector checks on such items as good management, presence of contaminating crops and weeds, plant diseases, and isolation. All certified seed must have an official tag attached to each container. This tag helps to identify the seed as to genetic origin and purity. Sealing is the last step prior to shipping the seed or holding it for the ultimate consumer.

While the percentage of forage-crop seed that is certified is still very small, there is evidence that it is increasing as growers recognize its advantages. Its more general adoption will aid materially in raising the productive level of our hay crops.

References

1. Beck, F. V.: Field seed industry in the United States; an analysis of the production, consumption and prices of leguminous and grass seeds, University of Wisconsin Press, Madison (1944).
2. Burton, G. W.: Factors influencing seed setting in several southern grasses, *Jour. Amer. Soc. Agron.*, **35**:465–474 (1943).
3. Burton, G. W.: Seed production of several southern grasses as influenced by burning and fertilizing, *Jour. Amer. Soc. Agron.*, **36**:523–529 (1944).
4. Carlson, J. W., and George Stewart: Alfalfa seed production, *Utah Agr. Expt. Sta. Tech. Bul.* 226 (1931).

5. Churchill, B. R.: Smooth brome grass seed production in Michigan, *Mich. Agr. Expt. Sta. Cir. Bul.* 192 (1944).
6. Crop Production, Annual Summary for 1945, U.S. Department of Agriculture, Bureau of Agricultural Economics, Crop Reporting Board.
7. Grandfield, C. O.: Alfalfa seed production as affected by organic reserves, air temperatures, humidity, and soil moisture, *Jour. Agr. Res.*, **70**:123–132 (1945).
8. Hollowell, E. A.: Registration of strains and varieties of sweet clover, *Jour. Amer. Soc. Agron.*, **35**:825–829 (1943).
9. Hollowell, E. A.: Registration of strains and varieties of red clover, *Jour. Amer. Soc. Agron.*, **35**:830–833 (1943).
10. Hollowell, E. A.: Legume seed production in the North, *Amer. Bee Jour.*, **84**:308 (1944).
11. Hollowell, E. A.: Registration of varieties and strains of alfalfa, *Jour. Amer. Soc. Agron.*, **37**:649–652 (1945).
12. Hollowell, E. A.: Registration of varieties and strains of grasses, *Jour. Amer. Soc. Agron.*, **37**:653–655 (1945).
13. Jenkins, L.: Harvesting seed of vetches, winter peas, and crimson clover, *Oreg. Agr. Ext. Serv. Bul.*, 597 (1942).
14. Madson, B. A.: Opportunities and problems in the production of ladino clover seed. *Calif. Agr. Dept. Bul.*, **34**:15–16 (1945).
15. Megee, C. R.: Influence of clipping treatment and rolling on the yield of clover seed, *Jour. Amer. Soc. Agron.*, **34**:841–843 (1942).
16. Newell, L. C., and F. D. Keim: Field performance of brome grass strains from different regional seed sources, *Jour. Amer. Soc. Agron.*, **35**:420–434 (1943).
17. Willard, C. J., and C. B. Rickey: Harvesting sweet clover seed with a corn binder, *Jour. Amer. Soc. Agron.*, **35**:540–543 (1943).
18. Wilsie, C. P.: Brome grass in Iowa, *Iowa Agr. Expt. Sta. Bul.* P75, (1945).

INDEX

Figures in **boldface** type refer to pages containing tables or illustrations.

Leguminosa

alfalfa — Medicago sativa

Med. Red Clover — Trifolium pratense

Mammot Alsike — Trifolium hybridum

als Ladino — Trifolium repens

Sweet Clover — Melilotus alba (white)
                    Melilotus officinalis (yellow)

(a) Huban — M. annua
(b) sickel — M. indicus.

Lespedeza { striata — common
           { stipulacea — Korean
    L. sericea — it is perennial.

Velvet Bean — Stizolobium deeringianum

Soybeans — Glycine max

Cowpeas — Vigna sinensis

Crimson clover — Trifolium incarnatum.